THE PHYLUM CHORDATA

THE MACMILLAN COMPANY
NEW YORK · BOSTON · CHICAGO · DALLAS
ATLANTA · SAN FRANCISCO

MACMILLAN AND CO., Limited
LONDON · BOMBAY · CALCUTTA · MADRAS
MELBOURNE

THE MACMILLAN COMPANY
OF CANADA, Limited
TORONTO

THE PHYLUM CHORDATA

BIOLOGY OF VERTEBRATES AND THEIR KIN

by H. H. Newman

PROFESSOR OF ZOOLOGY IN
THE UNIVERSITY OF CHICAGO

A Revision of Vertebrate Zoology

NEW YORK
THE MACMILLAN COMPANY

PREFACE

As a long-time student of vertebrate zoology the writer has had the good fortune to have had close contact with many varied methods of teaching the subject. Apart from courses in general zoology in which the classic frog is usually the only vertebrate type studied, many special methods of teaching vertebrate zoology are employed. In one institution with which we were connected for some years, a whole semester was devoted to the detailed study of one species of frog. In this so-called "Frog Course" the frog was used as a typical organism and its anatomy, behavior, ecology, physiology, and embryology were studied in some detail. Another, more advanced course dealt almost exclusively with the dissection of the cat. The type of vertebrate course most commonly offered in American colleges and universities is the Comparative Anatomy course, in which a few representative types are studied, system by system, in the laboratory; while the lectures, after a very brief survey of the living classes and orders of lower chordates and vertebrates, deal with systems of organs comparatively, with emphasis upon the embryonic development of these systems, and with little attention to any whole organism or to phylogenetic aspects. Another type of course given in a few institutions deals with the evolutionary history of vertebrates and concentrates attention upon the fossil record.

Still another type of course, which the writer has long favored, is one in which the laboratory and lecture parts of the course are essentially independent, though supplementary. The laboratory part of such a course deals with comparative anatomy, studied system by system; while the lectures cover the whole Phylum Chordata, with emphasis upon the evolutionary history of the group, the interrelations of surviving groups, general principles illustrated by the group, and significant aspects of their natural history. The present book presents the subject-matter of the lecture part of such a course and considerable additional matter used for supplementary reading. For many years the precursor of this volume, *Vertebrate Zoology*, has been widely used for supplementary reading in comparative anatomy courses and has, according to many reports, well served this purpose.

Our first experience with vertebrate courses was in every way most fortunate and has left an indelible impression. In 1898, as a beginning graduate student in the University of Chicago, we were advised to take an advanced course in vertebrates under that great naturalist, scholar, and teacher, the late William Morton Wheeler. Few zoologists know that this master in the field of entomology, especially of social Hymenoptera, was once an outstanding teacher of vertebrate zoology. Wheeler's course lasted a full year and was in some ways the best course we have ever taken. In the laboratory we had the opportunity to study and dissect almost every important type, including amphioxus, several tunicates, Balanoglossus, lamprey, hag-fish, dog-fish, skate, teleost, Necturus, turtle, lizard, alligator, pigeon, rabbit, and others. As additional projects, some of us were permitted to prepare demonstration dissections of rare vertebrates for the use of future classes. Our own contribution was a dissection of that rare, almost extinct reptile, *Sphenodon*. The lectures in the course were such as one might have expected from a great naturalist, who was also a master of language. They dealt with the natural history of chordates, including significant data about their modes of life, special adaptations, habitats, distribution, breeding habits, development, and phylogenetic relationships; constituting a well-rounded series of verbal pictures of the various animals as wholes.

It has always seemed to us that this course of Wheeler's was close to an ideal vertebrate course. It has strongly influenced our teaching and we have tried to perpetuate this influence in the present book.

When, after nearly twenty years, our *Vertebrate Zoology* seemed to demand revision it was found necessary to rewrite large sections of it in order to adapt it to new knowledge, new principles, and new interpretations. So extensively has the rewriting proceeded that when it was finished an almost entirely new book emerged. Since it is essentially a new book rather than merely a revision of an old one, it seems to deserve a new name—a name more nearly descriptive of its contents than the old one. It may be regarded as a successor of the old book, which in its time served a useful purpose but has now grown somewhat antiquated. It is our hope that *The Phylum Chordata* will be as useful for a number of years as was *Vertebrate Zoology* when it was new.

CHICAGO, ILLINOIS   H. H. NEWMAN
February, 1939

CONTENTS

CONTENTS

CHAPTER XIX. BIRDS OF TODAY

CHAPTER XX. EMBRYONIC DEVELOPMENT
OF THE BIRD

CHAPTER XXI. CLASS MAMMALIA
(GENERAL AND HISTORICAL)

THE PHYLUM CHORDATA

THE PHYLUM CHORDATA

CHAPTER I

CHARACTERISTICS, CONTENT, AND CLASSIFICATION OF THE PHYLUM CHORDATA

WHAT IS A PHYLUM?

A phylum, according to a standard dictionary, is a great division of the plant or animal kingdom ranking below a subkingdom and above a class. This definition, however, gives no information as to the significance of the group called a phylum. Actually a phylum is supposed to be the largest assemblage of genetically related individuals descended from a common ancestral stock.

A phylum is really an abstraction deduced from a set of criteria that have been decided upon by a group of biologists. Thus it has been decided that the criteria for membership in the great Phylum Arthropoda are: jointed appendages, metameric organization, chitinous exoskeleton, ventral non-tubular nerve cord, six-segmented head, coelom formed by hollowing out mesodermal cords and greatly reduced in adult. When all animals exhibiting these characteristics are brought together it is found that they are further divisible into several well-defined classes: (Crustacea, Arachnida, Myriapoda, and Insecta), but that there are also several rather obscure groups that resemble arthropods but do not fully meet all the agreed-upon arthropod criteria. There is, for example, the *Peripatus* group, definitely classed as an arthropod though it has almost as many annelid as arthropod features. Then there are the curious tardigrades that resemble simplified lice, but lack certain arthropod criteria. If they are not arthropods they are at least closely related to them. Next come the curious parasitic Pentastomida, more worm-like than arthropod-like. Yet the larvae resemble adult tardigrades. At best these forms are half-way arthropods and hence it would be stretching the criteria of the phylum to admit them to full membership. In fact, one of our colleagues declares that tardigrades, at least, are

1

not arthropods at all. Each of these aberrant groups might be given subphylum value rather than class value as is the practice.

From this brief survey of another great animal phylum, we may gain the impression that it is rather difficult to define a phylum in terms that will adequately cover all kinds of forms that seem to be sufficiently interrelated for inclusion in a phylum, and that it is difficult to set any but entirely arbitrary bounds to a phylum. An aberrant group, once admitted to the phylum, tends to drag in some poor relations and these to bring in their train still more distant relatives until one feels that all attempts to classify living beings into hard and fast categories are futile. Evidently nature did not have in mind man's craving for precise and positive pigeon-holing of organisms when she was evolving the multiplicity of types that crowd the earth. What she really produced was a vast branching system with innumerable diversified side twigs, or by-paths, and a few main thriving branches. It is the side branches that obscure the picture and give the phylogenist his hardest problems, but it is just exactly these side branches that lend strongest support to the general theory of evolution as a branching process.

Now the Phylum Chordata is like other phyla in that it is difficult to define and equally difficult to delimit. It is even more difficult to fence in the Chordata than the Arthropoda and there is somewhat less unanimity as to the validity and adequacy of the fences in the former group than in the latter.

The Phylum Chordata, as defined by most of the leading students in the field, includes primarily the vertebrates (Craniata), amphioxus (sometimes classed as an acraniate vertebrate), the tunicates and their kin, and, doubtfully, *Balanoglossus* and its distant sessile cousins, *Cephalodiscus* and *Rhabdopleura*. If the latter be admitted to the phylum it is difficult to exclude the Phoronidea and other groups somewhat like them. This is a motley crew ranging from man down to the acorn worm and the colonial microscopic *Rhabdopleura*, and one wonders what there may be in common among them to warrant their inclusion in the same phylum. Perhaps we can gain an understanding of the reasons underlying the classification of chordates if we make a preliminary examination first, of the characters that are unique for chordates and which all chordates possess; second, of a few characters that chordates *apparently* share with some invertebrates; and thirdly, a dozen or so characters that seem to be the most fundamental features of vertebrates as distinguished from non-vertebrate chordates. These three sets of characteristics will be discussed in the order named, after which a system of classification of the chordates, based upon these characters, will be presented.

THE THREE UNIQUE CHORDATE CHARACTERS

For a long time it has been customary to consider all animals as chordates if they possess a combination of three characters: *a, notochord; b, gill-slits;* and *c, dorsal tubular nerve cord.* Each of these three characters is said to be unique for chordates and the combination of three unique features in several kinds of animals is not at all likely to be due to coincidence, but must be due to the inheritance of all three from a common ancestor. No one would doubt for a moment that all animals actually possessing all three of these fundamental peculiarities should be placed in the same phylum, but perhaps we may be justified in questioning whether some of the things called notochord, gill-slits, or dorsal tubular nerve cord actually deserve to be considered as such. In order to be in a position to recognize and evaluate these structures even when much modified or disguised it is necessary to determine exactly what sort of thing each of them is.

Notochord. — It is the notochord that has given the name Chordata to the group. Hence we may regard this structure as of primary diagnostic value in judging the claims of any doubtful form to be classed as a chordate. Functionally, the notochord is a primitive internal skeleton consisting of an elastic rod acting as a fulcrum for the segmental muscles to pull against in locomotor movements. Positionally, the notochord typically lies beneath the nerve cord and above the alimentary canal, with paired muscle segments to right and left of it. The tissue of a typical notochord is like nothing else, consisting of large vacuolated cells of characteristic appearance. The rod itself is covered by one or two sheaths of tough connective tissue. According to Goodrich, "the notochord invariably develops from the dorsal wall of the archenteron as a thickening or upfolding which becomes nipped off from before backward, and continues to grow at its posterior end as the embryo lengthens." In vertebrates proper the notochord never extends further forward than about the middle of the brain, where lies the hypophysis. In brief then, the notochord is a definite structural entity recognizable by its position, its function, its histological structure, and its embryonic origin. It ought to be possible to recognize a notochord wherever it occurs even if somewhat disguised by secondary changes.

Gill-slits. — The term "gill-slit" is thoroughly intrenched in vertebrate morphology although several other terms have been used as alternatives, such as pharyngeal clefts, visceral clefts, pharyngeal or visceral pouches, etc. It seems best to use consistently in this book but one term and we shall use the term "gill-slit," with the understanding that we mean the whole complex described below. The gill-slits serve primitively for the passage of water from the pharynx to the outside. Whether the water current originally served primarily for food gathering, for respiration, or for both equally, is a question to be discussed later. In any event, water comes in through the mouth and goes out through the gill-slits. This type of water passage is not used by any animals other than those commonly classed as chordates, but is found in some members of all the groups thus classified. In vertebrates several pairs of gill-slits are always functional in the adults of fully aquatic classes, in the larvae of most amphibia, and in the neotenic adults of several amphibian genera, but are never fully broken through at any stage in the reptiles, birds, and mammals. Yet in all vertebrates the initial stages in gill-slit formation are obvious during embryonic life.

The passages known as gill-slits are developed by the meeting of rather deep paired outpouchings of the pharyngeal endoderm with corresponding relatively shallow inpouchings of the body ectoderm. The thin membrane at the point of meeting of the corresponding ingrowing and outgrowing pouches breaks through and a continuous passage is produced. Originally the paired gill-slits were doubtless metameric, or better, intermetameric, but in specialized or degenerate groups the slits do not correspond in numbers with primary body segments. The numbers of gill-slits range from 180 pairs in the adult amphioxus to one pair in *Cephalodiscus* and none in *Rhabdopleura*. The ancestral number was undoubtedly relatively high as compared with that in surviving forms of vertebrates, but was probably much lower than in amphioxus, which has doubtless increased the number of its gill-slits through secondary polyisomerism in adaptation to sedentary life. Our guess would be that the ancestral number of gill-slits was around ten or a dozen pairs. Embryonically, the gill-slits develop first in front and proceed backward. In phylogeny there is a progressive reduction in numbers of functional gill-slits. The lowest vertebrates, Ostracodermi and

Cyclostomata, having from ten to fourteen pairs, and the highest, only one.

Dorsal Tubular Nerve Cord. — Nerve cords are characteristic of all elongate and fairly complex organisms. The typical form of nerve cords found in invertebrates consists of paired solid ventral cords, swollen segmentally to form ganglia. In chordates there is a single, unpaired dorsal tubular nerve cord, without distinct ganglionic enlargements. The tubular condition is arrived at as follows: At first, in an early embryonic stage, the primordium of the nerve cord appears as a thickened dorsal plate of ectoderm, the medullary plate. This becomes depressed along the median dorsal axis to form the medullary groove, which becomes progressively deeper and finally, the lateral shoulders of the groove arch inward and fuse in the median line to form a hollow tube. Then the contiguous wings of ectoderm fuse to form the dorsal epidermis of the body-wall, leaving the neural tube cut off from the surface.

The dorsal origin and position of the nerve cord are regarded as related to the original mode of life of ancestral chordates. It is generally believed that concentration of nerve cells to form a central nervous system takes place in relation to the direction from which comes the greatest stimulation. In flatworms, annelids, and primitive arthropods, which typically crawl on the ventral surface, the central nervous system is close to the substratum, i.e., on the ventral side. The dorsal position of the nerve cord in chordates is regarded as evidence that the ancestral chordates were not crawlers, but free-swimming pelagic forms, receiving their chief stimulation from the sea surface above them.

These three major characteristics of chordates are found in typical form only in true chordates (Protochordata and Craniata), but structures somewhat resembling them are found also in the Hemichordata. Whether these structures in *Balanoglossus*, etc., are true homologues of those in the true chordates will be discussed in the appropriate place.

CHARACTERISTICS OF CHORDATES SUPPOSEDLY SHARED BY INVERTEBRATES

While notochord, gill-slits, and hollow dorsal nerve cord are the chief diagnostic features of chordates, there are a number of other fundamental characters in which the chordates agree among themselves and in which they are said to agree with members of certain other phyla.

Chordates are described as axiate organisms with antero-posterior axis, dorso-ventral axis, and bilateral symmetry; as coelomate; as triploblastic; and as metameric. The question arises as to whether in these respects chordates are actually homologous with members of all other phyla that are similarly characterized or whether the resemblances are sometimes merely superficial, the result of convergent evolution. Specifically, is the antero-posterior axis of a chordate homologous with that of an arthropod or an annelid; is the mesoderm of the chordate homologous with that of an annelid; is the coelom of the chordate homologous with that of an annelid or arthropod; is metamerism in vertebrates homologous with that in annelids? Let us examine these situations.

Axiate Organization. — Like most of the higher invertebrates, vertebrates have a head end, that end that ordinarily precedes in locomotion. The opposite end is sometimes called the tail end, and the axis running from head to tail end is most commonly called the antero-posterior axis. The question arises as to whether the "head end" of vertebrates is homologous with that of invertebrates. The head end of vertebrates is certainly not homologous with the oral end of a hydra or other coelenterate. It is also unlikely that the head end of vertebrates is homologous with that of annelids and arthropods, for the mouth of these invertebrates is derived from the blastopore of the embryo, whereas the anus of vertebrates is formed near the blastopore and the mouth breaks through near the anterior end of the archenteron. If, therefore, we are justified in the above statements, it is not correct to consider the antero-posterior axis of the vertebrates as strictly homologous with that of most invertebrates.

It also seems to be generally agreed that chordates have a *dorso-ventral* axis in contrast with the *ventro-dorsal* axis of such animals as flatworms, annelids, and arthropods. By this is meant that the central nervous system, occupying the apical region of the secondary axis, is dorsal in chordates and ventral in invertebrates. Both the "head-tail" axis and the "top-bottom" axis of chordates are, therefore, diametrically reversed in orientation as compared with those of invertebrates. Hence it would seem to be stretching the concept of homology to the breaking point to consider these axes as homologous in the two groups. It is more probable that these opposed axiate conditions are quite different and have been acquired independently by the two groups in the course of their evolution.

The axis of symmetry (or the bilateral axis) of vertebrates might seem to be more nearly equivalent to that of invertebrates, but even this third axiate feature may not be strictly homologous in the two groups. Bilateral symmetry may be regarded as an inevitable accompaniment of the other two axes. It is difficult to conceive of an organism possessing both antero-posterior and dorso-ventral (or ventro-dorsal) axes without bilaterality of some sort. Bilaterality is a third dimensional accompaniment of the other two axes.

In conclusion, then, it may be argued that, while the axiate organization of chordates seems to be, at least superficially, similar to that of many of the higher invertebrates, there are such fundamental differences between the two groups that it may be safer to regard them as analogous rather than homologous, and therefore as originating independently in evolution. From this point of view alone (and there are many others that might be mentioned) it seems entirely improbable that vertebrates could have been derived from any of the existing higher invertebrate phyla.

Origin of Mesoderm (Triploblastic Condition). — All Metazoa above the level of the Coelenterata are triploblastic, that is, they have introduced the third germ layer, the mesoderm. It has generally been assumed that the mesoderm of one group of triploblastic animals is homologous with that of all others. It is also implied that all triploblastic animals trace back to one ancestral type that introduced the mesoderm for the first time. It is possible, however, to entertain a very different view, namely, that mesoderm may have originated independently in two or more types of diploblastic (coelenterate-like) animals and that the different modes of mesoderm formation originated in different phylogenetic series.

In support of this idea let us cite some well-known facts. In annelids, mollusks, arthropods, and related groups the mesoderm originates as solid, cord-like outgrowths derived from paired pole cells or groups of cells that lie at the juncture of the ectoderm and endoderm in the gastrula stage. In another group of animals, including amphioxus, hemichordates, echinoderms, arrowworms, and brachiopods, the mesoderm is formed typically as the result of outpocketings of the archenteron as in Figure 16. It seems entirely unlikely that animals having one of these two distinct types of mesoderm formation could have descended from animals having the other type. This consideration deals a severe blow to the annelid and arthropod theories of vertebrate ancestry.

Coelom. — As already has been shown, some of the coelomic cavities of amphioxus are derived from a linear series of hollow outpouchings of the primitive gut (archenteron). The hollows of the anterior segmental coeloms are there from the beginning and were originally a part of the cavity of the primitive gut. If the archenteron of the larva be regarded as wholly endodermal, it may be claimed that the coelom is endodermal in origin. Because the coelomic pouches give rise to mesoderm, however, some biologists prefer to consider the archenteron as a mesentodermal structure. In annelids and arthropods the solid paired mesodermal cords are not derived in any way from entoderm, though the pole cells from which they arise are derived from near the lips of the blastopore and might therefore be regarded as originating from a region intermediate between ectoderm and endoderm, possibly equivalent to mesentoderm. Such an attempt to reconcile the two modes of origin of mesoderm seems, however, rather far-fetched.

One must, on the other hand, admit that in the vertebrates proper, in spite of early accounts of amphibian development, the origin of the segmental coeloms from outpouchings of the archenteron is far from clear. A short-cutting of the process, possibly because of the accumulation of yolk in the egg, makes it appear that the coelomic primordia are not originally hollow, but open up cavities only at a later time. The mesoblastic somites seem to be derived from the primitive streak, which is morphologically the closed blastopore, and the cells of the streak give rise to both mesoderm and endoderm. Even this situation, however, does not strengthen the view that vertebrate and invertebrate coeloms are homologous.

In view of these considerations it seems obvious that the coelom of chordates is very different from that of most invertebrates and can not be considered as at all homologous with the latter.

Metamerism (Segmental Organization). — Metamerism, or segmental organization, while definitely characteristic of vertebrates, is externally less obvious than in metameric invertebrates such as annelids and arthropods. While in the latter segmentation is clearly defined both externally and internally, it is visible only internally in higher vertebrates. External segmentation is a necessity in arthropods because of their external skeleton, which must be jointed to permit bodily movement, but their external segmentation does not necessarily correspond fully with internal segmentation. In the vertebrates that possess an external skeleton the elements of their armature are often metameric in arrangement, as in the scale rows of some fishes. But many higher vertebrates have no true exoskeleton and therefore do not express their metamerism externally.

Internally, however, vertebrates are almost as thoroughly metameric as are the higher invertebrates. Even the body-wall musculature is primitively segmental and many of the internal systems, such as the nervous system, the circulatory system, the excretory system, etc., are, in origin at least, thoroughly segmental.

In searching for a possible invertebrate ancestor for the vertebrates it has been customary to select some group exhibiting metamerism, and theories have been elaborated involving both annelids and arthropods as possible ancestors of the vertebrates. These theories are based on the assumption that metamerism in one group must be homologous with that in another group and that segmental organization has arisen only once in the course of evolution. There are many cogent reasons for taking exception to this view. In the first place, metamerism in the annelids is arrived at by a method involving repeated hollowing out of the paired mesodermal cords derived through the proliferation of paired pole cells lying near the lips of the blastopore. In amphioxus, on the contrary, the initiation of metamerism is accomplished through the segmental outpouching of the archenteron, a totally different mode of origin from that in annelids, as has been explained above in the discussion of the coelom. Another great difficulty faced by proponents of the annelid or arthropod ancestry of vertebrates is that some of the chordates, notably the tunicates, are non-metameric. According to the annelid-arthropod ancestry theories, we would then have to suppose either that the tunicates are not related to vertebrates or else that they have secondarily lost their metamerism. Both of these suppositions are untenable.

These and other considerations favor the idea that metamerism in vertebrates is not homologous with that in metameric invertebrates, but at best only analogous. Hence there is no point in attempting to derive vertebrates from annelids or arthropods merely because metamerism is a feature common to all of them. A more defensible view is that metamerism arose independently in the groups under discussion.

SOME DISTINCTIVE CHARACTERS OF CRANIATA
(VERTEBRATES)

In addition to the characters already enumerated and discussed in which the vertebrates agree with the non-vertebrate chordates and those in which they agree at least superficially, with members of certain other phyla, there is a large number of purely vertebrate characters that are not shared by other animals at all or are shared only in a very general way.

Vertebrates constitute the main division of the Phylum Chordata. In spite of the striking diversity of both superficial and internal organization between the lowest and highest vertebrate (say hagfish and man), there is so much in common between them and such a fundamental unity of body plan running throughout the whole subphylum that there can be no question but that the entire group came from a common ancestral stock. The list of vertebrate characters is a long one and it is difficult to decide where to set a limit. Those that seem most characteristic and significant are the following: *1*, internal and external skeleton; *2*, vertebral column; *3*, cranium; *4*, cephalization; *5*, dorsal and ventral nerve roots; *6*, sympathetic nervous system; *7*, pituitary and pineal bodies; *8*, ventral heart; *9*, hepatic portal system; *10*, red blood corpuscles; *11*, paired appendages, when present, originating from several segments; *12*, postanal tail; *13*, endocrine glands. A brief discussion of each of these characteristics follows:

Both Internal and External Skeleton. — All vertebrates and other true chordates have a unique type of skeletal equipment not found in any invertebrate, namely, the internal skeleton consisting of the notochord. In addition, the vertebrates very commonly have an external skeleton consisting of scales or dermal plates. In the earliest vertebrates of which we have a fossil record (the ostracoderms) the external armor-like skeleton was composed of rather large, flat, bony plates, which may represent fused scales, covering the anterior part of the body. It may be significant that these early vertebrates show about equal development of internal and external skeletons. In the higher vertebrates it frequently happens that some of the external skeletal elements sink beneath the surface and reinforce the internal skeleton, thereby ceasing to exist as external skeletal elements. Further discussion at present of these relations would carry us too far afield.

Vertebral Column. — The possession of a vertebral column must have made a strong impression on the early anatomists, for they named the vertebrates after this character and called all other animals lacking this character invertebrates. While the vertebral column is doubtless a very important character it is totally absent in some lower chordates and present only in a very rudimentary form in some true vertebrates, the Cyclostomata, which may, however, be degenerate in this respect. The vertebral column in its developed condition is made up of a series of segmental bones or cartilages that are organized about the notochord. Cartilage cells penetrate and invade the sheaths of the notochord and displace partially or completely the notochordal tissue to form the centrum of the vertebra. Neural arches above and haemal arches below surround respectively the neural tube and the vertebral blood vessels. These arches and their accessories in higher vertebrates fuse with the centrum to make the solid vertebrae. The vertebrae are articulated to one another by movable joints of many different shapes characteristic of different major groups.

Cranium. — The possession of a cranium, sometimes called skull or brain-case, must also have seemed to anatomists to be highly important, for the true vertebrates are commonly called Craniata in contrast with Acraniata, of which amphioxus is a representative. The brain-case arises from several flat cartilaginous plates beneath and beside the brain. These plates expand, fuse together and coalesce with the cartilaginous capsules surrounding the main sense organs to make a continuous brain-box, or *chondrocranium*. In bony fishes and higher vertebrates this primitive cranium is further boxed in above and below by the sinking in of bones of the exoskeleton, the armor bones of the head region. These fuse with the original brain-case to make an extremely complex skull. In higher vertebrates the cartilaginous elements of the skull are gradually replaced by bone.

Cephalization. — All vertebrates have a well-defined head, characterized by a rather complex brain and specialized sense organs. In amphioxus the head is very poorly represented, if present at all. In the lowest vertebrates the head is rather small and not clearly marked off from the trunk. As one surveys the ascending series of vertebrate types from the hag-fishes to man he is impressed with the steady increase in relative size and specialization of the head, and especially of its nervous components.

This steady trend toward greater and greater prominence and domination of the head over the rest of the body is called cephalization.

The study of the problem of segmentation in the head has occupied the attention of many leading morphologists and the solution of the problem is still incomplete. De Beer claims that the clue to the puzzle lies in the recognition that there are two more or less independent heads, the "neural head" which is dorsal, and the "visceral head," which is ventral. The posterior extent of the neural head is marked by the occipital arch and that of the visceral head by the last visceral arch. These two heads are both involved in cephalization but in opposite ways. The neural head tends to extend its territory by borrowing and incorporating one after the other in the course of evolution additional trunk segments, while the visceral head tends to become progressively shorter and shorter by losing segments or telescoping them more and more beneath the neural head. The neural head of the lowest vertebrates occupies four segments, that of some sharks seven; Amphibia seem to be degenerate with only six segments; while in reptiles, birds, and mammals the neural head occupies eight segments. The number of segments in the visceral head is highest in some of the cyclostomes and becomes progressively less as one proceeds up the scale to the land vertebrates.

Dorsal and Ventral Nerve Roots. — While most of the higher invertebrates possess paired segmental nerves branching off from the nerve cords, only vertebrates and amphioxus possess two sets of nerve roots, a dorsal pair and a ventral pair coming off from the nerve cord of each metamere. The ventral roots are purely efferent or motor in function, carrying impulses from the brain or spinal cord to effectors such as muscles and glands. The dorsal roots are of mixed character, carrying mainly afferent impulses from the peripheral sensory neurones to the central nervous system, but some of the fibers are efferent. The dorsal root is usually provided with a large swelling, the spinal ganglion, in which lie many neurone bodies. After remaining separate for a short distance the dorsal and ventral roots usually unite to form the mixed common spinal nerves. This complex is characteristic of most vertebrates, but in amphioxus and in the lampreys the two roots remain separate throughout. The whole system of nerves and ganglia outside of the brain and spinal cord constitute the *peripheral nervous system* in contradistinction to the *central nervous system.* A special part of the peripheral system will be next discussed.

Sympathetic Nervous System. — An elaborate system of ganglia, some segmentally arranged in two rows paralleling the spinal cord and others irregularly placed, constitutes an internal co-ordinating system. This system is also referred to as the *autonomic* or as the *visceral system*, both terms being partly descriptive. The term "autonomic" refers to the fact that this system is not under voluntary control and operates without arousing consciousness. The term "visceral" suggests that the system lies in the body cavity and controls the activities of the internal organs or viscera. The whole system has hook-ups with the various centers in the central nervous system, notably the medulla oblongata.

Pituitary and Pineal Bodies. — These two characteristic structures are usually associated in the minds of biologists and therefore will be dealt with as one topic even though they are quite different and unrelated except in that they are both in a sense "appendages" of the brain.

The *pituitary body* lies beneath the fore-brain and has a dual origin, being composed of *a*, the *hypophysis* that grows in from the embryonic ectoderm in front of the head; and *b*, the *infundibulum*, a down-growth from the floor of the fore-brain, which is therefore of nervous origin. In all vertebrates except the cyclostomes the two components are more or less fused into one complex endocrine gland producing several different hormones essential to normal growth and functioning of various systems of organs. Further details about the pituitary gland must be deferred till later in the course.

The *pineal body*, or epiphysis, is in higher vertebrates a vestigial organ of no known present function which is morphologically a diverticulum from the roof of the diencephalon, or 'tween-brain. In lower vertebrates the pineal body is clearly a small median third eye, which looks directly upward from the top of the head. In its best developed state, as in some of the reptiles, there is a retina and a lens and the organ doubtless has a visual function.

Ventral Heart. — The heart is morphologically a specialized region of the main ventral vein. In amphioxus there is no definite heart enlargement but merely a pulsating region of the large vein beneath the pharynx. In cyclostomes the heart is a muscular S-shaped tube, in fishes the auricle and ventricle are better defined, in Amphibia and reptiles the auricle is subdivided into right and left halves and the ventricle partly divided, and in birds and mammals the ventricle is fully divided into right and left ventricles. Gradual specialization of the heart constitutes one of the main evolutionary trends in vertebrates. In those invertebrates that have specialized hearts the position of the heart is dorsal or else consists of a series of segmental heart arches as in the annelids. Both conditions in invertebrates are thus in sharp contrast to those in vertebrates and other chordates.

Hepatic Portal System. — A peculiarly vertebrate portion of the circulatory system is that part of the venous trunk which sidetracks the food-laden blood from the intestine into the great filtration or purifying plant known as the liver. Even in the lowly amphioxus with its primitive liver diverticulum there is a hepatic portal loop as shown in Figure 10. Invertebrates have glands that have been naïvely called livers but are not true livers in the sense that they are homologous with or function like vertebrate livers.

Red Blood Corpuscles. — While some invertebrates have red blood, due to the presence of a red pigment, *haemoglobin*, they carry the latter in colloidal solution in the blood plasma. In contrast with this, the vertebrates carry haemoglobin in specialized cells, the red blood corpuscles, or *erythrocytes*, which are typically formed in the red bone marrow, but also have other sources of origin. The blood of amphioxus is colorless and there is, of course, no need of erythrocytes. Curiously enough, however, there are variously colored corpuscles in the blood of tunicates that may function similarly to the erythrocytes of vertebrates.

Paired Appendages Each Originating from Several Segments. — While no modern vertebrate has more than two pairs of paired appendages, some of the primitive extinct fishes possessed additional pairs. Invertebrates also possess paired appendages, but in them a single pair of appendages is derived from but one metamere. In the vertebrates, however, the muscular, nervous, and skeletal elements of several adjacent metameres combine to form a single appendage. The number of metameres involved in an appendage differs somewhat in fore and hind limbs and shows some variation in different groups of vertebrates. The presence of paired appendages is not universal among vertebrates, for the cyclostomes are entirely limbless. Needless to say, amphioxus has no paired appendages although the metapleural folds are sometimes regarded as the primordial homologues of paired fins.

Postanal Tail. — The tail may be described as a posterior pro-longation of the trunk without a body cavity (splanchnocoel). It usually possesses vertebrae, muscle segments, nerve cord, and blood vessels, but never contains visceral organs. The tail is characteristic also of amphioxus and of larval tunicates. In certain Amphibia the tail is absent in the adult but present in the larva, while in man and apes it is reduced to a vestigial structure in adults, though well de-fined in the embryo. The original function of the tail seems to have been that of aquatic locomotion. In many aquatic and in some terrestrial vertebrates it is still an important locomotor organ.

Endocrine Glands. — Endocrine glands are glands of internal secretion, in contrast with exocrine glands that emit their secretions into digestive and excretory passages, or to the body surface. Endo-crine glands discharge their products, called *hormones*, directly into the blood stream. While it is certain that some invertebrates possess glands that meet the above definition, the possession of an elaborate system of endocrine glands seems to be a peculiarly vertebrate char-acteristic often overlooked in listing vertebrate characters.

The role of the endocrine glands seems to be that of co-ordinating the functions of the internal organs. In this they share the duties of the nervous system. The most important of the endocrine glands are the thyroid, the pituitary, the islet cells of the pancreas, the parathyroids, the adrenals (suprarenals), and the glandular parts of the male and female gonads. It is no mere chance that the verte-brates, the largest, most highly specialized and most completely integrated of organisms, should have not only the most highly spe-cialized nervous systems, but also the most elaborate system of chemical integrators and co-ordinators, the endocrine gland system.

The above list of vertebrate characteristics is by no means ex-haustive. One immediately thinks of the characteristic sense organs, the peculiar and unique digestive tract with its digestive glands, the unique excretory system, and the unique features of embryonic de-velopment. It seems advisable, however, to omit these features here, as any general statement about them would be inadequate, while a detailed account would doubtless be unintelligible in advance of a study of the systems in the laboratory.

CLASSIFICATION OF THE PHYLUM CHORDATA

Taxonomy is at best somewhat arbitrary. Almost every treatise of vertebrate zoology or monograph on a class of vertebrates uses a different classification. The writer has had access to the best authorities in the field and can do no more than attempt to select from those classifications available the best parts of each and to put them together into a single system. Our plan is that of following the classification preferred by a leading authority in each class or in some cases to combine what seem to be the best features of two or more classifications. This method may produce something different from any other hitherto published, but we have made a strong effort to arrive at a classification that will meet the needs of students and teachers everywhere and at the same time express something of the individual views of the writer himself. In this classification there are several types of intermediate categories between the more familiar ones such as Phyla, Subphyla, Classes, and Orders.

The broadest divisions of a phylum are the subphyla. A subphylum such as Craniata is first divided into two main **Branches** (Monorhina and Gnathostomata), the two largest categories of vertebrates. The Gnathostomata are then divided into two primary groups called GRADE Ichthyopterygii (fish-like or finned gnathostomes) and GRADE Tetrapoda (four-footed gnathostomes). The GRADE Ichthyopterygii consists only of the *Class* Pisces, which is broadly divisible into two *Subgrades* Chondrichthyes (cartilage fishes) and Osteichthyes (bony fishes). The GRADE Tetrapoda is broadly subdivided into **Subgrade** Anamnia (without an amnion) including only the *Class* Amphibia, and **Subgrade** Amniota (with an amnion) including the *Classes* Reptilia, Aves, and Mammalia.

Several intermediate taxonomic categories such as Subclass, Infraclass, Superorder, Subdivision, Group, Section, etc., are introduced when such categories seem to serve a useful purpose.

PHYLUM CHORDATA

SUBPHYLUM I. PROTOCHORDATA (ACRANIA)

 Class I. Urochordata
    Order 1. Ascideacea
    Order 2. Thaliacea
    Order 3. Larvacea

 Class II. Cephalochordata

 APPENDIX. PHYLUM (?) HEMICHORDATA

 Class I. Enteropneusta
 Class II. Pterobranchia
 Class III. Phoronidea (?)

SUBPHYLUM II. CRANIATA (VERTEBRATA)

BRANCH A. MONORHINA (AGNATHA)

Class Cyclostomata
Subclass Myxinoidea
Subclass Petromyzontia

Class Ostracodermi
Order 1. Anaspida *
Order 2. Cephalospidomorphi *
Order 3. Pteraspidomorphi *
Order 4. Pterichthyomorphi *

BRANCH B. GNATHOSTOMATA (AMPHIRHINA)

GRADE ICHTHYOPTERYGII

Class Pisces
Subgrade Chondrichthyes
Subclass Elasmobranchii
Order Selachii
Order Holocephali
Order Pleuracanthoidei *
Subclass Cladoselachii *
Subclass Acanthodii *
Subclass Coccosteomorphi
Order Anarthrodira *
Order Arthrodira *
Subgrade Osteichthyes
Subclass Choanichthyes
Order Dipnoi
Order Crossopterygii
Suborder Osteolepidoti *
Suborder Coelacanthini *
Subclass Actinopterygii
Subdivision A.
Order Chondrostei
Order Polypterini
Subdivision B. Holostei
Group a.
Order Amioidei
Order Lepidosteoidei
Group b.
Order Teleostei

* Extinct orders (sometimes subclasses) are indicated by an asterisk.

GRADE TETRAPODA (CHEIROPTERYGII)

Subgrade Anamnia
Class Amphibia
Order Labyrinthodontia *
Order Phyllospondyli *
Order Lepospondyli *
Order Gymnophiona (Apoda)
Order Caudata (Urodela)
Order Salientia (Anura)

Subgrade Amniota
Class Reptilia
Subclass Anapsida
Order Cotylosauria *
Order Chelonia
Subclass Ichthyopterygia (validity doubtful)
Order Mesosauria *
Order Ichthyosauria *
Subclass Synaptosauria (validity doubtful)
Order Protorosauria *
Order Sauropterygia *
Subclass Lepidosauria (validity doubtful)
Order Eusuchia *
Order Rhynchocephalia
Order Squamata
Subclass Archosauria
Order Thecodontia *
Order Crocodilia
Order Pterosauria *
Order Saurischia *
Order Ornithischia *
Subclass Synapsida
Order Pelycosauria *
Order Therapsida *
Class Aves
Grade Archaeornithes *
Grade Neornithes
Section 1. Odontormae
Order Ichthyorniformes *
Section 2. Odontolcae
Order Hesperornithes *
Section 3. Ratitae
Order Casuarii
Order Struthiones

           Order Rheae
           Order Dinornithes *
           Order Aepyornithes *
           Order Apteryges
        Section 4. Carinatae
          Group a. Palaeognathae
           Order Tinamiformes
          Group b. Neognathae
           Order Sphenisciformes
           Order Colymbiformes
           Order Procellariiformes
           Order Pelicaniformes
           Order Ciconiiformes
           Order Anseriformes
           Order Falconiformes
           Order Galliformes
           Order Opisthocomiformes
           Order Gruiformes
           Order Charadriiformes
           Order Columbiformes
           Order Cuculiformes
           Order Psittaciformes
           Order Coraciiformes
           Order Passeriformes

Class Mammalia
  Subclass Prototheria
      Order Monotremata
  Subclass Allotheria
      Order Multituberculata *
  (Mammalia incertae sedis)
      Order Triconodontia *
  Subclass Theria
    Infraclass Pantotheria
      Order Pantotheria *
      Order Symmetrodonta *
    Infraclass Metatheria (Didelphia)
      Order Marsupialia
    Infraclass Eutheria (Monodelphia)
      Order Insectivora ⎫
      Order Dermoptera ⎪ Insectivore
      Order Chiroptera ⎬ Assemblage or
      Order Primates   ⎭ Superorder
      Order Rodentia

Order Edentata ⎫
Order Pholidota ⎬ Edentate Assemblage or Superorder
Order Tubulidentata ⎭

Order Carnivora ⎫
Order Cetacea ⎬ Carnivore Assemblage or Superorder

Order Perissodactyla ⎫
Order Artiodactyla ⎪
Order Hyracoidea ⎬ Ungulate Assemblage or Superorder
Order Proboscidea ⎪
Order Sirenia ⎭

Although much of the classification here presented depends upon a study of the comparative anatomy and embryology of living groups, even a larger part of it has to do with extinct groups. Without a background of the chordates of the past those of the present can not be adequately understood. The real heart and spirit of vertebrate zoology is that part which deals with the evolution of the group. Hence it seems necessary for us to divert attention for a time from a consideration of the pure morphology of the vertebrates in order to consider some of the broader principles that to some extent guide the further discussion of the various groups of chordates.

CHAPTER II

PRINCIPLES AND FACTORS OF VERTEBRATE EVOLUTION

VERTEBRATES AS MATERIAL FOR THE STUDY OF ORGANIC EVOLUTION

The actual course of vertebrate evolution is better known and understood than that of any other group of animals. Hence a course dealing largely with vertebrates should, we believe, center about the theme of evolution and should present the best illustrations of the various modes and trends of evolution that seem to be discernible from a careful study of vertebrate history.

The reasons why the vertebrates are especially favorable for the objective study of evolutionary processes are mainly four: *a*, the group is of *relatively* recent origin and therefore fossil vertebrates are confined to rocks and other depositories that are available for study on account of their relative nearness to the surface and their relatively unchanged character; *b*, most vertebrates possess external or internal skeletons or both, and these hard parts are especially well adapted for fossilization; *c*, the vertebrates are now and have been for a long time large and abundant animals; and *d*, living vertebrates have been more extensively studied than any other animals, with the possible exception of insects, a fact that facilitates the interpretation of the fossil remains of extinct forms.

THE TIME SCALE OF VERTEBRATE EVOLUTION

When it was stated that vertebrates are of relatively recent origin, the word "*relatively*" was italicized because otherwise the statement might be misleading. As a matter of fact, the earliest fossil fragments of vertebrates have been found in rocks of the Silurian Period, which were deposited approximately 400,000,000 years ago. These extinct vertebrates, known as ostracoderms, were fish-like creatures with well-developed head armature. They had already become specialized into a considerable number of diverse groups. From this fact it

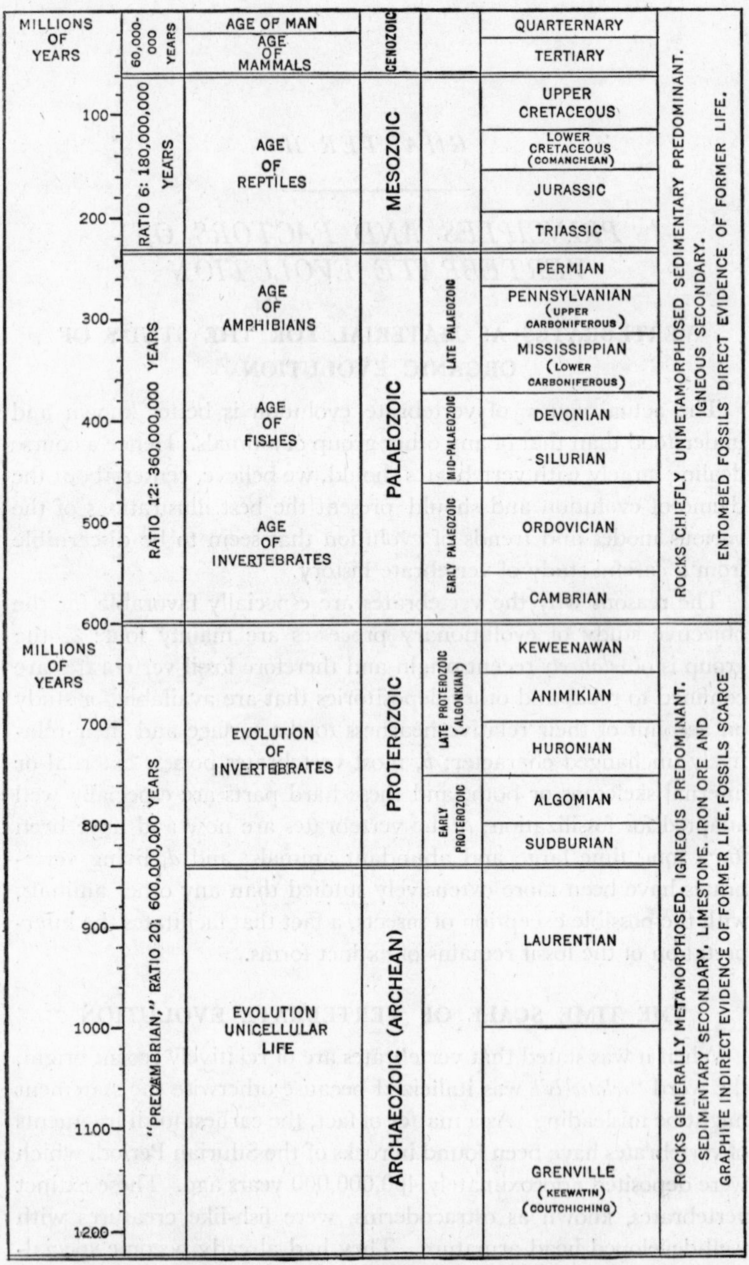

MILLIONS OF YEARS		AGE OF MAN	CENOZOIC		QUARTERNARY	
	60,000,000 YEARS	AGE OF MAMMALS			TERTIARY	ROCKS CHIEFLY UNMETAMORPHOSED SEDIMENTARY PREDOMINANT. IGNEOUS SECONDARY. ENTOMBED FOSSILS DIRECT EVIDENCE OF FORMER LIFE.
100—	RATIO 6: 180,000,000 YEARS	AGE OF REPTILES	MESOZOIC		UPPER CRETACEOUS	
					LOWER CRETACEOUS (COMANCHEAN)	
					JURASSIC	
200—					TRIASSIC	
		AGE OF AMPHIBIANS		LATE PALAEOZOIC	PERMIAN	
300—	RATIO 12: 360,000,000 YEARS				PENNSYLVANIAN (UPPER CARBONIFEROUS)	
			PALAEOZOIC		MISSISSIPPIAN (LOWER CARBONIFEROUS)	
400—		AGE OF FISHES		MID-PALAEOZOIC	DEVONIAN	
					SILURIAN	
500—		AGE OF INVERTEBRATES		EARLY PALAEOZOIC	ORDOVICIAN	
					CAMBRIAN	
600— MILLIONS OF YEARS		EVOLUTION OF INVERTEBRATES	PROTEROZOIC	LATE PROTEROZOIC (ALGONKIAN)	KEWEENAWAN	ROCKS GENERALLY METAMORPHOSED. IGNEOUS PREDOMINANT. SEDIMENTARY SECONDARY, LIMESTONE, IRON ORE AND GRAPHITE INDIRECT EVIDENCE OF FORMER LIFE. FOSSILS SCARCE
700—	"PRECAMBRIAN," RATIO 20: 600,000,000 YEARS				ANIMIKIAN	
					HURONIAN	
800—				EARLY PROTEROZOIC	ALGOMIAN	
					SUDBURIAN	
900—		EVOLUTION UNICELLULAR LIFE	ARCHAEOZOIC (ARCHEAN)		LAURENTIAN	
1000—						
1100—						
					GRENVILLE (KEEWATIN) (COUTCHICHING)	
1200—						

Fig. 1. Total Geologic Time Scale, estimated at 1,200,000,000 years. (From Newman, after Osborn, modified to agree with the more recent estimates.)

may be deduced that our first glimpse of vertebrate history is ob-
tained after a long, slow preparatory period that may well have
begun at least another 50,000,000 years earlier. A reasonable guess
would place the dawn of vertebrate history at a period about
450,000,000 years ago. After admitting for them such great antiquity it may, therefore, seem ironic to speak of vertebrates as in any
sense recent, but when we take into consideration that some fossil
invertebrates probably date back nearly a billion years and that most
invertebrate phyla are well represented in Cambrian rocks 650,-
000,000 years old, the term *"relatively recent"* seems justified for the
vertebrates.

The accompanying Geologic Time Scale (Fig. 1) gives in condensed form the order of succession of the ages, eras, and periods,
together with estimates, based largely on the degree of disintegra-
tion of radio-active elements found in various rocks, of the age
and duration of these periods. It will be useful for the student to
memorize this table at least from Silurian times on, as a basis of
reference, for in the succeeding chapters we shall have occasion to
state that, for example, flying reptiles originated during Jurassic
times and lasted till the end of Cretaceous times, without explain-
ing what is meant by these terms.

For our purposes we may confine attention to three geologic eras:
Palaeozoic, Mesozoic, and Cenozoic. Some authorities have dig-
nified the last half million years of the Cenozoic by the term Psychozoic Era, involving the time since the dawn of Man. The Palaeozoic Era is subdivided into three sub-eras: early Palaeozoic;
mid-Palaeozoic (the Age of Fishes); and late Palaeozoic (the Age of
Amphibia and of Primitive Reptiles). The whole Mesozoic Era
is known as the Golden Age of Reptiles; while the main part of the
Cenozoic, the Tertiary sub-era, is known as the Age of Mammals,
leaving the last and most recent part of this era, the Quarternary,
to be termed the Age of Man, or the Psychozoic sub-era.

THE ROCKY PAGES OF GEOLOGICAL HISTORY

The successive layers of rock from the lowest to the highest,
from the most deeply buried to the most recent surface deposits,
constitute a readable history of the various changes in the earth's
crust during the last billion years. The whole series of strata may be
regarded as a vast volume consisting of pages superimposed one
upon another, containing the records of the physiographic conditions,

the climates, and the animals and plants existing at the time each "page" was "written." Experts in geology and paleontology are able to read and interpret these pages of the earth's history with a reasonable degree of accuracy. Many parts of the story are still missing either because the pages containing these parts have not yet been exposed for inspection, have been largely destroyed by erosion, or rendered illegible by other geologic processes. Considering the relatively small part of the whole record at present available to students of geology, it is indeed remarkable that the history of vertebrate evolution is, at least in its main outlines, so nearly complete.

Some of the main facts derived from the study of the vertebrate fossil record are as follows:

The earliest complete vertebrate fossils are those of ostracoderms: aquatic, fish-like forms with relatively generalized (unspecialized) organization. After these, in succession appeared the jawed (gnathostome) cartilaginous fishes, bony fishes, amphibians, reptiles, birds, and mammals, and the peculiar mammal, man. The accompanying chart (Fig. 2) serves to visualize this story. There has been a somewhat orderly advance in general efficiency and dominance over the adverse factors of the environment, resulting at present in the partial control of the environment by the most advanced vertebrate now living, *Homo sapiens*.

During the period of vertebrate evolution immense numbers of evolutionary lines have been started, only to meet with failure either because of overspecialization or because the main schemes of their evolutionary changes were out of step with the current geologic or organic changes. The result has been the total extinction of many thousands of vertebrate types and the survival of only a relatively few. The following story has repeated itself over and over again. In some existing group which has recently been an offshoot of an earlier group and has not as yet gone very far in the specialization of the new characters that distinguish it from its ancestral stock, some novel and rather radical change has given rise to the pioneers of another new group. Such a new group, once it has gained a firm foothold, begins a process of *adaptive radiation*, during which many specialized types arise that are adapted to a great variety of different environments. During a single geologic period specialization goes farther and farther, each divergent type becoming better adapted to some particular environmental complex, but less adapted to other environments. The close of each geologic period is characterized by more or less radical geologic changes, involving increasing climatic vicissi-

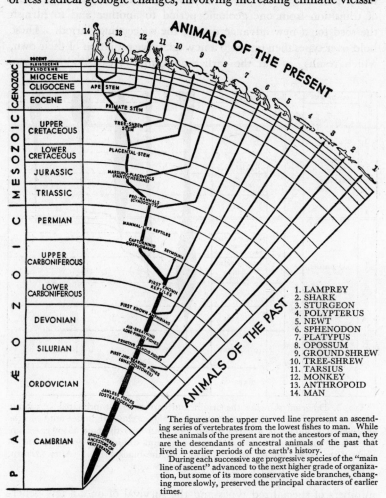

1. LAMPREY
2. SHARK
3. STURGEON
4. POLYPTERUS
5. NEWT
6. SPHENODON
7. PLATYPUS
8. OPOSSUM
9. GROUND SHREW
10. TREE-SHREW
11. TARSIUS
12. MONKEY
13. ANTHROPOID
14. MAN

The figures on the upper curved line represent an ascending series of vertebrates from the lowest fishes to man. While these animals of the present are not the ancestors of man, they are the descendants of ancestral animals of the past that lived in earlier periods of the earth's history.

During each successive age progressive species of the "main line of ascent" advanced to the next higher grade of organization, but some of its more conservative side branches, changing more slowly, preserved the principal characters of earlier times.

Fig. 2. Phylogenetic tree of vertebrate evolution, especially emphasizing the ancestral history of man, with other groups shown as side lines. (From W. K. Gregory, courtesy of the American Museum of Natural History, New York.)

tudes and continental uplifts. The natural result has been that the most specialized types of each period, unable to adjust themselves to the on-coming changes, have almost without exception become extinct. Fortunately for progressive evolution as a whole, however, a few representatives of each of the main groups have remained relatively generalized and plastic, sufficiently so to withstand the rigors of transition from one geologic period to another and to furnish the seed for a new advance during the succeeding period.   These hold-over types then undergo a new adaptive radiation of their own, which results, as did the earlier ones, in the extinction of large

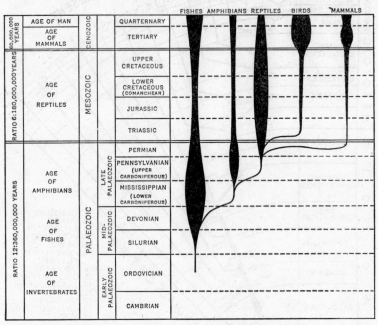

FIG. 3. Diagram showing the origin and careers of the principal vertebrate classes, showing especially the fact that each higher class originates not from the specialized members of a lower group, but from near the base of lower group. Periods of maximum radiation (expansion) and diminution (contraction) of each of the classes are shown graphically by the black areas. (After Osborn, *Origin and Evolution of Life*, Charles Scribner's Sons.)

numbers of specialized types and the survival of only a few generalized representatives that become the starting-points for further adaptive radiation.

An analysis of this story might lead one to the conclusion that over the long-time period no real evolutionary progress is made, for the specialized types of each period leave no survivors and only the conservative, relatively unprogressive types persist. Such a conclusion, however, is not justified by the facts, for these conservative stem stocks are themselves not at a standstill. They do not change much with respect to such characters as would especially adapt them to peculiar or temporary environments, but they do change slowly and surely with respect to their deeper-lying organization in such a way that they steadily improve in general efficiency and in their abilities to cope with geologic crises or with changing environments in general.

The accompanying chronological chart of vertebrate succession (Fig. 3) pictures graphically the story just told. The relative widths of each black area during successive periods indicates the small beginning, the maximum success, and the decline of each of the vertebrate classes. It also shows how each new class comes off from near the base of the earlier class, not from its later, more specialized members.

TWO KINDS AND PACES OF EVOLUTIONARY CHANGE

From what has been said it may be inferred that there are two distinct kinds and paces of evolutionary change: *a*, the relatively rapid type of evolution known as adaptive radiation, according to which a generalized group becomes progressively more and more split up into numerous subtypes specialized for the diverse existing environmental complexes, the most specialized representatives becoming extinct during or at the end of the geologic period in which they arose; and *b*, the relatively slow type of evolution of the mainstem forms that remain generalized with regard to special adaptive features, but steadily add to their equipment for general adaptability and efficiency.

Both kinds of evolution exhibit elements of orderliness. In evolutionary parlance, they are orthogenetic in character. In those branches that undergo adaptive radiation, each line of specialization follows definite trends toward increased fitness for particular environments. As a good example of this kind of special adaptive evolution one may be pardoned for mentioning the classic but somewhat hackneyed case of the evolution of the horse family (Fig. 4). The horse tribe might be regarded as the vertebrates' response to a highly important evolutionary advance in the plant world. During late Eocene times, when mammals were just beginning an extensive adaptive radiation, the first grasses arose and gained a foothold. These highly efficient plants spread rapidly over vast areas of territory unsuitable for other plants and offered a new energy source for any animals capable of exploiting it. This was doubtless the chief incentive back of the evolution of those highly efficient grazing types, the horses. Steadily the horses became larger, swifter of foot and longer of neck. Their teeth became more and more specialized for grinding the harsh grass tissues. As the horses grew more numerous they become the prey of swift-footed carnivores, and speed on foot was a prime necessity for survival. What the horses did in response was to specialize for longer legs and tip-toe running, resulting in the steady loss of their hoofed toes until the more recent horses came to possess but one functional toe on each foot, a toe armed with a massive modified claw, the hoof. Through the millenniums succeeding the Eocene, at which time the first primitive horses appeared, one can trace steady, progressive trends, involving increasing size, length of legs and neck, reduction of toes, and tooth specialization. Such a series of orderly evolutionary changes is an example of what evolutionists commonly call *orthogenesis* (literally translated as straight-line evolution). Scores of other examples of orthogenetic series have been described for both vertebrates and invertebrates.

Various theories have been offered in explanation of the genetic mechanisms underlying the undisputed facts of orthogenesis, but as yet none seems quite adequate. Natural selection of mutations remains at present the most acceptable, though various modern students of evolution have attempted to discredit it.

Not less regular and orderly are the evolutionary changes exhibited by vertebrates in their long, slow progress from period to period of geologic time. Those plastic and relatively generalized stem types that survive through the vicissitudes of transition from period to period exhibit certain steady, progressive trends which make for increasing general efficiency. Chief among these trends is that of steadily advancing intelligence, which from the morphological aspect means increase in the size and specialization of the brain and the sense organs of the head. This trend has already been referred to on pages 11, 12 under the title of cephalization. Thus the brain and sense organs of the ostracoderms are relatively quite small and generalized with little specialization of the fore-brain. Steadily, throughout the ages the vertebrate brain has increased in size relative to that of the body and in regional specialization. The fore-brain has progressively increased in size and importance, especially that part of it known as the cerebral hemispheres, until in man the cerebral cortex, or neopallium, far overshadows the rest of the brain

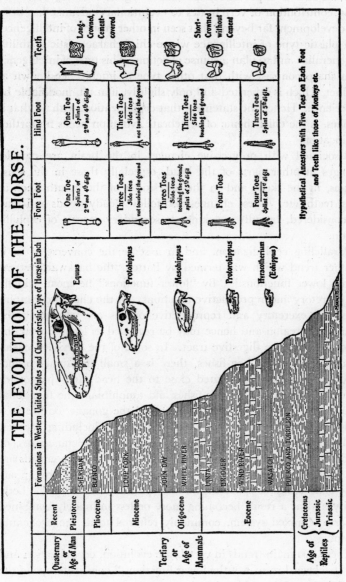

The table in the image contains the following content:

THE EVOLUTION OF THE HORSE.

Age	Formations in Western United States and Characteristic Type of Horse in Each	Fore Foot	Hind Foot	Teeth
Quaternary or Age of Man — Recent, Pleistocene	SHERIDAN, BLANCO — Equus	One Toe Splints of 2nd and 4th digits	One Toe Splints of 2nd and 4th digits	Long-Crowned, Cement-covered
Tertiary or Age of Mammals — Pliocene	LOUP FORK — Protohippus	Three Toes Side toes not touching the ground	Three Toes Side toes not touching the ground	
Miocene	JOHN DAY			
Oligocene	WHITE RIVER — Mesohippus	Three Toes Side toes touching the ground; splint of 5th digit	Three Toes Side toes touching the ground	
Eocene	UINTA, BRIDGER, WIND RIVER — Protorohippus	Four Toes	Three Toes Splint of 5th digit	Short-Crowned without Cement
	WASATCH, PUERCO AND TORREJON — Hyracotherium (Eohippus)	Four Toes Splint of 1st digit		
Age of Reptiles { Cretaceous, Jurassic, Triassic	Hypothetical Ancestors with Five Toes on Each Foot and Teeth like those of Monkeys etc.			

FIG. 4. Graphic presentation of the evolution of the Horse. (From Matthew, 1926.)

29

and has become a peculiarly specialized organ of intelligence. The main contribution of vertebrates to evolutionary advance has been the development far beyond that seen in other groups of intelligence, of a plastic type of intelligence whose chief characteristic is ability to generalize and to plan a course of action. This type of intelligence is in sharp contrast with that other type of intelligence known as instinct, which is inherited and only slightly, if at all, modifiable by experience. Hence the statement that cephalization, with all that it implies, is the chief theme of vertebrate evolution needs no further justification.

Associated with progressive changes in the brain are parallel changes in other parts of the head, especially those in the sense organs, in the skull, and in the accessories of the mouth, such as jaws, teeth, etc. These changes also follow steady trends and may be considered, broadly speaking, as secondary aspects of cephalization.

Paralleling cephalization, and in a sense the converse of it, is another trend which was termed by Patten "the backward retreat of the lower functions." By "lower functions" he meant chiefly the excretory and reproductive functions. In the chordate, amphioxus, the excretory and reproductive organs are present in the pharyngeal region and hence may be regarded as located near the head region of the digestive tract. In some of the surviving cyclostomes, notably the hag-fishes, there is a small functional pronephros, or fore-kidney, situated close to the head, and the gonads extend far forward. In true fishes and amphibians the functional kidney (mesonephros or mid-kidney) and the gonads too are in a mid-trunk region. In the higher vertebrates, including reptiles, birds, and mammals, the functional kidney (the metanephros, or hind-kidney) occupies a more posterior position and the gonads are still further back, the ducts and accessories of the two systems apparently competing for space in the most posterior region of the body cavity and as a result becoming more or less intimately combined to form a mixed system, commonly referred to as the urogenital system.

These two main trends in vertebrate evolution, cephalization and the "backward retreat of the lower functions," constitute two of the chief themes of the study of the comparative anatomy of vertebrates and will be amply illustrated in chapters dealing with various vertebrate and lower chordate classes.

Minor, but important additional trends are obvious accompaniments of the two chief trends dealt with above. Notable among these are trends in the circulatory system, in the organs of locomotion, and in the exo- and endoskeleton. While these trends are less obviously orthogenetic than are the two main trends there are in them elements of steady progress and increasing efficiency of function that can not be overlooked.

From the ecological standpoint, still another trend is clearly defined, a trend from the reproduction of very large numbers of potential offspring, left at the mercy of the inimical environment with the survival of only a few in each brood, to the reproduction of one or a few offspring that are given a good start in life and are sheltered and nurtured by the parents over more and more extended periods of infancy. The prolonged infancy of the human offspring represents the climax of the evolution of parental care and has had much to do with the success of the human species.

Finally, one more orthogenetic trend, not quite so obvious as some of the others but none the less real, is a trend from aquatic to terrestrial or even aerial life. The earlier vertebrates were all thoroughly aquatic and had not at all invaded the dry land and the open air. The conquest of the land by vertebrates began with the lobe-finned fishes, was partially accomplished by the Amphibia, greatly accelerated by the reptiles, and still further advanced by the birds and mammals. The mammals have remained essentially terrestrial, though many are arboreal, some secondarily aquatic, and a few (the bats) have developed powers of flight. The birds are primarily aerial, only relatively few of them remaining terrestrial or having become secondarily aquatic. The chief systems concerned in this slow transition from aquatic to terrestrial and aerial life are the respiratory system and associated circulatory system, the paired appendages, and the brain and sense organs. These changes have involved the substitution of lungs for gills, double-barreled for single-barreled heart, legs and wings for fins, and changes from aquatic to terrestrial sense organs. We shall of course, have much to say about these changes in subsequent connections.

THE SEGMENTAL ORGANIZATION OF VERTEBRATES

While in all probability the earliest chordates were simple forms, with possibly three pairs of body cavities, a preoral pair and two pairs of postoral coeloms, amphioxus and the vertebrates have secondarily become elaborately metameric through a process of segmenting the mesoderm into somites that form the basis of additional body parts essentially like the last of the three primary segments.

A vertebrate then is a secondarily compound organism composed of a linear series of potentially equivalent compartments. A simple vertebrate is roughly analogous to a railroad train with an engine in front and a series of cars behind. Each car may be thought of as fundamentally like all the others. Each has its walls and floor and roof, its wheels, its doors and windows, etc., but the different units may be modified in various ways to serve different functions of transportation. Thus the first car behind the engine is the coal car which has become an accessory of the engine. Then come the mail car, the express car, the baggage car, the day coaches, the sleepers, the diner, and the observation car. Some trains carry other, more specialized units; other are much simpler. A primitive type of train is a freight train which lacks the specialized passenger units and consists of nothing but the engine, a coal car, a long series of freight cars of the same type, and a caboose on behind.

Now the head of the vertebrate may be compared with the engine, and the postcephalic metameres with the rest of the train of cars. In very primitive vertebrates the "cars" are much alike, as in a simple freight train, but in higher, more specialized vertebrates practically every "car" is different in form and function. But let us not push the train analogy too far.

The Vertebrate Head. — It is now well established that not only the body but the head also is composed of segments. The best evidence of the segmental character of the head is derived from a study of the mesoblastic somites which are easily recognizable in the embryos of such favorable forms as lampreys and some sharks. The three anterior somites form the eye muscles. The fourth somite is in the region of the ear and persists in cyclostomes throughout life, but in fishes the fourth somite degenerates after formation and does not persist in the adult. Five to seven metaotic (back of the ear) somites are recognized, the exact number being unsettled. Further indications of metamerism in the head are seen in the cranial nerves, in the gill-slits and in the branchial skeleton; but none of these parts corresponds fully in its segmental character to the more fundamental mesoblastic somites or muscle segments.

The head segments and body segments correspond in most of

their structural features but differ in a few. Kidney tubules appear at some time in all body metameres but are entirely absent in the head; whereas aortic arches, gill-slits, and visceral skeleton are characteristic of the head and never appear in the body metameres.

In vertebrates proper, as we know them, the head and body are fully segmental throughout, but the head segments have become specialized in some ways and the body segments in others. It is believed, however, that the present vertebrates have descended from metameric ancestors somewhat like amphioxus, in which the whole body from end to end is clearly segmental, and there is no marked distinction between head and body segments.

GREGORY'S THEORY OF POLYISOMERISM AND ANISOMERISM

W. K. Gregory, perhaps the leading American authority on vertebrate evolution, has attempted to clarify the course of evolution of this group by introducing a new terminology which we shall find extremely useful for descriptive purposes. He considers that the original ancestor of the vertebrates consisted of a linear series of equivalent metameres. The equivalent parts are known as *polyisomeres* (meaning many equal parts). In the course of evolution these originally equal segments undergo various kinds of secondary modification, thus becoming *anisomeres*, unequal parts. In higher vertebrates the original polyisomeric condition has become obscured by fusions of adjacent metameres, atrophy of some and distortion of others. These changes may be induced by emphasis of some originally equal parts and de-emphasis of others. The terms polyisomerism and anisomerism apply not only to original metameres but also to any serially repeated structures even though not strictly metameric. A series of structures like rows of teeth, for example, may be at first all alike (polyisomeres) or may become specialized into incisors, canines, premolars, and molars (anisomeres).

Some structures, such as the gill-slits of amphioxus, may become secondarily multiplied so that there may be several of them to each original muscle segment. Such a process is known as secondary polyisomerism. Similarly the vertebrae of eels and other elongated vertebrates may become secondarily multiplied beyond the number characteristic of the ancestors. As a descriptive device Gregory's theory and terminology are useful, but offer no explanation of the causal mechanisms responsible for the changes and trends described.

Assuming that vertebrates are essentially compound organisms composed of serially repeated compartments, it seems necessary to discuss the implications of this view. It is implied that each metamere is serially homologous with all the rest. Each has an inherent potency for developing all the structures that any other develops. According to this view each system of organs is able to appear in every segment unless differential influences are brought to bear, affecting some metameres in one way and others in other ways. The problem is that of accounting for the fact that some metameres realize some of their prospective potencies and other metameres other potencies, so that in higher vertebrates nearly every metamere develops somewhat differently. Thus in higher vertebrates the head metameres develop gill-slits, visceral skeleton, specialized sense organs, and specialized brain lobes, but lack kidneys, gonads, paired and unpaired appendages; while the body metameres lack these specialized head characters, but develop specialized structures for circulation, excretion, reproduction, digestion, and locomotion. The differences in the expression of potencies in different metameres can not be due to different genetic factors, for every cell of the body is assumed to possess the same assortment of genes. Hence we must seek for the mechanisms of differentiation of metameres either in the environment (internal or external) or else in the cytoplasmic organization of the egg and early embryo.

THE METABOLIC GRADIENT THEORY AS A POSSIBLE EXPLANATION OF CEPHALIZATION AND METAMERIC DIFFERENTIATION

According to C. M. Child's theories, there is a fundamental physiological basis for cephalization and the differentiation of metameres down the primary, or antero-posterior axis. He and his associates have demonstrated for many lower axiate organisms and for the embryos of higher axiate organisms, including vertebrates, that the apical region, or head end, of the axis has a higher rate of metabolism than other regions, that the parts nearest the apical end have a slightly lower metabolic rate than the latter and that there is a gradient of decreasing metabolic rate down the axis until the basal region is reached. The apical region, being the most active, sends impulses down the axis, each lower region passing on these impulses with decreasing strength to more posterior regions. In terms of metameres, this means that no two metameres have developed from regions with exactly the same metabolic rate or receiving exactly the same growth-controlling or organizing impulses from the apical end.

There exists between the apical region and regions posterior to it a relation of physiological dominance and subordination. The head region, having the highest metabolic rate, especially favors the development and specialization of nervous and sensory organs that require a high rate of metabolism for their complete expression. In addition to this, the head region seems to exercise an inhibiting influence upon more posterior regions, an influence that prevents them from realizing whatever potencies they may have for developing parts characteristic of the head. That posterior regions probably have such potencies is indicated by experiments upon lower axiate organisms such as flat-worms. In Planaria, for example, the young, vigorous worm has a brain and special sense organs only in the head, but if the head is cut off, that portion of the trunk adjacent to it readily regenerates a complete new head. Even parts of the worm cut out of the middle or posterior regions, when released from the dominance of the original head, form complete heads for themselves. Similar powers of developing heads from posterior levels are exhibited by segmented invertebrates such as annelids. In these forms it appears that each metamere, if emancipated from the control of the head, has a potency to develop head parts or any other parts characteristic of any level of the axis. In vertebrates, however, posterior regions, if severed from the head, have no such power to develop a new head.

Although every cell in an embryo is now believed to possess the same genetic constitution as every other cell, and therefore has the genetic potency for developing all the tissues characteristic of the species, the realization of these potencies seems to be determined and limited by the particular metabolic rate present at a given level of the axis. The metabolic rates of posterior levels is in turn influenced by the degree of dominance of the head, or apical region, which seems to vary in different groups.

That important evolutionary trend in vertebrates, known as cephalization, seems to involve a progressively increasing physiological dominance of the head. Not only does the head inhibit the development of "lower functions" in the more anterior metameres, but it exercises this inhibition further and further down the axis as the head becomes more and more dominant. Moreover, the head profoundly modifies the differentiation of metameres adjacent to itself in very special ways. Assuming that in the earliest vertebrates the true head involved only an anterior segment and possibly one or two of the adjacent metameres, the course of evolution seems to have involved the incorporation into the head itself of more and more of the metameres adjacent to it, so that progressively more and more metameres are appropriated by the head and become subordinate parts of an increasingly complex segmented head.

What physiological changes are responsible for the orthogenetic trend toward cephalization and its accompaniments can at present only be guessed at, but it seems reasonable to assume that there has occurred during the ages a relative increase in the metabolic dominance of the head end of the axis. Whether this has been a secondary effect of gene changes or of a gradual steepening of the gradient in the cytoplasm of the germ cells, or both, we have no means of ascertaining.

The author of the gradient theory has always been reluctant to extend its implications into phylogenetic fields, but the present writer feels that, although such an extension of the theory must be regarded as at present purely speculative, such speculation may at least help to rationalize the main trends of vertebrate evolution.

THE ORGANIZER THEORY IN RELATION TO THE AXIAL GRADIENT THEORY

In the above discussion of the axial gradient conception and some of its corollaries such as dominance and subordination, we have not suggested any mechanism through which such influences between parts can operate. It is in this connection that the *Organizer Theory* of Spemann comes to the aid of the axial gradient theory of Child.

Spemann discovered that in vertebrate embryos after the completion of gastrulation a region of the embryo at or near the dorsal lip of the blastopore is a dominant region that acts as an organizer for the whole embryo and determines the next stages of differentiation. If a piece of the dorsal-lip region of an amphibian larva be removed and grafted upon the belly of another larva this grafted piece induces the development of a new individual. It changes the prospective course of development of the belly tissues and causes them to develop quite differently, and an orderly new individual arises out of tissues that would normally form only belly tissues. Spemann found that a chemical extract of the organizer would induce the formation of a new axis about as well as the whole piece of tissue did. From this it would appear that the way in which one part controls the differentiation of another part is through the production of chemical substances which pass from one tissue to another. Thus the organizer substances act in such a way that the tissues immediately adjacent to the organizer can not develop characters just like those of the organizer, but become somewhat different. These tissues next to the organizer would in turn act as organizers for tissues adjacent to them and through their chemical products influence the differentiation of such tissues. If we follow this conception to its logical conclusion and confine our attention for the moment to the primary axis of vertebrates, the following theory of axiate differentiation would seem to be warranted.

As soon as a primary axis of an embryo is established the anterior or apical end of the axis becomes an organizer. Through its chemical products it influences the course of differentiation of the adjacent metameres and determines which of the potencies of this region shall be realized. This metamere in turn chemically influences the differentiation of the next metamere, and this the next, and so on down the axis. If this were to happen as suggested, the result would be a series of metameres each somewhat different from all the others.

Phylogenetically, it is conceivable that gene mutations might influence the activity of the first organizer, the apical end of the new axis, and cause a change in the chemical substances produced by it, causing the next metamere to be more or less limited in the realization of its potencies. A change in the original organizer might in this way produce changes throughout the axis. According to this view the orthogenetic changes involved in cephalization and backward retreat of the lower functions might be due to a series of gene mutations each of which merely accelerated the rate of chemical activity in the primary organizer, the other changes down the axis being secondarily due to this primary change.

Doubtless this theory of axiate differentiation is too simple, but that something of this sort happens in development we regard as more than probable. It is conceivable, however, that gene mutations may occur that do not affect the organizer directly, but affect special regions of the body. Thus one localized tissue may be relatively accelerated and another retarded and we may have an upset in the timing of different growing regions. This leads us to the discussion of another rather new theory of vertebrate morphology, called the *Theory of Heterogony*.

THE PRINCIPLE OF HETEROGONY

Julian Huxley and his associates have within the last few years proposed a new and rather simple theory of morphogenesis, known as the *Theory of Heterogony*, a theory which may be thought of as supplementing in a sense the theories of Child, Gregory, and others. According to this view, the increased size and specialization of any metamere or outgrowth of a metamere is the secondary result of an increased rate of growth, probably due to a localized increase in the rate of cell division of such a part in relation to those of adjacent parts. The term heterogony may be translated literally to mean a differential timing of developmental rates.

The favorite instances of heterogony cited by the authors of the theory have to do with the horns of ungulates. In the deer family, for example, it has been found that the size and complexity of horns are related to body size, but that the horns are not merely larger in the larger species, but they are larger in proportion to body size. Thus the smallest deer have either no horns or at best quite rudimentary ones, while the largest members of the deer family, such as the moose and reindeer, have very large and elaborate antlers. In the words of Huxley, "The bigger the individual of any such species, the greater are his horns in proportion to the rest of him." The extinct Irish elk, a giant among his kind, had such a tremendous burden of horns that evolutionists believe the excessive development of horns had much to do with the extinction of the species.

In order to account for what might appear to be an orthogenetic trend of horn size and complexity in the deer family, one merely has to posit the origin of an increased division rate of certain cells in the body that are the primordia of horns. The larger the individual grows, the more chance will it have to produce disproportionately large horns. On this assumption, what might appear to be a steady evolutionary trend in horn growth, an alleged example of orthogenesis, turns out to be only an incidental accompaniment of progressive increase in size.

The bearing of this view on orthogenesis theories is as follows: It has been claimed by Osborn and other writers that certain of these trends in horn evolution are little, if at all, controlled by natural selection, for the same kinds of trends are found in diverse groups with very different habits of life. Moreover, it is claimed that horn development sometimes goes far beyond the adaptive needs of the species and in some cases, notably the extinct Irish elk, the excessive growth was not only non-adaptive but positively detrimental. According to the theory of heterogony, horn increase is simply a secondary consequence of increase in size, which is, at least up to certain limits and under most conditions, positively advantageous and of high survival value. In the deer family, for example, greater size of individuals or of species confers greater strength and greater speed for self-defense or in the contest for mates. Moreover, a greater size or a more advanced condition at birth gives the individual an initial advantage over its fellows in securing food and escaping enemies.

Huxley has therefore attacked one of Osborn's favorite instances of alleged orthogenesis of horns, namely, that in the extinct Titanotheres, great rhinoceros-like mammals which throve during the Eocene and Oligocene periods and became extinct before the end of the latter period. These animals, at first small, grew toward the end of their career to be in some instances nearly as large as elephants. Four lines of these animals, each derived from the primitive Eocene common stock, evolved independently of each other. One line remained stocky in build and retained the incisor teeth; a second line grew longer-limbed and speedier, lost its incisors and became grazers; a third line remained relatively small, but lost its incisors; while a fourth line retained its incisors and went in for great bulk and slow, browsing habits. The common ancestor of these four lines was small and had no horns. In each of the four lines, however, long after they had diverged from each other, nose horns of a peculiar Y-shape appeared and underwent parallel courses of evolution. Thus the smallest members of each line had no nose horns or only small ones, the largest ones had horns largest in proportion to body size, and there was in each of the lines the same apparent orthogenetic trend toward large flat Y-shaped horns.

Osborn's explanation of this situation implies that, since the four separate stocks have specialized for such different life habits, the similar horns are not likely to have any special adaptive significance. Rather, the course of horn evolution was predetermined in the germ-plasm of the hornless common ancestor of the different stocks. Something in the germ-plasm was, as it were, wound up like clockwork and continued to carry on mechanically in a predestined fashion quite independently of any advantage or disadvantage to the various stocks. The horns simply had to appear at a certain stage in evolution and had to go through the same course of increasing size and specialization quite irrespective of the need or lack of need for them. The reader will already have guessed what would be Huxley's criticism of the above theory. He summons to his aid the principle of heterogony, according to which horn development is simply an incidental consequence of increase in size, which in turn is decidedly advantageous. Then, since the larger individuals of a species in each generation survive in larger numbers than smaller ones, there would be a steady progressive increase in size over long periods of time. Thus the apparent orthogenesis is regarded as nothing more than a very simple instance of progressive adaptive change through natural selection, or survival of the fittest.

Huxley and his associates, as indeed most English biologists, are strong selectionists and lose no opportunity to support the selection principle as the chief guiding factor in progressive evolution. They are inclined to believe that all other instances of progressive evolution of apparently non-adaptive structures would, if properly analyzed, turn out to be the result of changes correlated with adaptive changes that in turn are guided by natural selection.

Geneticists in general are inhospitable to all orthogenesis views that are in any way tinged with mystical factors. Osborn's view of a predetermined course of events in the germ-plasm seems to involve some mystical unknowable force that has no parallel in known genetic machinery. If it is to be thought of as due to any known type of genetic machinery at all it would imply that mutations of a definite sort occur in a definite sequence and that this sequence is predetermined before the first change in the series appears. This runs counter to the experience of geneticists regarding the occurrence of mutations, for if one thing is more obvious than another about mutations it is their random character and their unpredictability.

On the whole, then, it seems wise, in the present state of our knowledge of the mechanics of evolution, to hold in abeyance our final judgment about the mechanisms of orthogenesis until such time as experimental evidence of the existence of such factors is forthcoming. For the present, it seems best to regard all that fabric of concepts that goes by the name of orthogenesis as descriptive rather

than explanatory. That there have been in the evolution of vertebrates real orthogenetic trends such as those discussed above no one
will deny, though some of the described trends may be less definite
than descriptions of them would lead us to believe.

THE RECAPITULATION THEORY AND
VERTEBRATE PHYLOGENY

The Recapitulation Theory, when critically employed, is of great
value in solving many problems of vertebrate evolution. In its
original form, as posited by Haeckel, this theory may be stated as
follows: The life history of the individual presents a brief, condensed
résumé of its ancestral history. Some one has paraphrased this
theory in somewhat facetious terms: "the individual climbs its own
ancestral tree." It is now generally agreed that the recapitulation
theory does not hold in the literal sense. Certainly the stages of
embryogenesis are not in any sense equivalent to a series of adult
ancestors. But there can be no question but that many transitory
embryonic structures of higher vertebrates are similar to permanent
structures of lower forms. Thus the embryonic pronephros of a
mammal is homologous with the adult pronephros of the hag-fish;
and the embryonic notochord of a mammal is homologous with the
adult notochord of amphioxus and the cyclostomes. In this limited
sense the mammalian embryo repeats in its ontogeny some of the
adult structures of lower forms. It is not true, however, that the
embryo of a higher type is ever as a whole anything like an adult
stage of an ancestor.

F. R. Lillie has stated the real facts about recapitulation in an
acceptable form:

"If phylogeny is to be understood to be the succession of adult
forms in the line of evolution, it cannot be said in any real sense that
ontogeny is a brief recapitulation of phylogeny, for the embryo of a
higher form is never like the adult of a lower form, though the anatomy of embryonic organs of higher species resembles in many particulars the anatomy of homologous organs of the adult of the lower
species. However, if we conceive that the whole life history is necessary for the definition of a species, we obtain a different basis for the
recapitulation theory. The comparable units are then entire ontogenies, and these resemble one another in proportion to the nearness
of relationship, just as the definitive structures do. Thus in nearly

related species the ontogenies are very similar; in more distantly related species there is less resemblance, and in species from different classes the ontogenies are widely divergent in many respects."

If then the ontogeny of a higher form completely paralleled that of a lower form through the developmental period, except for the adult stage, the higher form would differ from the lower only in the last stages. But this is not the case, for there are differences between the two somewhat parallel ontogenies at all stages. There is a general tendency for higher forms to condense the early stages, some structures being pushed back to earlier and earlier stages. Moreover, some stages in the ontogeny of lower forms may be omitted altogether or appear only as transitory structures that soon disappear. Also new structures frequently appear in the middle of ontogeny that have no parallel in the ontogeny of ancestors. Thus various kinds of adaptive structures that have a value only for the larval or fetal life are interpolated into the ontogeny of higher forms. These interpolated structures are sometimes so prominent as to obscure the true ancestral conditions and thus tend to confuse the picture of recapitulation.

Every ontogeny is therefore a curious admixture of ancestral structures and new interpolated structures. The true ancestral characters are called *palingenetic* and the new structures, *cenogenetic*. It is the task of the student of ancestral histories to disentangle these two sets of structures and to eliminate from the phylogenetic picture the cenogenetic structures and their effects on ontogeny. This is not an easy task and many mistakes of interpretation have been made.

Some of the more significant changes in ontogeny have been due to differences in timing of some structures with respect to others. We have already referred to the tendency of higher forms to compress and shorten the early embryonic stages. In this way structures that appear relatively late in the ontogeny of a lower form may appear quite early in a higher form. The reverse of this process is also not uncommon, for embryonic, larval, or fetal structures or systems may persist into adult life thus preventing some of the end stages (adult structures) from coming to expression. Thus in various tailed amphibia many of the larval structures, such as external gills, lidless eyes, fins on the tail, etc., remain even after the animals become sexually mature. This condition is known as *neoteny*, and will be discussed at length in a later connection. It has been suggested that the human proportions of head, face, etc., are persistent fetal characters, and that man is therefore a somewhat neotenic type. In support of this view is the fact that human adults are more like fetal apes and monkeys than like the adults of these forms.

An explanation of these distortions of ontogeny offered by G. R. De Beer and others harks back to the theory of heterogony. If a structure in some way increases its developmental pace as compared with other structures, it may come to full expression earlier than it did in the ancestors and this may alter the timing of the development of the various systems. Structures that appear thus prematurely may inhibit or otherwise modify the development of other structures. Conversely, a structure that loses developmental momentum at an early time may progressively lose ground and ultimately become vestigial or even be reduced to nothing. Thus vestigial structures and lost structures may be the result of differential reduction of growth rate, or negative heterogony.

Local changes in developmental rate can rather readily be accounted for by gene changes, for genes are regarded as organic catalysts that accelerate or retard cellular processes. They also are highly specific in their action both as regards the time when they produce their effect and the parts of the body which they are able to influence. They do not affect all tissues alike.

As the organism grows and becomes more complex various correlating, regulating, and integrating factors come into play. These mechanisms are largely nervous and hormonal. When the nervous system appears it has definite growth controlling or organizing properties and it is doubtless at least partly through such mechanisms that the nervous system of the head, the brain, exercises its dominance over the body regions. The beginning of functional activity of the endocrine glands also affects differentiation of all tissues. Any genetic change in the thyroid or pituitary glands, for example, will doubtless be effective in altering bodily proportions. The mechanisms of differentiation are many and varied, and their interactions exceedingly complex, but it seems probable that they are all explicable on a genetic basis. Gene changes may affect any or all parts of these mechanisms and the resulting changes in bodily form and proportions are not too difficult to understand.

THE RACIAL AGE THEORY AND RACIAL SENESCENCE

In the discussion just concluded it has been emphasized that, although ontogeny does not in any literal fashion recapitulate phylogeny, there are undoubtedly parallels between individual and racial development. If then ontogeny parallels phylogeny, to some extent the reverse must also be true, that phylogeny to the same extent parallels ontogeny.

Recognition of this parallel has given rise to the Racial Age Theory and to that particular aspect of it known as the Racial Senescence Theory. This general theory assumes that there are certain basic resemblances between the life career of a race (using the term in a very general sense) and that of an individual. Just as an individual starts out as a zygote, goes through a period of development and specialization of parts, reaches a period of full maturity, and then enters a period of senescence terminated by death; so a race or stock of animals may be thought of as starting out in a small way as a stem type of a very generalized sort, the various descendant groups becoming differentiated for different modes of life, each of these becoming more and more specialized along some particular line, and the whole race reaching maturity when the maximum of adaptive radiation has been accomplished. A group might be regarded as in its full maturity when it is at the height of its dominance and adaptive success and might then be termed a climax, or adult, group. When a group reaches the height of its success it begins a slow decline, becomes progressively racially senescent, most of its specialized members become extinct and, as a dominant group, it dies. It often lives on, however, through the survival of a few of its more plastic, generalized types that act as the germ or seed for a new period of racial development.

The theory of Racial Age implies that, just as an individual has a definite and fixed lifetime and inevitably runs a predestined course, so a race as such has a fixed span of life and must sooner or later become extinct. It implies also that just as an individual as such must die, but produces offspring through the setting aside of generalized cells, germ-cells, from which new life cycles take their origin; so races that for the most part must become extinct, usually give off some generalized, plastic descendants that evade racial extinction and furnish the material for starting other racial age cycles. In a previous connection these same conceptions have been expressed as part of the interpretation of the fossil record.

It is difficult to decide whether the apparent parallel between ontogenetic and phylogenetic history is merely an artificial analogy or whether there is some real and fundamental basis for the attractive concept. Smith-Woodward, Osborn, Lull, and other paleontologists write about racial senescence as though it were self-evident and real beyond question, while Huxley and others have vigorously criticized the whole theory, claiming that it is based on nothing more than an analogy, and a loose analogy at that. They assert that about the only real evidence back of the theory is that excessive size, over-development of hard parts, degeneration of active structures, and general exuberance of form were often displayed by stocks that soon afterwards became extinct. They also state that many highly specialized forms exhibiting various "criteria of racial senescence" have actually survived over long periods of time without undergoing much further change. Thus tortoises, whales, king crabs, crocodiles, and many other forms that exhibit some or many "senescent" features, have succeeded in stalling off extinction for many millions of years, though they should, according to the racial senescence theory, have long ago passed out. Apparently it is only when such highly specialized types are confronted with so radically changed an environmental set-up as to overtax their adaptive equipment that they must necessarily become extinct. Hence there appears to be for these overspecialized forms no inevitable racial death that is a consequence of their having run through a predetermined life cycle. If then racial extinction should turn out to be no more than the elimination of those types that are highly specialized for one particular environment and can not withstand the hardships incident to climatic change, we would have nothing more than another case of the cold-blooded operation of natural selection.

In spite of these criticisms of the racial age theory, and especially of that particular phase of it known as racial senescence, the writer can not but feel somewhat sympathetic toward these concepts, at least when they are viewed as mere descriptive devices and when freed from the taint of any mystic inner driving forces. It may well be that certain of the most fortunate members of senescent groups have been able to find environments that favor their prolonged survival, just as occasionally a centenarian among mankind, either through his individual vigor or through a fortunate environmental experience, has lived on without much evidence of change for decades after his contemporaries have died.

It seems more than a mere metaphor when we speak of primitive plastic stocks representing a race in its infancy; of stocks at the height of their adaptive radiation as in the mature or climax stage of their evolution; and of races becoming large and sluggish, heavily armored, with reduced brains and with various bizarre excrescences, as senescent end products of a race verging upon inevitable racial extinction.

CRITERIA OF RACIAL SENESCENCE

Among the authors who have advocated the theory of racial senescence none, perhaps, has stated the theory so plainly as Smith-Woodward, the eminent English paleontologist. He lists as the chief marks of racial senescence three types of characteristics: relative increase of size, spinescence, and degeneracy.

Relative Increase in Size. — In almost all types of animals, past and present, some species have become giants among their kind, far exceeding their relatives in this respect. These giant forms are, except possibly the whales and the elephants, sluggish, and stupid. They are slow to reach maturity and hence have a lowered rate of increase. Examples of senescent giants among vertebrates are the Mesozoic dinosaurs, especially those vast herbivorous forms such as *Brontosaurus* and *Brachiosaurus;* the existing giant whales, such as the sperm whale, the Greenland whale, and the sulphur-bottom whale, all gigantic as compared with their relatives the dolphins and porpoises.

Spinescence. — By spinescence is meant that tendency so common among rather sluggish forms to develop spiny or horny excrescences of the exoskeleton. One need mention only such exemplars of spinescence as the extinct Palaeozoic reptile *Dimetrodon,* the extinct Jurassic *Stegosaurus,* and the living hedgehogs and porcupines, all slow and sluggish types. Various heavily armored forms might also be regarded as examples of spinescence. Among these one may include the tortoises, the armadillos, and scaly ant-eaters. As special examples of spinescence one might also include horned animals or even heavily tusked forms such as the elephants.

Degeneracy. — The most important examples of degeneracy have to do with the loss or reduction of the brain, the higher sense organs, and limbs. Examples of great brain reduction are *Stegosaurus* and perhaps amphioxus and the tunicates. There are countless cases of the loss or reduction of eyes, and some examples of reduced efficiency of the olfactory apparatus. Loss of some or all of the teeth is one of the commonest phases of degeneracy. Loss or reduction of limbs and of tail are other striking aspects of degeneracy.

A special type of degeneracy is that of the secondary evolution among many different groups of the so-called *eel-type* of body form. As a rule, these forms are exceedingly long and have far more vertebrae than members of allied groups. Doubtless this great increase in serially repeated parts is the result of secondary polyisomerism. Strangely enough, the eel-type phase of degeneracy is usually accompanied by loss of limbs, sometimes loss of tail, frequently loss of eyes and of teeth, and not infrequently, loss of scales. In our account of vertebrate groups we shall have occasion to label a good many types, some in almost every group, as "eel-type" degenerates. No doubt the student can readily anticipate what some of these forms are.

Many degenerates are interpreted as neotenic or permanent larval forms. This situation is especially well illustrated by many genera of newts and salamanders. Neoteny may then be regarded as one expression of racial senescence. A race that, after once reaching adult status, reverts to a permanent larval condition is, so to speak, in its second childhood.

Whether or not the theory of racial senescence serves as an explanation of evolutionary mechanisms, it seems to have at least some descriptive value. We shall henceforth use the theory critically and without accepting any of its doubtful implications.

HOMOLOGY THE GUIDING PRINCIPLE IN VERTEBRATE COMPARATIVE ANATOMY AND IN PHYLOGENY

The Principle of Homology is almost a corollary of the Recapitulation Theory. Any two or more structures in different groups of animals that have a similar embryonic origin and parallel each other in development for a reasonable length of time are by definition homologous. So the only sure test of homology must come from a study of embryology. What is implied in the principle of homology is that two or more forms possessing truly homologous structures must have been derived from a common ancestor that possessed the characters in question. In other words, homologous structures in different groups imply a certain common genetic origin for these groups. Thus the wing of a bird, the arm of a man, the flipper of a whale, the one-toed fore leg of a horse, and even the pectoral fin of a lobe-finned fish, are regarded as homologous because they start out in development from similar rudiments and follow for some time the same plan of differentiation, only diverging in relatively late stages to produce very different end products. One must, however, be extremely cautious in the application of the principle of homology. Many very doubtful homologies have been introduced into the fabric of phylogenetic biology. One need merely mention the two very questionable homologues of the Hemichordata, the so-called notochord and the so-called dorsal, tubular central nervous system, as illustrations of a common habit of morphologists of overstraining an otherwise valuable principle.

Another very common error, less likely to occur nowadays than in earlier times, is that of assuming that organs that look alike and function alike are homologous, without putting them to an embryological test. It often happens that these superficially similar organs or systems are merely *analogous*, the result of a tendency of tissues of different origin independently to meet the demands of a common environmental situation in similar fashion, but arriving at their results in entirely different ways. Thus the eyes of vertebrates and those of the cephalopod mollusks (squid, octopus, etc.), look alike, function alike, and seem to be situated in equivalent parts of the body, but they have an entirely different mode of embryonic origin and pattern of development. They are, therefore, not homologous at all, but only analogous. Other alleged homologies are of a more fundamental nature. We have already in Chapter I given evidence to show that such important correspondences between vertebrates and invertebrates as the antero-posterior axis, the coelom, and metamerism are not homologous but at best only analogous.

Many other concepts dealing with morphology occur to the writer, some of which might perhaps be appropriately dealt with in this chapter, but enough of theory for the present. It is our belief that at least a general perusal of the contents of this chapter is advisable in advance of the study of the more concrete materials of chordate and vertebrate anatomy. After the factual background of the student has been at least partially built up, a rereading of this chapter should be of service in integrating and rationalizing what might otherwise be a somewhat unorganized mass of facts. With this background of general principles in mind, let us now resume the factual description of chordate animals.

CHAPTER III

PRIMITIVE TRUE CHORDATES
(PROTOCHORDATA)

(CLASS CEPHALOCHORDATA)

INTRODUCTORY STATEMENT

The introduction of the Subphylum Protochordata, combining the old Subphyla Urochordata and Cephalochordata into one subphylum and reducing these groups to the rank of classes, is not without precedent. Other writers have done the same thing. The exclusion of the Hemichordata from the ranks of the true chordates is done on our own responsibility and may or may not be justified.

There can be no doubt, however, that the Urochordata and Cephalochordata are related too closely to be assigned to two separate subphyla. They show evidences of having been derived from a common ancestral stock which was perhaps closer to the craniates than are the survivors of either class today, for the Urochordates are, as adults, extremely degenerate and, according to our interpretation, the cephalochordates may also be degenerate, secondarily decephalized forms and therefore less advanced than the original ancestral chordates from which they and other chordates were derived. This view of the classic amphioxus as a degenerate, however, is not held by some leading specialists who prefer to regard the acephalic condition as primitive. The facts brought out later in this chapter will help us to decide which of these alternative views is the more tenable.

It should also be pointed out that our classification of chordates into two subphyla — a, Protochordata (including Cephalochordata and Urochordata), and b, Craniata (Vertebrates) — is quite out of harmony with that of Goodrich, who is perhaps the leading scholar among vertebrate morphologists today. For some strange reason Goodrich chooses to create a Phylum Vertebrata with two subphyla: a, Acrania, including only the cephalochordates; and b, Craniata, the true vertebrates. Apart from the impropriety of classing amphioxus, which has no trace of vertebrae, as a vertebrate, this classification leaves no room for the Urochordata, which in our opinion are unquestionably related to the Cephalochordata. In his scholarly treatises, *Vertebrata Craniata* (1909) and in his more recent *Studies in the Structure and Development of Vertebrates* (1930) no mention is made of the Urochordata, while amphioxus is discussed in detail. One wonders what sort of taxonomic status Goodrich would assign to the far-from-negligible tunicates and their kin. If they are to be excluded from the phylum containing amphioxus and the craniates they would have to be assigned to a separate phylum, a disposition of them that we, personally, would not be willing to accept.

In presenting an account of the primitive chordates we shall begin with the Cephalochordata, for it is difficult to understand the Urochordata except by comparison with amphioxus. A thorough knowledge of the latter is also generally regarded as fundamental for an understanding of vertebrates.

CLASS I. CEPHALOCHORDATA

This class comprises a compact assemblage of small marine organisms belonging to two genera, *Branchiostoma* and *Asymmetron*. For convenience we shall use the well-intrenched name amphioxus, not capitalized, as a common name for any sort of cephalochordate, just as one would use the term "tunicate" for any typical member of the urochordates.

Amphioxus is a small, fish-like creature ranging from about one to three inches in length. It is, considering the amount of biological literature inspired by it, a decidedly unimpressive creature, looking like a pale, skinned sardine. It is often called the "lancelet," a name suggested by the fact that it is sharp at both ends.

Geographic Distribution. — There are recognized about sixteen species of cephalochordates though some of these may be only varieties. Nine are assigned to the genus *Branchiostoma* and seven to the genus *Asymmetron*. The various species of *Branchiostoma* have an almost world-wide distribution, being found on the sandy shores of all continents and on many oceanic islands. *Asymmetron* is confined to the Indo-Pacific waters except for one species native to the Bahamas. Most of the species are tropical, being confined to a belt between 40° N. and 40° S. latitudes. A few, however, are found as far north as the coast of Norway and as far south as the southern tip of Africa.

The species most thoroughly investigated, *Branchiostoma lanceolatum*, is itself extremely widely distributed, occurring in the Mediterranean, in northwestern Europe, in Ceylon, and off the eastern coast of the United States. Such an almost cosmopolitan species must be a very old and very stable one, for the distribution by slow migration of a relatively sedentary form over such tremendous stretches of territory as that between North America and Ceylon must have required millions of years. Yet during this time no further splitting up into species has occurred. The two genera of cephalochordates and all the species are also very similar to each other, showing that only slight evolutionary changes have occurred since their derivation from a very ancient common ancestral species. All of these facts of distribution tend to support the theory that amphioxus, although in its present condition somewhat degenerate, is not so very different from its very ancient ancestors.

Taxonomic Status. — Amphioxus has been known to biologists for nearly one hundred and fifty years, and has doubtless been used as a food delicacy for a much longer time. Dried lancelets are today sold in vast quantities in Mediterranean markets and the trade goes back beyond the memory of man. The little animal was first described, so far as is known, by Pallas in 1778 and was regarded by him, on account of a fancied resemblance to a common terrestrial mollusk, as a kind of slug, and he named it *Limax lanceolatus*. In 1804 Costa, an Italian naturalist, described it more accurately as a fish-like creature with vertebrate affinities and gave it the name *Branchiostoma lanceolatum*, the generic name implying the mistaken notion that the oral tentacles are branchiae, or gills. A year or so later Yarrel investigated it independently and named it "Amphioxus," a name that has come to be so nearly universal that, even though the Law of Priority requires us to respect the name *Branchiostoma*, it will doubtless continue in common use for a long time.

Slowly our knowledge of the true nature of amphioxus has increased through the detailed studies of its anatomy, embryology, physiology, and ecology during the last hundred years. Many of the world's most famous zoologists have studied it and experimented with it, rendering it one of the best understood of zoological classic types. The consensus of opinion as to the taxonomic status of amphioxus may be expressed in the words of Willey, one of the most thorough of the students of its biology: "Though specialized in some particulars and degenerate in others, amphioxus represents a grade of organization not far removed from the main line of early chordate ancestors." Whether it be primitively simple or secondarily degenerate, the fact remains that in its structure and development it displays in a strikingly diagrammatic way the general pattern of chordate organization. On this account it has long been a laboratory favorite in educational institutions throughout the civilized world and is studied annually by many thousands of students.

Some difference of opinion exists as to whether the lack of a true head (the acephalic condition) is primitive or secondary. Most writers prefer to regard this condition as primitive and to assume that the acquisition of a brain came in only with the true vertebrates. The writer, however, regards the headless condition as one of the consequences of the assumption of sedentary life, for sedentary and sessile forms have a way of losing their heads. One needs only to mention the clams and barnacles as familiar examples of this phenomenon of secondary acephaly. This view is supported by the fact that the notochord, which in typical chordates extends only part way under the brain, actually juts far out in front of the tiny brain in amphioxus, suggesting that the ancestral brain was once much larger and has undergone secondary regression. Further, the brain of amphioxus is hardly as large as some portions of the nerve cord, while the brain of even the tunicate larva is much larger than its nerve cord and is far more highly differentiated even as a larval brain than is the adult brain of its relative, amphioxus. Most writers agree that, like that of the tunicates, the pharynx of amphioxus is much more specialized and has many more gill-slits than had the ancestral chordate. This secondary multiplication of gill-slits may be only an acquisition to facilitate the ciliary mode of feeding, which we regard as an adaptation for sedentary life.

THE DOUBLE LIFE OF AMPHIOXUS

The innocent little lancelet leads a double life. It spends most of its time buried in the sand with only the head end protruding (Fig. 5), but from time to time it emerges from the sand and swims swiftly with vibratory lateral bendings of its narrow body until it finds another suitable spot for a burrow. When the writer visited the famous zoological laboratory at Naples he was shown about the aquarium by the director, Dr. Dohrn, and was especially interested in the amphioxus aquarium where hundreds of these animals were lying quietly in the sand. Dr. Dohrn, for our edification, poked a few lancelets out of their burrows and gave us a chance to watch them bury themselves again. This they do with almost unbelievable swiftness. The little creature, almost as soon as dislodged from one

FIG. 5. A group of lancelets (*Branchiostoma lanceolatum*) in normal habitat, some in the sedentary position with only the anterior end protruding from the sand burrow, one in the foreground beginning to dig a new burrow, and others swimming about in fish-like fashion. (Redrawn from indistinct photograph after Willey.)

burrow, points toward the bottom and with a vibratory motion almost too rapid to be seen, darts head-first into sand almost as if the latter were so much water. In a second or so it makes a U-turn, the head end emerges above the surface, and it comes to rest in the feeding position. Judging by the quietude of the whole colony whenever one chanced to observe it one gets the impression that the lancelet spends at least 90 per cent of its daylight time in its burrow, and that when it changes feeding stations it does so rapidly. Doubtless there is good reason for being in a hurry when swimming free, for the animal would make a tender morsel for any fish lurking in the neighborhood. And this is all the more evident when we consider that amphioxus has no true eyes, but only a crude eyespot which affords no vision of an approaching enemy. At night, however, the animal is said to swim about quite freely, exercising its muscular system and keeping up its efficiency.

The sharply pointed anterior end with the stiff protruding noto-chord, the fine segmental muscular equipment and the median fin-fold with its enlarged caudal fin might be regarded as adapta-tions for the free life of swift swimming, but all of this equipment is equally efficient as a burrowing device. Surely most of the other bodily characters are associated with the sedentary phase of its life.

ANATOMY AND PHYSIOLOGY OF AMPHIOXUS

Food-concentrating mechanisms. — A large share of the life of amphioxus is spent in a sand burrow with only the head end pro-truding as shown in Figure 5. While in the burrow the main business of life is feeding and breathing. The method of feeding is a variant of the general ciliary method commonly adopted by sedentary or sessile organisms and by small organisms such as ciliate Protozoa and the larvae of many higher forms. Doubtless this method of feeding is a very primitive character and was probably the original habit of the earliest tiny ancestral chordates.

The food of amphioxus consists of microscopic organisms sus-pended in sea water, which are so abundant in warm waters as to constitute a veritable "sea soup." The suspension as it exists in the water, however, is far too dilute to be passed through the digestive system. It needs to be filtered out and concentrated and the excess water removed from it. This is done by an elaborate food-concen-trating mechanism.

The greatly enlarged pharynx (Fig. 6) is lined with cilia, which beat synchronously backward and downward, causing a stream of water to be sucked in through the mouth. Most of the water passes out through the numerous pairs of gill-slits, but the food particles are captured by a sort of flypaper-like apparatus, the endostyle (Fig. 7). This structure consists of a glandular ciliated groove run-ning the length of the pharynx on the ventral side. The groove is composed of four tracts of mucous glands separated by tracts of ciliated cells (Fig. 8). The glands secrete a sticky mucus, and the cilia whip the mucus into a twisted rope and propel it forward and upward both along the gill-bars and around the peripharyngeal grooves that encircle the mouth. This traveling food conveyor is then

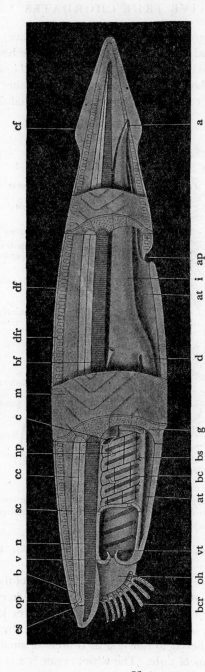

FIG. 6. General anatomy of amphioxus. a, anus; ap, atriopore; at, atrium; b, brain; bcr, buccal cirri; bc, branchial cleft; bf, brown funnel; bs, branchial skeletal rod; cc, central canal of neural tube; c, coelom; cf, caudal fin; d, liver diverticulum; df, dorsal fin; dfr, dorsal fin ray; es, eye spot; g, gonad; i, intestine; m, myotome; n, notochord; np, nephridium; oh, oral hood; op, olfactory pit or funnel; sc, spinal cord or neural tube; v, velum; vt, velar tentacles. (Redrawn after Parker and Haswell.)

picked up by a dorsal groove (the hyperpharyngeal groove) the cilia of which beat backward so as to propel the mucous rope back to the intestine, where its food load is digested. The mucus and indigestible wastes are discarded through the anus. A number of other features of amphioxus may be considered as accessories of the ciliary mode

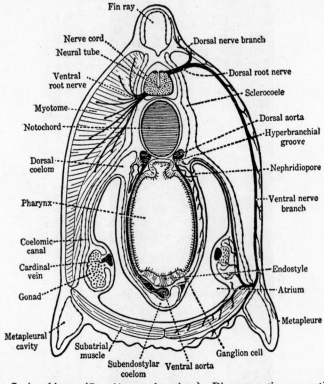

FIG. 7. Amphioxus (*Branchiostoma lanceolatus*). Diagrammatic *cross section* in the pharyngeal region showing various internal structures including coelomic cavities. (After Goodrich.)

of feeding: oral hood, wheel organ, velum and velar tentacles, atrium and atriopore.

The oral hood (Fig. 6) is a sort of half funnel in front of the mouth. It helps to focus the water vortex into the mouth. The free margins of the hood are provided with tentacle-like structures known as buccal cirrhi (Fig. 6), which were originally considered by Costa as gills, but are now believed to function as bearers of small sensory organs, possibly organs of taste. The wheel organ is a rather conspicuous ciliary structure at the base of the oral hood near the mouth, whose cilia beat in such a way as to suggest a turning wheel. This organ helps to create a vortex of water and to focus it toward the mouth. The mouth is an opening in the center of the velum, a muscular sheet that opens or closes the mouth and thus regulates the amount of water that may enter. Surrounding the mouth and

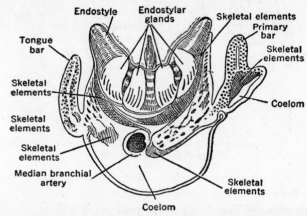

Fig. 8. Transverse section through ventral part of pharynx of amphioxus. (From Herdman, after Lankester.)

projecting from it are the slender velar tentacles that, when bent across the mouth opening, form a fine grating that probably serves to keep out sand grains or other indigestible particles.

The atrium and atriopore constitute a system characteristic of all the Protochordata and may be regarded as an essential part of the food-concentrating mechanism. Because of the fact that the pharynx is distended and thin-walled and is so elaborately split up by the numerous gill-slits, it is a delicate structure and would be readily damaged or clogged if exposed to the exterior. The atrium is essentially a sheath of the body-wall formed by paired ventro-lateral folds of the latter that grow downward toward the middle, meet and fuse in the median ventral line (Fig. 9), and enclose a water-filled space between itself and body proper. The cavity of this sheath is the atrial cavity. On account of its origin from paired folds of the body-wall, the cavity of the atrium is lined with ectoderm and is really a part of the outside world. Paired flanges of the atrium, running along the ventro-lateral regions, are called meta-pleural folds (Fig. 9) and are regarded by some biologists as a sort of

prophecy of the paired fins of fishes. The atrial cavity is closed in
front, but opens to the exterior through the atriopore situated near
the anus. Water passes out of the gill-slits into the atrial cavity and
then is given off through the one narrow nozzle, the atriopore, in a

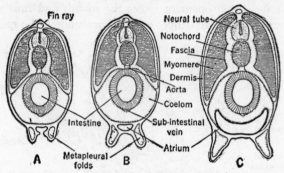

Fig. 9. Three stages in the development of the atrium in amphioxus.
(After Parker and Haswell.)

strong, continuous stream which forces its way to the surface
through the sand passage made when burrowing.

Respiration. — The cavity of the pharynx is well supplied with
blood vessels and the passage of water through it serves for respiration as well as for feeding. There are no specialized gills, but each
gill-bar between adjacent gill-slits contains a blood vessel with
lateral branches in which the blood circulates so close to the surface
that it is able to take up oxygen from the water and give off carbon
dioxide. The rather thin-walled pharynx is supported by a system
of rods of chitin-like substance forming the supports of the gill-bars.
Each primary gill-slit is divided lengthwise by a secondary tongue
bar with its skeletal rod. A very similar arrangement of gill-slits is
found in *Balanoglossus*, and some biologists regard this as an indication of relationship between amphioxus and the Hemichordata.

Digestive System. — Back of the pharynx the alimentary tract
narrows somewhat to form a continuous straight intestine without
loops, the size of which becomes steadily smaller as it proceeds
posteriorly and ends in a small opening, the anus. There is no specialized stomach enlargement. A short distance back of the anterior
end of the intestine a blind outpouching is given off from the right
side, called the liver diverticulum (Fig. 6). The whole gut is provided with a thin muscular layer, enabling it to contract peristalti-
cally, and is suspended throughout by a dorsal mesentery.

Integument and Body-wall. — The skin is soft, thin, and transparent. The epidermis consists of but a single layer of cells without any thickened protective covering. The dermis is soft and composed of gelatinous connective tissue.

The body-wall is composed almost entirely of muscle segments (myotomes) which are V-shaped (Fig. 6), when seen from the side, with apex of the V directed forward. Myotomes run from almost the tip of the anterior end back to near the end of the tail. These myotomes appear to be primitively segmental or metameric structures. Each metamere is enclosed in a sort of compartment or box, composed of connective tissue, the muscle fibers being attached between the front and back ends of the box. The vertebrates possess the same sort of muscular pattern, and it is believed that much of the vertebrate skeleton is derived through elaboration of the connective-tissue partitions between the muscle segments.

Skeleton and Fins. — The skeleton of amphioxus is entirely an internal one and consists mainly of the *notochord* (Fig. 6). It runs from end to end of the body and has but a single protective sheath. In every way, except that it projects in front of the brain, it is a typical notochord such as has been described as characteristic for chordates. It serves the main function of preventing the shortening of the body when muscles contract, but permits the muscles first on one and then on the other side to bend the body laterally and thus to propel it through the water in fish-like fashion. Other parts of the skeleton are the supports of the gill-bars, those of the buccal cirrhi, already mentioned, and the so-called fin-rays, box-like masses of gelatinous substance covered by tough connective tissue.

The **fin system** consists of a continuous fin-fold which is for the most part single and median, but in some regions is paired. On the entire dorsal side the fin-fold is single and continues to be single around the caudal region, where it is expanded into a flat paddle, the caudal fin, and on the ventral side up to the anus, where it divides and becomes double for the short distance up to the atriopore. Forward of the atriopore the right branch of the double portion of the ventral fin-fold is continuous with the right metapleural fold of the atrium. These facts support the theory that the paired fins of fishes have been derived from the double portion of the continuous fin-fold system. Only part of the fin system, however, is supported by skeletal elements, the fin-rays. The part of the fin system thus supported consists of the whole dorsal region except the tip of the head and tip of the tail. All the other parts, though continuous with the ray-supported regions are without skeletal elements and therefore may not be strictly homologous with the ray-supported fins.

Circulatory System (Fig. 10). — This system is almost diagrammatically simple but, except for lack of specializations, resembles that of aquatic vertebrates. There is a single vessel in the ventral wall of the alimentary tract, the subintestinal vein, in which the

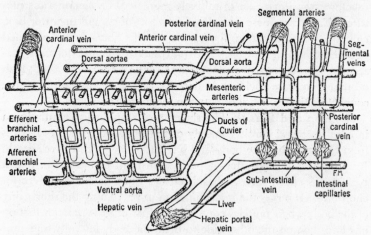

FIG. 10. Diagram of the main blood vessels of amphioxus. The arrows indicate the direction of blood flow. (From Messer, after De Beer.)

blood moves forward. This vessel makes a detour through the liver diverticulum, which detour is therefore interpreted as a primitive hepatic portal system. Returning from this detour to the median line the vessel goes forward under the pharynx as a pulsating tube, which acts as a heart although not specialized as such. This ventral aorta splits up into afferent branchial arteries that enter the gill-bars and emerge as efferent branchial vessels, which in turn unite to form the paired dorso-lateral aortae in which oxygenated blood is carried both forward into the oral-hood region and backward to the rest of the body, giving off branches segmentally to all parts of the trunk. These branches, after traversing the various organs, unite to form the subintestinal vein, and the circuit is completed. It is important to note that the circulatory system is closed, i.e., the blood is contained in vessels throughout its course. The blood is colorless and carries no pigmented blood corpuscles.

Coelom. — The coelom, or true body cavity, of amphioxus is essentially like that of vertebrates but is secondarily distorted and restricted by the immense size of the atrium, which pushes into the body in such a way as to crowd the coelom off into corners. An examination of Figure 7 will make this clear. This figure represents a typical transverse section through the pharyngeal region. The large cavity, *p*, is the atrium. If the atrium were not there the whole space between the pharynx and the body-wall would be filled with coelom. As it is, however, the coelom consists of a series of segmental cavities above and to the sides of the pharynx, known as the dorsal coeloms (*sc*), a small unsegmented space (*ec*) below the pharynx which communicates with the dorsal coeloms by means of slender canals, and in sexually mature individuals lateral segmented spaces filled with gonads (*g*).

Behind the pharynx the coelom is much simpler. There the gut is suspended by the dorsal mesentery representing a union of the walls of the right and left coeloms, and the whole gut lies in a spacious non-segmented splanchnocoel, as in vertebrates.

The **excretory system** consists of true nephridia, which resemble those of many invertebrates but are distinct from vertebrate excretory organs, all of which are coelomoducts. Each nephridium (Fig. 11, A) is a short, bent tube ending blindly in the coelom, but with a

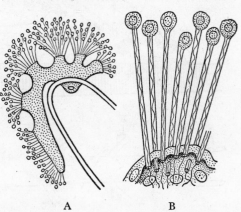

A   B

Fig. 11. A. A single nephridium of amphioxus showing several processes ending blindly in the coelom and a single opening into the atrial cavity. B. One nephridial process enlarged to show the group of flame-cell-like solenocytes. (After Boveri and Goodrich.)

nephridiopore opening into the atrium (really the outside world). The nephridium does not obtain wastes from the coelom, but from blood vessels that surround it. One of the strangest features of amphioxus is the fact that extending from several knob-like extensions of the nephridium on the coelom side are groups of single cells on long stalks, looking like bunches of tiny balloons on strings (Fig. 11, B). These cells are flame cells, or solenocytes. The stalk of each is hollow and from the body of the cell is given off a very long flagellum that whips about in such a way as to flush out the wastes from the cell stalk. These solenocytes correspond very closely with those of some polychaete annelids, a fact that lends some color to the otherwise untenable theory that chordates have been derived from annelid ancestors. Amphioxus is the only chordate known to possess true nephridia.

Nervous System. — The central nervous system of amphioxus (Fig. 12) consists of a slender hollow tube lying above the notochord.

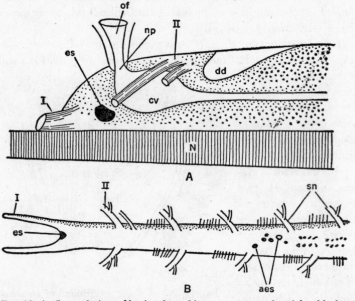

FIG. 12. A. Lateral view of brain of amphioxus. cv, central vesicle; dd, dorsal dilatation of the neural canal; es, eye spot; of, olfactory funnel; np, neuropore; I, first cranial nerve, olfactory; II, second (optic) cranial nerve, showing dorsal and ventral roots. B. Dorsal view of brain and spinal cord of amphioxus. aes, accessory dorsal eye spots, some median, some paired; es, eye spot; I and II, first and second cranial nerves; sn, spinal nerves. (Redrawn from Willey, after Hatschek and Schneider.)

The brain, if it deserves the name, is a slightly specialized region of the nerve cord, at its anterior end. In the adult lancelet the diameter of the brain is even less than that of the rest of the nerve cord, while in the larva it is considerably larger than the nerve cord, a fact which we regard as clear evidence that the brain is secondarily degenerate.

The cavity, or central vesicle, of the brain is considerably larger than that of the nerve cord and is open for a time to the exterior through a neuropore but is closed in the adult and is represented by the so-called Köllicker's pit. There is also a dorsal extension of the neural canal that further reduces the amount of nervous tissue in the tiny brain.

Paired "olfactory" nerves run forward to innervate the organs of the oral hood. A single median eyespot lies between these nerves at the front end of the brain. This is a primitive visual organ which is no more than a pigment spot and is not regarded as homologous with the eyes of vertebrates. It is probably sensitive to light, and may give information as to which direction is up toward the light. Other, smaller pigment spots are scattered irregularly along the dorsal side of the nerve cord.

The nerve cord gives off branches more or less segmentally, which are nerve roots (Fig. 12, B). In each segment there is on each side a dorsal nerve root and a bunch of small ventral nerve roots that are never united with the dorsal nerve root to form mixed spinal nerves as in most vertebrates. Sensory impulses go directly from the periphery to the central nervous system instead of running, as in vertebrates, to nerve cells in the dorsal ganglion whence they are relayed to the nerve cord. On account of the general bilateral asymmetry of the body the right and left pairs of nerve roots are not opposite each other, but alternate. This is also true of the myotomes that are innervated by these nerve roots.

Reproductive System. — This system is primitive and segmental. The sexes are separate, in contrast to urochordates which are hermaphroditic. The gonads are simple pouches (Fig. 7) derived from the walls of the coelom at about the 10th to the 30th segments. These become large and bulge out into the atrium, rupturing into the latter when distended with ripe eggs and sperms. There are no genital ducts. From the atrium the eggs and sperms are carried to the outside in the water current and fertilization occurs in the open. Spawning occurs at or near sunset when simultaneously males and females discharge swarms of eggs and sperms. Development takes place in the open sea water, the eggs and embryos floating about not far from the surface.

DEVELOPMENT OF AMPHIOXUS

Since the embryology of amphioxus is known in minute detail it should be an easy matter to write a simple history of its development, but it is not at all simple. For our purposes a few of the salient

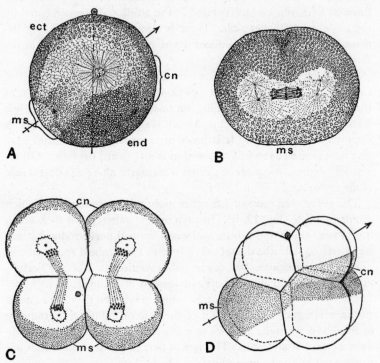

Fig. 13. Egg and early cleavage stages of amphioxus. A and B. Actual sections of eggs in first cleavage; A, in median plane; B, in frontal plane. Substance of mesodermal crescent (ms) at posterior pole; area of chorda-neural crescent (cn), dorsal to anterior pole; endodermal area (end) full of yolk, on dorsal side; ectodermal area (ect) opposite on ventral side. Figure B shows initial spindles for second cleavage diverging anteriorly. C, telophase of second cleavage, viewed from animal pole. Posterior cells containing mesodermal crescent (ms) smaller than anterior cells containing chorda-neural crescent (cn). D, eight cells, 4 micromeres shifted forward on 4 macromeres. Shading of mesodermal (ms) and chorda-neural (cn) crescents schematic. (From Conklin.)

points must suffice and only those points that seem to have special comparative or phylogenetic significance will be described, following the recent careful account of early stages given by Conklin.

The egg is microscopically small, about one-tenth of a millimeter in diameter, and contains a very small amount of food yolk. Immediately after fertilization the cytoplasmic materials of the egg are

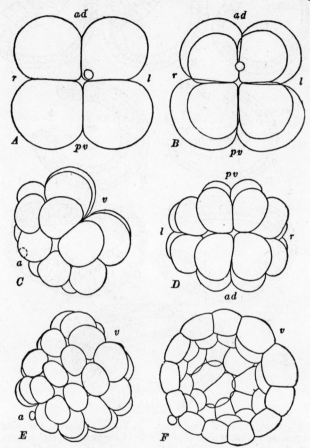

Fig. 14. Cleavage of amphioxus. A. Four-cell stage viewed from the animal pole. The two antero-dorsal cells are the smaller. B. Eight-cell stage viewed from the animal pole showing the four sizes of cells. C. Sixteen-cells viewed from the left side. D. Thirty-two cells viewed from the vegetal pole. E. Thirty-two passing into sixty-four cells, viewed from the antero-dorsal region. F. Optical section of right-half of young blastula. About 128 cells. a, animal pole; ad, antero-dorsal; l, left; pv, posterior ventral; r, right; v, vegetal pole. (From Kellicott, *Outlines of Chordate Development*, Henry Holt and Company, after Cerfontaine.)

so precisely arranged as to foreshadow the future axiate relations of the embryo. The antero-posterior axis, dorso-ventral axis, and bilateral symmetry are already clearly defined before cleavage begins.

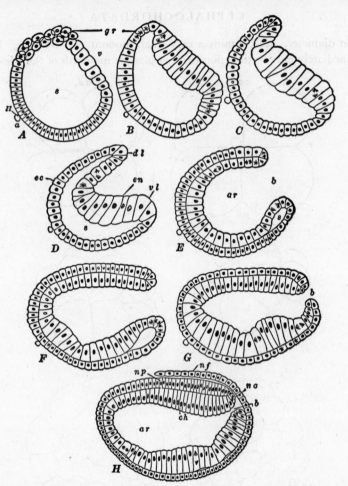

Fig. 15. Gastrulation of amphioxus. A. Blastula showing flattening of the vegetal pole and rapid proliferation of cells in the posterior region (germ ring). B. Flattening more pronounced; mitosis in cells of germ ring. C. Commencement of the infolding (invagination) of the cells of the vegetal pole. D. Continued infolding, and inflection, or involution, of ectoderm cells in the dorsal lip of the blastopore. The blastocoel becoming obliterated and the archenteron being established. E. Invagination complete. Continued involution of the dorsal lip of blastopore. Mitoses in germ ring. F. Constriction of blastopore and commencement of elongation of the gastrula. Remnants of blastocoel in ventral lip of blastopore. H. Neurenteric canal established by overgrowth of neural folds. Continued mitosis in germ ring. a, animal pole; ar, archenteron; b, blastoporal opening; ch, rudiment of notochord; dl, dorsal lip of blastopore; ec, ectoderm; en, endoderm; gr, germ ring; nc, neurenteric canal; nf, neural fold; np, neural plate; s, blastocoel or segmentation cavity; v, vegetal pole; vl, ventral lip of blastopore; II, second polar body. (From Kellicott, *Outlines of Chordate Development*, Henry Holt and Company, after Cerfontaine.)

Figure 13, A, shows a section of an egg in the median plane looking from the right side. The polar body marks the original animal pole of the egg and the arrow marks the antero-posterior axis, which does not coincide with the original primary axis of the mature egg. Note the four regions of cytoplasm destined to form ectoderm (*ect*), endoderm (*end*), the mesodermal crescent (*ms*), and the chorda-neural crescent (*cn*). This precocious localization of materials in the uncleaved egg is strikingly like that of the tunicates, though not quite so sharply defined as in the latter, and is regarded as strong evidence of the relationship of the two groups.

The first cleavage plane (Fig. 13, B) lies in the plane of bilateral symmetry and divides the egg into right and left halves. The second cleavage occurs at right angles to the first and produces two some-what larger antero-dorsal cells and two somewhat smaller postero-ventral cells (Fig. 13, C). From the antero-dorsal cells come the neural plate, the notochord and some of the general ectoderm and endoderm. The postero-ventral cells give rise to mesoderm and also some ectoderm and endoderm.

The third cleavage (Fig. 13, D) is latitudinal and cuts off four ventral micromeres, containing about one-third of the volume of the egg from four dorsal macromeres containing about two-thirds of the egg volume. The entire pattern of the egg and of early cleavage is essentially the same as in tunicates. Figure 14, A, B, does not agree with Conklin's recent account with respect to dorsal and ventral orientation, but serves our purposes as to later stages.

After the eight-cell stage the cleavage is not quite so diagram-matic (Fig. 14, C, D, E), but after a few more cell-divisions a hollow one-layered sphere of cells is produced, the blastula, with a large cavity, the blastocoel (Fig. 14, F).

The older blastula flattens dorso-ventrally in the region of the mesodermal crescent (Fig. 15, A, B). Then follows an infolding of the cells of the endodermal plate (Fig. 15, C, D, E) and this invagina-tion obliterates the blastocoel and gives the embryo, now a young gastrula (Fig. 15, F), the appearance of a hemispherical bowl with the endoderm in the hollow. The endoderm-lined hollow is the primitive gut, or archenteron, and the margin of the bowl is the wide-open blastopore. The invagination stage of gastrulation is the embolic phase. The blastopore now becomes reduced to small diam-eter by a growing across the opening of the ventral lip of the blasto-pore, the epibolic phase of gastrulation (Fig. 15, G, H). The closed

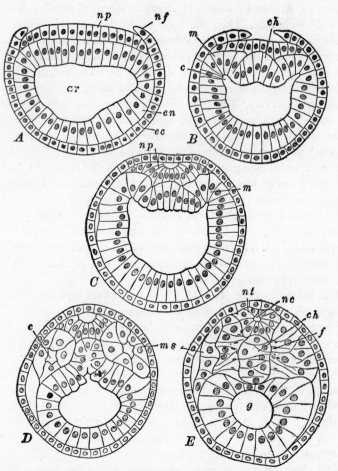

Fig. 16. Transverse sections through young embryos of amphioxus, showing formation of nerve chord, notochord, and mesoderm. A. Commencement of the growth of the superficial ectoderm (neural folds) above the neural plate (medullary plate). B. Continued growth of the ectoderm over the neural plate. Differentiation of the notochord, and first indications of mesoderm and enterocoelic cavities. C. Section through middle of larva with two somites. Neural plate folding into tube. D. Section through first pair of mesodermal somites now completely constricted off. E. Section through middle of larva with nine pairs of somites. Neural plate folded into a tube. Notochord completely separated. In the inner cells of the somites muscle fibrillae are forming. ar, archenteron; c, enterocoel; ch, notochord; ec, ectoderm; en, endoderm; f, muscle fibrillae; g, gut cavity; m, unsegmented mesoderm fold; ms, mesoblastic somite; nc, neurocoel; nf, neural fold; np, neural plate; nt, neural tube. (From Kellicott, *Outlines of Chordate Development*, Henry Holt and Company, after Cerfontaine.)

blastopore marks the region of the future anus. While this has been taking place the embryo has elongated greatly in the antero-posterior axis (Fig. 15, H), at which stage one can recognize the dorsal and ventral lips of the blastopore, the ventral lip being pigmented (*pg*); the flat neural plate (*np*); the notochordal plate (*ch*) and the mesodermal pouch or groove (*mp*) of the right side. At this stage the future adult condition is plainly foreshadowed.

From here on we shall mention only a few of the most significant facts about the development of systems, such as the formation of the mesoderm, the neural tube, the mouth, the gill-slits, and the notochord.

Development of the Nervous System. — The neural tube is formed from the neural, or medullary, plate by a dual process of pushing in of the lateral ectoderm bordering the neural plate and an active sinking in of the center of the neural plate itself to form a neural groove (Fig. 16, A, B). This does not close to form the neural tube until after the lateral wings of ectoderm have closed over it (Fig. 16, C, D, E). The hollow of the neural tube for a time communicates with the archenteron at the blastopore region, the open passage being known as the neurenteric canal (Fig. 15, H). The anterior end of the neural canal for some time also remains open to the exterior at the point known as the neuropore. This opening is regarded as equivalent to the temporary embryonic neuropore of vertebrates.

The Origin of Mesoderm. — The mesoderm of amphioxus has a complicated origin somewhat difficult to explain. The first indication of mesoderm appears when a pair of hollow pouches (enterocoelic pouches) is pinched off from the archenteron near, but not at the anterior end (Fig. 16, B, C, D). This first pair of pouches forms the first pair of mesoblastic somites. Posterior to this first pair of pouches the archenteron folds out into a pair of elongated ridges or grooves. The grooves open widely into the archenteron and before these grooves pinch off from the archenteron the hollow is continuous with the archenteron. Subsequently this elongated closed groove becomes broken up into a series of mesoblastic somites (Figs. 17, B, and 18, A), which constitute the primary set of segments and are relatively few in number. Many new somites are added later from cells derived from the dorsal lip of the blastopore. Thus only the anterior somites are derived directly from the archenteron and the rest of them originate in a very different fashion, equivalent to that found in true vertebrates.

In addition to the first pair of enterocoelic pouches and the paired enterocoelic grooves a pair of anterior head cavities somewhat later

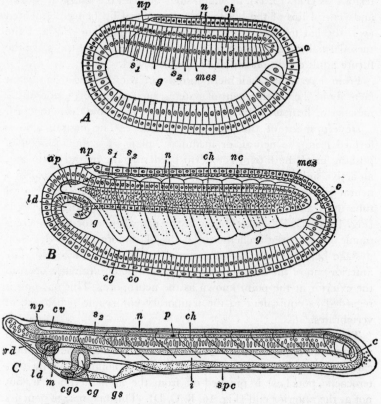

FIG. 17. Optical section of young embryos of amphioxus. The cilia are omitted. A. Two-somite stage, approximately at the time of hatching, showing relation of neuropore and neurenteric canal. B. Nine-somite stage, showing origin of anterior gut diverticula. C. Fifteen-somite stage. End of the embryonic period. ap, anterior process of first somite; c, neurenteric canal; ch, notochord; cgo, external opening of club-shaped gland; co, coelomic cavity of somite; cv, cerebral vesicle; g, gut cavity; gs, rudiment of first gill-slit; i, intestine; l, left anterior gut diverticulum; m, mouth; mes, unsegmented mesoderm; n, nerve cord; p, pigment spot (eye spot); rd, right anterior gut diverticulum; s_1, s_2, first and second mesoblastic somites; spc, splanchnocoel (body cavity). (From Kellicott, *Outlines of Chordate Development*, Henry Holt and Company, after Hatschek.)

become nipped off from the anterior end of the archenteron. These two cavities, at first nearly equal in size, have different fates. The right one becomes large and fills the space between gut and body-wall in front of the first pair of somites, while the left one remains small and gives rise to a depression known as the preoral pit, or *Hatschek's* pit, an organ of unknown function.

The entire mesoderm of amphioxus is segmented and derived directly or indirectly from outgrowths of the archenteron. There is a stage in development when the embryo might be regarded as in the "tri-segmented condition," with *a*, a pair of head coeloms; *b*, a pair of coeloms formed from the first enterocoelomic pouches; and *c*, the paired pinched-off mesodermal grooves. This trisegmented condition is thought by some writers to suggest a relationship with the trisegmented larva of *Balanoglossus* (Fig. 36) and other forms, a view that will be discussed later. Other features of late embryonic and early larval development are shown in Figures 17 and 18.

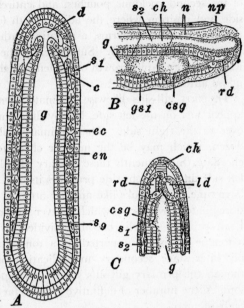

FIG. 18. Sections through young amphioxus embryos showing the origin of the anterior gut diverticula. A. Frontal section through embryo with nine pairs of somites. (See Fig. 19, B.) The dotted line marks the course of the gut wall ventral to the level of the section. B. Optical sagittal section through anterior end of embryo with thirteen pairs of somites showing position of right anterior gut diverticulum. C. Same in ventral view. c, coelomic cavity of somite; ch, notochord; csg, rudiment of club-shaped gland; d, rudiment of anterior gut diverticulum; ec, ectoderm; en, endoderm; g, gut cavity; gs_1, rudiment of first gill-slit; ld, left anterior gut diverticulum; n, nerve cord; np, neuropore; rd, right anterior gut diverticulum; s_1, s_2, s_9, first, second, ninth mesodermal somites. (From Kellicott, *Outlines of Chordate Development*, Henry Holt and Company, after Hatschek.)

The Development of Asymmetry. — We have already cited one feature of asymmetrical development, namely, that of the paired head coeloms. This is merely one indication of profound asymmetrical development affecting nearly the whole body, which is especially evident in the mouth and the gill-slits. The mouth (Fig. 17, C) first appears well back from the anterior end at about the level of the second coelomic pouches, and entirely on the *left* side (the side and position where the adult mouth forms during metamorphosis in the echinoderms, a situation rather intriguing from the phylogenetic viewpoint). Subsequently the mouth is pushed forward by more rapid growth of the left side than the right and takes up an anterior position.

The first gill-slits likewise originate asymmetrically and again appear first on the left side, but by differential growth are pushed over to the right side. These primary gill-slits number about a dozen, which may be the number characteristic of the ancestral chordate. Subsequently these primary left gill-slits move back to the left side and the right side produces its own gill-slits, but only at a later time. This looks like another attempt of the organism to restore bilateral symmetry, which it never succeeds in doing completely. Each primary gill-slit becomes divided by a dorsal infolding of a tongue of tissue supported by a tongue bar. At a considerably later stage secondary multiplication of gill-slits occurs, and though the primary gill-slits strictly correspond to the number of somites, the number of definitive gill-slits far exceeds the number of body segments.

SUMMARY

Amphioxus is regarded as in its fundamental organization not very far removed from the hypothetical ancestral chordate condition. It is, however, a curious mixture of primitive, specialized, and degenerate features. In this respect it resembles many other organisms.

We may regard as primitive characters:
1. The notochord, except its anterior projection.
2. The complete myotomic segmentation from end to end.
3. The diagrammatic circulatory system, without a specialized heart.
4. The straight intestine, without loops.
5. The simple liver diverticulum.
6. The simple epidermis, one layer thick.
7. Segmental nephridia, which are not coelomoducts.
8. Segmental gonads, without ducts.
9. Lack of biting jaws.

10. Lack of paired fins, unless the short double ventral region be regarded as such.
11. The formation of anterior coelomic pouches.
12. The ciliary method of feeding, but not the more extreme specialization of it.
13. The small, almost yolkless eggs.
14. The hollow, spherical blastula.
15. The embolic phase of gastrulation.
16. The endostyle.
17. The separate dorsal and ventral roots of the spinal nerves.

We may regard as specialized features:
1. The greatly enlarged and elaborate pharynx.
2. The very large number of gill-slits, which have increased far beyond the number of metameres in which they occur and are probably multiplied by secondary polyisomerism.
3. The elaborate velum and oral-hood equipment.
4. The atrium and atriopore, and the distortions of the coelom associated with the atrial system.

We regard as degenerate features:
1. The reduced brain and sense organs, probably an accompaniment of the assumption of sedentary living.
2. The forward projecting notochord, which may be merely the result of the retreat of the brain from the anterior end.

It is difficult to interpret as either primitive or specialized the characters in which amphioxus resembles the Hemichordata. It would, perhaps, be logical to consider them primitive, for it is customary to regard such correspondences as a heritage from a common ancestor. The specializations, however, are in the same direction as those in the Urochordata and indicate that amphioxus, as it is today, has departed somewhat on a side line and is therefore not in the main line of vertebrate ancestors.

CHAPTER IV

PRIMITIVE TRUE CHORDATA (CONTINUED) *(CLASS UROCHORDATA)*

TAXONOMIC STATUS AND DISTRIBUTION

During recent years most biologists have become convinced that the Urochordata are related to the Cephalochordata and that they must be assigned to the same subphylum as the latter. The best evidence of a relationship closer than was formerly suspected comes from the newer studies of the early development of amphioxus that have already been discussed and will be again called to mind in a later part of the present chapter.

In contrast with the Cephalochordata, which consists of but one family, two genera, and only a few species of very similar forms, the class Urochordata is divided into three orders, two of which are divided into two suborders, each with a dozen or more taxonomic families, many subfamilies, scores of genera, and hundreds of species. In contrast with the almost uniform body-plan, habits, and habitat of the Cephalochordata, the Urochordata exhibit a high degree of diversity in all these respects. They range from completely sessile tunicates (which may be large or small, solitary or colonial), to free-swimming solitary or colonial salpians, and the peculiar neotenic, or permanent larval forms, the Larvacea. Figure 19 shows a few of the diverse types of urochordates in a variety of habitats.

Distribution. — The urochordates are exclusively marine, but, unlike the cephalochordates, they occur in nearly all parts of the sea and at nearly all latitudes and depths. They are found in Arctic and Antarctic waters as well as in tropical seas and they thrive along the shores as well as at abysmal depths of two miles or more.

The fact that all urochordates are hermaphrodites, even though many of them are now free-swimming forms, suggests that they are all derived from a sessile common ancestor, and that therefore the most generalized condition for the group is to be found in the tunicates, an example of which we shall proceed to describe.

74

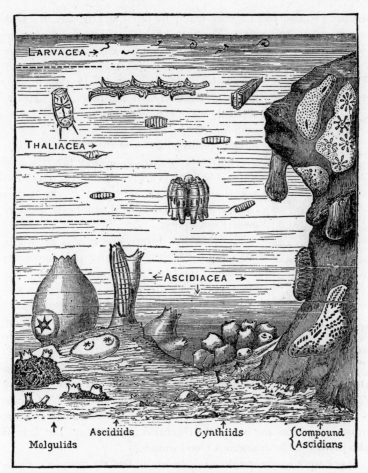

FIG. 19. Sketch of the chief kinds of Urochordata found in the sea showing their distribution and habits. The dotted lines on the left indicate the life zones of the sea: the surface or pelagic zone; the middle zone; and the sea-bottom zone. (From Herdman in the *Cambridge Natural History*, Vol. VII.)

MORPHOLOGY AND DEVELOPMENT OF A TUNICATE

STRUCTURE OF THE ADULT

A typical tunicate is one of the most inanimate of animals, rivaling a sponge in inertness. Superficially, at least, it bears no resemblance to a living animal, much less to a vertebrate. A common type of tunicate (Fig. 20) has the general appearance of a somewhat wrinkled leather bag fastened firmly by root-like processes to a rock or a piece of wharf piling. The "bag" has two apertures which seem

to be puckered about the edges, the puckering being due to the constriction of sphincter muscles. One of the apertures, that at the top, is the oral funnel and the other, opening on the side, is the atrial funnel or atriopore. Currents of water can be seen to enter the oral funnel and to pour out of the atrial funnel. If the animal is pulled loose and taken out of water it will squirt a stream of water out of the atrial funnel, a bit of behavior which has caused them to be labeled, somewhat humorously, "sea squirts."

Fig. 20. External appearance of a typical Ascidian (*Ascidia*) seen from the right side. (From Parker and Haswell, after Herdman.)

The wrinkled, brown covering is known as the tunic (or test), a character that has given the name "tunicates" to the group. This tunic, often quite thick and tough, is doubtless a sort of armor for an otherwise defenseless creature. The tunic itself is non-cellular, is secreted by the mantle, and is composed of a substance called tunicin, which is closely similar chemically to cellulose. It is not homogeneous in consistency but is made up of cells of many sorts, largely mesodermal cells that have wandered into it. These cells are embedded in a general matrix of tunic substance, reminding one of the condition in cartilage. The tunic is also permeated by numerous blood sinuses.

If one were to remove the tunic he would find the body of the animal still sac-like with the two apertures referred to above, but the exposed sac is composed of living tissue, though still not the body-wall proper (Fig. 21). The real body is found, by cutting through this second sac, or mantle, to be attached along the ventral side of the mantle and to be surrounded by water. Hence we at once correctly suspect that this cavity corresponds to the atrial cavity, that the mantle is the equivalent of the atrial folds, and that the atrial funnel is the homologue of the atriopore of amphioxus.

Lying free in the atrial cavity, except for its attachment to the mouth and along the ventral side, is a greatly enlarged, sac-like pharynx, perforated with numerous lengthwise slits, stigmata, that give the whole sac the appearance of a grating. The stigmata (Fig. 21) are not gill-slits proper, but are elaborate subdivisions of one or a few primitive gill-slits. The oral funnel (mouth) is partially separated from the pharynx by a velum with velar tentacles, just as in amphioxus. Along the side of the pharynx that is fixed to the mantle is an endostyle, which marks this side as ventral, and on the opposite side is the dorsal lamina that is connected with the endostyle

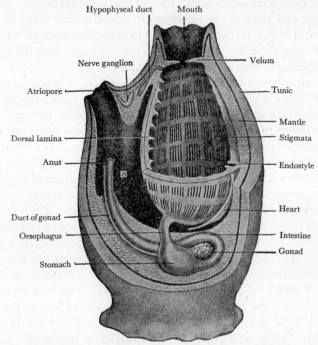

Fig. 21. Internal anatomy of an ascidian, revealed by cutting away of structures of the right side. a, atrial cavity. (Considerably modified after Hertwig.)

by means of peripharyngeal ciliated bands or grooves. The whole apparatus is merely a more specialized and somewhat more efficient food-concentrating (and respiratory) apparatus than is the pharynx of amphioxus. With the more complete sedentary habit has come a more specialized apparatus for ciliary feeding.

The most significant difference between the adult tunicate and amphioxus has to do with the shape of the body, especially of the digestive tract. In amphioxus the gut is a straight tube with mouth at one end and anus at the other; whereas in the tunicate the gut is U-shaped with mouth and anus opening in the same direction, a condition characteristic of sessile and tube-dwelling animals in general (Fig. 21). The dorsal food path of the pharynx leads straight back into a short, narrow oesophagus, which in turns enters the well-defined stomach. This lies almost at right angles to the axis of the pharynx and enters the intestine which in turn loops anteriorly and dorsally so that the anus opens into the atrial cavity pointed in the same direction as the mouth. Part of the oesophagus, the whole stomach, and most of the intestine are buried in the tissue of the mantle. There is no liver, but many delicate, microscopic tubules ramify along the outer wall of the intestine and open into the stomach. These are regarded as digestive glands.

The **circulatory system** is a biological oddity. It is composed of a "heart" consisting of a ventral muscular tube, lying close to the stomach and surrounded by a pericardium, believed by some but not by others to be derived from the coelom. Anteriorly the heart tube connects with a ventral branchial aorta which gives off branches into the pharynx, while posteriorly it connects with a visceral aorta, that ramifies among the viscera. The peculiar feature of tunicate circulation is that blood does not go around a true circuit but shuttles back and forth through the heart. The direction of blood flow through the heart is periodically turned about by a reversal of peristalsis of the heart muscles. For a time the blood is pumped anteriorly into the branchial sac (pharynx), where it becomes oxygenated; then the direction of flow is changed and this freshened blood is pumped backward into the viscera and mantle where food products and metabolic wastes are added. Another reversal of flow carries the visceral blood to the branchial sac and elsewhere. In a sense, we have here a double circulation, physiologically speaking, comparable to the pulmonary and systemic circulations of mammals and birds, but different in that at one time the heart acts as a "respiratory" pump and at others as a "systemic" pump. Nowhere else in the animal kingdom is such a rhythmically reversed circulation known.

The **nervous system** of the adult tunicate (Fig. 21) is a poor thing for a chordate. It consists of a single elongated, solid ganglion lying between the oral and atrial funnels, this space representing all there is left of the dorsal body-wall. This ganglion sends nerves to various parts of the body, especially to the sphincter muscles of the oral and atrial funnels (siphons) and to the velum, thus serving to regulate the water flow. Closely in contact, and indeed partly embedded in the ventral surface of the ganglion, is a peculiar hollow, branching structure, sometimes known as the *neural gland*, whose function is unknown. This structure opens through a small tubercle into the branchial sac near the velum. The fact that this structure arises partly from the stomodaeum (ectodermal mouth lining) and partly from the ventral floor of the brain, has suggested that it is homologous with part of the pituitary gland of vertebrates. There are no well-defined sense organs in the adult tunicate, though sensory cells of various kinds are found in connection with siphons, velum, and other movable parts.

The **coelom** in tunicates is absent, or at least greatly reduced. There is no extensive body cavity in which the viscera lie free, as in vertebrates. (It will be remembered that in amphioxus also the coeloms had been reduced to relatively small size apparently due to the encroachment of the atrial cavity.) In the tunicate this encroachment of the atrium has gone still further, resulting in a disappearance of the coelom as a true body cavity and in the retention of only a few somewhat doubtful derivatives, such as the pericardial cavity, the renal gland, and the gonads. These questionable coelomic structures are derived only indirectly from the archenteron. They do not arise as paired hollow pouches, but as a pair of originally solid mesodermal plates. This great reduction of the coelom, or, according to some, its complete absence, may be regarded as one result of degeneracy. Never at any time does the mesoderm show any tendency toward metameric segmentation.

The **non-metameric organization** of the tunicates is worthy of special comment in this connection. Since, as has just been pointed out, the mesoderm does not become segmented, whereas in amphioxus and the vertebrates segmentation is initiated in the mesoderm, it might be concluded that the tunicates represent an offshoot from the chordate ancestral stock prior to the evolution of metamerism. The only suggestion of metamerism in the tunicates is seen in the repetition of gill-slits, but, as has been indicated, this may not be metamerism at all but merely a case of secondary polyisomerism in Gregory's sense.

A rather large mass closely associated with the rectum and lower intestine is called the renal organ, believed to have an excretory function. This organ seems not to be homologous with either true nephridia or coelomoducts. The lack of metameric repetition of the renal organ is only to be expected in a form that is in other respects non-metameric.

The **reproductive system** consists of a single ovary with oviduct and a single testis with vas deferens. Thus, in gonads as in the renal organ, there is no metameric repetition. The gonads are derived from the mesoderm, as in amphioxus and other chordates. The ducts of ovary and testis are closely associated with the rectum and open beside the anus, emptying their products into the atrial cavity.

A Comparison of the Adult Tunicate with Amphioxus. — On the basis of the adult anatomy of the tunicate, without considering developmental conditions at all, the conclusion can not be avoided that the ascidians and cephalochordates are definitely related. The main correspondence exists in the food-concentrating mechanism, including velum, endostyle and its accessories, and the whole atrium complex. These structures are so evidently closely homologous in the two classes that they constitute convincing evidence of the common ancestry of the groups that possess them. Even more impressive correspondences are found in their embryonic and larval peculiarities.

EMBRYOLOGY, LARVAL STAGES, AND METAMORPHOSIS

The eggs of tunicates are usually rather minute, corresponding roughly to those of amphioxus in size. Like the latter they are almost colorless and contain but little yolk. Some genera, notably *Cynthia*, have relatively large eggs with cytoplasmic contents distributed in such a way as to indicate the future pattern of organization of the embryo, in which case the cleavage is of a highly determinate type and there is a relatively long embryonic life.

Conklin has recently called attention to the striking similarity of certain ascidian eggs to those of amphioxus. In both there is much the same pattern of morphogenetic substances, with an ectodermal area in the animal hemisphere, an endodermal area in the vegetative hemisphere, and between these two areas a mesodermal crescent on the posterior side and a chordo-neural crescent on the anterior side. Correspondences of this sort afford convincing evidence of relationship between amphioxus and the tunicates.

Apart from the fact that the tunicates have a much longer embryonic life and do not become free-swimming larvae at the gastrula stage, as does amphioxus, the early stages of development are so similar to those of amphioxus that an account of them would be almost a repetition of that already given for the latter.

Statements differ as to whether there are several pairs of primary gill-slits or only one. It seems more probable, in view of the nonmetameric character of the tunicate, that only one pair of true primary gill-slits is produced and that these divide by a process of secondary polyisomerism into about six pairs of secondary gill-slits which in turn become further subdivided into the definitive stigmata.

After about three days the embryo is hatched as the "ascidian tadpole," which swims about freely for some time while further developmental changes take place. The advanced larva then settles down, attaches itself by suckers to some solid surface, and undergoes a profound metamorphosis into the sessile adult. A study of the advanced ascidian tadpole is highly instructive.

The Advanced Ascidian Tadpole Larva. — When the tadpole larva (Fig. 22) is full grown and before degeneration sets in, it is un-

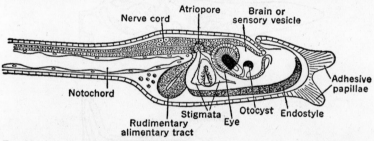

FIG. 22. Anterior end of an advanced ascidian "tadpole" larva (*Ascidia millata*) in optical section. (From Parker and Haswell, after Kowalevsky.)

questionably a chordate, in some respects more advanced than amphioxus. The central nervous system is dorsal and tubular and is enlarged at the anterior end into a good little brain (sensory vesicle) which opens at its anterior end into the pharynx near the mouth, a point called the neuropore, probably homologous with that of amphioxus. This little brain has a single median eye derived from the interior wall of the hollow vesicle, an eye far more specialized than that of amphioxus, since it possesses retina, pigment layer, a lens, and cornea. On the ventral floor of the brain vesicle and inside of the brain vesicle lies an otocyst, doubtless an organ of equilibrium. The nerve cord is slender and not much differentiated, yet hollow throughout. There is present an unmistakable notochord which extends from the tip of the tail up to but not into the pharyngeal region. It is regarded as belonging to the tail only (hence the name Urochordata), but actually extends into what appears to be the trunk of the tadpole body. In the larva there may be seen the well-developed pharynx, with endostyle and only two pairs of stigmata.

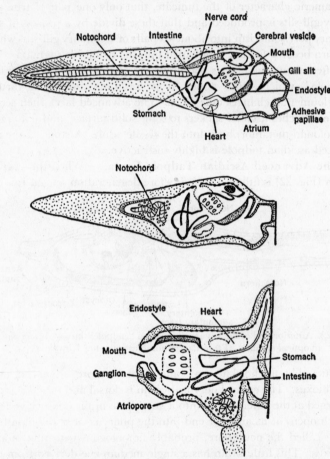

FIG. 23. Metamorphosis of the ascidian larva. (After Seeliger.)

The atrium and the postpharyngeal digestive tract are developing, the latter still in quite a rudimentary condition. Very little else has as yet been differentiated internally. Externally, the tail has well-defined dorsal and ventral fin-folds. Special larval adhesive papillae, "chin warts," are present at the anterior end.

Metamorphosis. — After swimming about for a short time — the time must be short since there is as yet no provision for feeding — the larva becomes sluggish and sinks to the bottom, where it attaches itself by its sucker-like papillae, or "chin warts," and stands erect but with head down. It then undergoes a profound series of metamorphic changes (Fig. 23), which may be regarded as due partly to differential growth and partly to destruction of already differentiated tissues. The region between the adhesive organs and the mouth, which is morphologically ventral, grows very rapidly, while the true dorsal region ceases to grow and becomes degenerate. This moves the oral funnel up to the free end and leaves only the space between the oral and atrial funnels to represent the whole dorsal side. The whole tail with its good notochord, muscles, fins, and nerve cord undergoes complete destruction, largely by phagocytosis, though external parts may be actually shredded off and lost. The very promising little brain degenerates to form the ganglion and the neural gland. Progressive changes are concerned chiefly with the specialization of the elaborate food-gathering apparatus, involving gill-slit multiplication, the extension of the atrium, the development of the velum, etc. At the conclusion of metamorphosis the animal may be regarded as little more than an animate food-sieve with necessary accessories for digestion, circulation, the excretion of wastes, and just enough brain to regulate these activities.

One is tempted to speculate as to what kind of an adult form the ancestors of the tunicates had before they entered upon the senescent period of racial degeneration. One might be justified in picturing a non-metameric, free-swimming organism with a good brain and sense organs, but probably the animals were of minute size and without any hard parts. Such a form probably lived near the sea surface and fed upon microscopic organisms that could be swept into the pharynx by ciliary suction. One would not expect these hypothetical forms to be hermaphroditic, but to have separate sexes. One might also guess that originally the coelom was formed by one or even three pairs of archenteric outpouchings such as are found in amphioxus, *Balanoglossus*, and Echinoderms, though this type of coelom formation seems to be absent in present-day urochordates. One suspects that a true picture of the common ancestor of the vertebrates, amphioxus and the tunicates would not be so very different from the ascidian tadpole advanced a few stages further than it now attains, and possibly showing at least the first steps toward metamerism.

COLONIAL ORGANIZATION

Quite in contrast with any other true chordates, the Urochordata, particularly the ascidians and salpians, form colonies by budding off new individuals from a single parent. It is customary to divide the order Ascidiacea into two suborders: Ascidiae simplices and Ascidiae compositae. The simple ascidians reproduce by budding also, but the new individuals thus produced are complete in every way, each having a separate test and retaining only a mechanical connection with the parent individual.

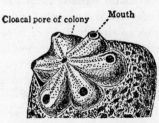

FIG. 24. A single rosette-shaped system of colonial ascidian individuals belonging to the species *Botryllus violaceus*. (After Milne-Edwards.)

The compound ascidians, on the other hand, are formed by budding colonies of new individuals that are buried in a common test, or investing mass, in which open canals occur that connect the atrial cavities of groups of individuals. This condition is well illustrated in Figures 24 and 25, which show surface and sectional views of typical compound forms. In *Botryllus* (Fig. 24) the individuals form groups arranged like rosettes, each having

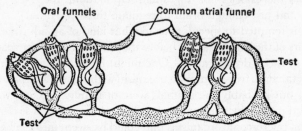

FIG. 25. Sectional view of a colonial ascidian (part of a colony). (From Herdman.)

a separate oral funnel at the ends of the radii and a common atriopore (cloacal pore) in the center.

Most of the compound ascidians occur as sessile colonies that form sheets of matter on the surface of rocks, piles, or other smooth surfaces. A well-known type on our Atlantic coast is called by the fishermen "sea pork," owing to the fact that the common investment of the colony is spread in a rather thick sheet over a rock and the whole looks like a slice of pinkish fat pork.

Far more interesting than the sessile composite types are the less numerous pelagic colonials, such as *Pyrosoma* (Fig. 26). In this form we have an illustration of the biological principle that units of a lower order of organization sometimes combine to form a compound individual of a higher order. The separate ascidiozoöids of a *Pyrosoma* "individual" are arranged in organized fashion, so that they form a hollow cylinder, closed at one end but open at the other. The oral

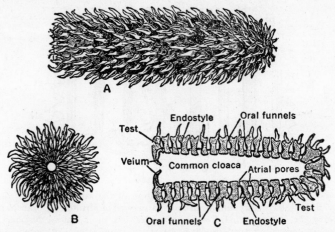

FIG. 26. The free-swimming colonial ascidian, *Pyrosoma*. A, lateral view, natural size; B, view of open end; C, diagram of longitudinal section. (From Herdman.)

funnels all open on the outside and the cloacal funnels all open into the hollow of the cylinder. The aperture into the latter can be opened and closed by means of a velum, or diaphragm, which acts as a regulator of water flow and therefore of locomotion for the whole colony. All of the ascidiozoöids in the compound "individual" are oriented in the same way, with anterior end outward, posterior end inward, dorsal side toward the open end, and ventral side toward the closed end of the cylinder. This compound individual behaves as a unit, and to our mind *is* a unit, of a higher order than is a single ascidian.

ORDER THALIACEA (SALPIANS)

The salpians are free-swimming pelagic forms, sometimes solitary and sometimes colonial. They might be regarded as emancipated descendants of the tunicates: the stolid, sessile "sea squirt" ancestors having been transfigured into beautiful, gracefully-swimming, almost transparent descendants.

A typical salpian, such as the classic *Doliolum* (Fig. 27), is shaped like a barrel with top and bottom removed. The resemblance to a barrel is enhanced by the presence of seven or eight muscle bands that look for all the world like barrel-hoops. The open ends of the "barrel" are fringed with lobes, or tentacles, which are elaborations

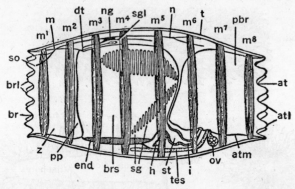

Fig. 27. Individual of the sexual generation of the salpian *Doliolum tritonis* × 10. at, atrial aperture; atl, atrial lobes; atm, wall of atrium; br, branchial or oral aperture; brl, branchial lobes or tentacles; brs, branchial sac or pharynx; dt, dorsal tubercle; end, endostyle; h, heart; m, mantle; m^1–m^8, circular muscle bands; n, nerve; ng, nerve ganglion; ov, ovary; pbr, peribranchial or atrial cavity; pp, peripharyngeal band; sg, stigmata; sgl, subneural gland; so, sense organ; st, stomach; t, test or tunic; tes, testis; z, prebranchial zone. (After Herdman.)

of the oral and cloacal funnels. The test, or tunic, is thin and transparent and contains no cells. The whole body is about as transparent as that of a jelly fish, making it possible to study the internal anatomy from the outside. The oral funnel opens broadly into the voluminous pharynx, or branchial sac, which is suspended from the dorsal wall of the atrium and is perforated by a dorsal and a ventral row of stigmata, or secondary gill-slits. The pharynx is provided with an endostyle and a peripharyngeal ciliated band, but there is no representative of the dorsal lamina. Locomotion is accomplished by means of contraction of muscle bands. When the posterior bands contract water is forced out of the cloacal funnel and the body is pushed ahead. In a sense one may regard the mechanism of locomotion as due to peristaltic waves of contraction of muscle bands from the front to the back which causes the water to be sucked in at the front

and forced out at the rear. The oesophagus opens out of the ventral
part of the pharynx, there is a small stomach and a short intestine,
and the anus opens almost posteriorly but is bent into a partial
U-shape.

The dorsal side of the body is more extensive than in tunicates
and the dorsal ganglion and subneural gland are situated a little
nearer the anterior than the posterior. The ganglion is evidently a
better central nervous system than that of the tunicate for it has more
to superintend in the way of co-ordinated activities. Salpians are
hermaphrodites, though fully free-swimming, a fact that suggests their
derivation from a sessile ancestor. The rest of the anatomy is much
like that of a tunicate.

Development and Alternation of Generations in Doliolum. —
The early development is much like that of a tunicate. After the

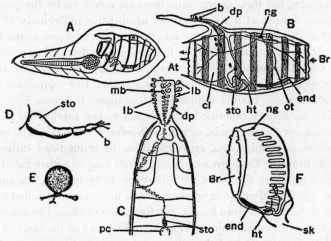

Fig. 28. Life history of *Doliolum*. A. Tailed larval stage; B. "Nurse" or *oözooid*,
showing buds (blastozoöids) migrating from the ventral stolon to the dorsal process; C, posterior part of much later oözooid to show buds arranged in three rows
on the dorsal process. D. Stolon segmenting. E. Young migrating bud. F. Troph-
ozoöid developed from one of the buds of a lateral row. at, atrial aperture; b,
buds; br, branchial or oral aperture; cl, cloaca; dp, dorsal process; end, endostyle; ht, heart; lb, lateral buds; mb, median buds; ng, nerve ganglion; ot, otocyst; pc, pericardium; sk, stalk; sto, stolon. (From Herdman, after Uljanin and
Barrois.)

embryonic period there is produced a tailed tadpole larva (Fig. 28, A)
in which the caudal appendage is relatively short and small as compared with the trunk and acts as a locomotor organ for a short time.

A period of metamorphosis occurs without the larva becoming fixed to the substratum, and the tail with its notochord is lost. This metamorphosed individual constitutes the asexual nurse generation. Such a nurse has on its ventral side near the heart and stomach a body process known as a cadophore, reminding one of a similar structure in *Cephalodiscus*, which buds off tiny new embryonic buds (blastozoöids). These buds look like amoebae as they crawl over the surface of the parent body and locate themselves on the stolon, a dorsal process of the body-wall, and proceed to grow into infant salpians. The first buds to arrive at the dorsal process move out to the end and attach themselves. Subsequent arrivals place themselves in rows, forming military ranks, with the youngest nearest the parent body. In some species the young individuals form a ring rather than rows. Some of these budded progeny grow up into individuals of the sexual generation, but those of the outer rows are sacrificed for the good of the community, as it were, and act as nutritive individuals. Even some of the individuals in the middle rows act as foster forms that contribute food to the relatively few individuals destined to grow up into sexual individuals. The few individuals of the sexual generation develop for a time as attached forms and then free themselves and become sexually mature salpians like that shown in Figure 27.

The life history described here applies to one subdivision of the salpians, the Cyclomyaria, of which *Doliolum* is the type. The other subdivision, Hemimyaria, represented by the genus *Salpa*, differs in details from the Cyclomyaria, but it would take us rather far afield to attempt a description of the differences in body form, the somewhat different alternation of generations, the curious so-called budding of male forms from female, the formation of chain-like colonies, and the direct embryonic development of the ova in the body of the mother, with the tadpole larval stage omitted. Suffice it to say that the whole life history constitutes one of the most unusual and fascinating chapters in chordate biology.

ORDER LARVACEA (APPENDICULARIA)

These tiny free-swimming pelagic animals received the name Larvacea because they are regarded as neotenic, retaining the larval form throughout adult life. The alternative ordinal name, Appendicularia, refers to the fact that the tail, with its supporting notochord is rather loosely articulated like an appendage to the trunk.

The body proper of the tiny animal (Fig. 30) is short and not unlike that of the larva of the genus Doliolum. The well-developed paddle-shaped tail is attached near the posterior end of the body and in swimming position bends forward toward the oral end. It is loosely articulated to the trunk by a sort of ball-and-socket joint. The attitude of the tail with respect to the main axis of the body is thus very different from that of the ascidian larva, in which the tail extends straight back from the body. The tail itself is an efficient locomotor organ, supported by a notochord that does not extend into the trunk. It possesses muscles and a dorsal nerve cord connected with the dorsal ganglion. It has a continuous fin-fold, dorsal and ventral folds uniting smoothly around the end of the tail. Both muscular and nervous structures in the tail show slight traces of segmentation, but no true metamerism.

The most curious feature of the life of a larvacean is the fact that it makes a "house" out of its test, a relatively large jelly-like dwelling with a front and a back door. In Figure 29, the arrow pointing inward indicates the oral end of the main hallway, or the front door, and the arrow pointing out, the atrial end, or back door. The little animal itself dwells in the living room at the center and is responsible for producing a steady current of water for food gathering and ventilation. It is not very proud of its house, for from time to time it abandons it and swims about actively near the sea surface. When a period of rest and retirement is necessary, another "house" is secreted and is occupied for another term.

Fig. 29. An individual belonging to the order Larvacea (Oikopleura) in its gelatinous "house." Only the small hammer-shaped object in the main passage-way is the animal itself. The arrows show the current of water through the "house." (From Herdman after Fol.)

Internally, a larvacean is like a simplified salpian (Fig. 30), with only one pair of stigmata, or primary gill-slits. The presence of but one pair of gill-slits suggests that this is the primitive number for urochordates, and that the larger number of stigmata in tunicates and salpians is the result of secondary polyisomerism in Gregory's sense. A large hermophrodite gland (ovary and testis) occupies a considerable part of the posterior end of the trunk. The hermaphrodite condition, together with the fact that the alimentary tract is U-shaped, the anus opening in same direction as the mouth, suggests that the Larvacea are not much like the ancestral chordate, but

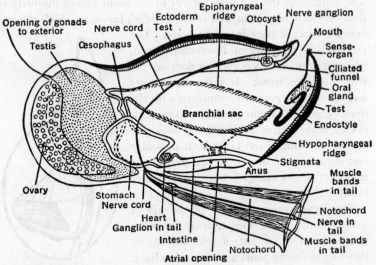

FIG. 30. Sagittal optical section of *Oikopleura*, a larvacean. Part of tail cut off. (From Herdman.)

that they are the neotenic descendants of a sessile ancestor much like a tunicate. They may even be direct neotenic derivatives of a salpian group.

In conclusion, it should be reiterated that the Urochordata constitute a highly successful side line of chordate evolution in which the sessile aspects of the double life exhibited by amphioxus have become the dominant feature of their organization. Both salpians and larvaceans may be regarded as secondarily emancipated free-swimming descendants of sessile ancestors. Few groups afford such fascinating material for biological research.

CHAPTER V

THE HEMICHORDATA AND THE
PHYLOGENY OF THE CHORDATES

GENERAL STATEMENT

The group called Hemichordata consists of marine forms of two main sorts: Enteropneusta, sand-burrowing worm-like forms, such as *Balanoglossus;* and Pterobranchia, minute tube-dwelling, sessile forms, including *Cephalodiscus* and *Rhabdopleura.* Though there is more evidence against the view than for it, some biologists regard the Phoronidea as aberrant chordates, related to *Cephalodiscus.*

The name Hemichordata carries the implication that the animals of that group are chordates. Literally, the name means half-chordates, and perhaps that is what they really are. A careful study of the adult anatomy and of the embryonic and larval stages brings to light some resemblances between them and the true chordates, but it appears to us that in some instances the principle of homology has been strained almost to the breaking point in an attempt to prove the chordate affinities of the Hemichordata. Undoubtedly the inclusion or non-inclusion of a group within the bounds of a given phylum is, at best, an arbitrary procedure, for phyla are no more than man-made concepts, and their distinguishing characteristics are only as rigid or as elastic as man sees fit to make them. Hence it is a matter of trivial import as to whether the hemichordates are regarded as true chordates or only half-way chordates. On either basis there can be little question but that the hemichordates and the fully accepted chordates are related, however distantly, and have been derived from the same ancient ancestral stock. If the writer had his choice as to how to classify the Hemichordata he would prefer to give them a small phylum to themselves and to arrange them at the end of a side branch of the ancestral tree that would come off the main stem somewhere between the Echinodermata and the true chordates. This view rests upon descriptions of the morphology of the group, which are soon to follow.

CLASS I.   ENTEROPNEUSTA

These marine, worm-like, sand-burrowing forms range in length from 25 mm. to 2500 mm. For the most part they are found living on the bottom of shallow waters, though some species are found at a depth of 2500 fathoms. The class consists of the following genera: *Balanoglossus* (Figs. 31, 33, A), *Glossobalanus, Dolichoglossus* (Fig. 33, D), *Ptychodera, Glandiceps* (Fig. 33, B), *Schizocardium* (Fig. 33, C), *Harrimania, Spengelia,* and *Steorobalanus.* Of these *Balanoglossus* is much the largest genus, with an almost world-wide distribution.

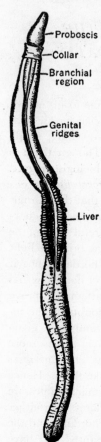

The members of the class are all rather closely similar in fundamental body-plan. On that account we may describe the anatomy of *Balanoglossus* with assurance that this description will cover the essential features of the class.

Instead of having as the three main body regions a head, trunk, and tail (as vertebrates do), the natural divisions of the body are proboscis, collar, and trunk, the latter being further differentiated into an anterior branchial region, a middle genital region, and a posterior abdominal region terminating at the anus (Fig. 31). The proboscis sits in the collar somewhat like an acorn in its cup, a character that has given the name "acorn worms" to the group. The mouth, which is always wide open and incapable of closing completely, lies on the ventral side and its lips are the ventral edges of the collar region.

Both proboscis and collar are hollow and their cavities communicate with the exterior by pores that permit water to be taken into or expelled from the cavities. The proboscis has a single asymmetrical pore on the left side near its base, while the collar has paired pores. These water-filled cavities are coelomic in character and the pores may be regarded as primitive coelomoducts. The trunk region also possesses paired coeloms but without pores opening to the exterior.

The functional significance of the cavities and water pores in

Fig. 31. *Balanoglossus.* (From Lull, after Spengel.)

proboscis and collar may best be explained through a description of
the burrowing habits. When on the surface of the sandy bottom
Balanoglossus pushes the tip of the proboscis into the sand, moving it
around by muscular contractions until a shallow, cylindrical hole is
made. Then the proboscis empties its water content through its
pore and collapses. This allows the collar to enter the hole. By taking in water through the pores the collar expands so as to fit tightly

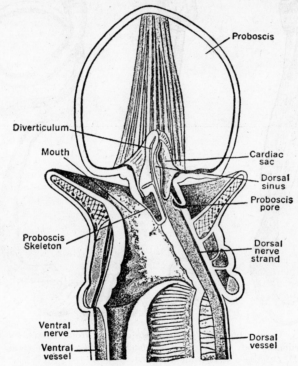

FIG. 32. *Balanoglossus*, diagrammatic sagittal section. (From Parker and
Haswell, after Spengel.)

into the hole like a cork in a bottle. The well-filled collar then gives
a point of resistance for further rooting movements of the refilled
proboscis, which loosens sand and stows it into the scoop-shovel
mouth. Then both proboscis and collar relax and the latter squirms
deeper into the hole before tightening its hold again. Once the collar
gets a firm grip, the animal makes rapid progress and soon buries
itself. The tail end is left near the surface, and at intervals comes

out and deposits a pile of castings somewhat after the fashion of earthworms. One can easily locate the burrows of "acorn worms" by the piles of castings. It will be seen that *Balanoglossus* literally eats its way through the sand. In eating sand it of course obtains whatever nourishment it contains, and this may be considerable, for large

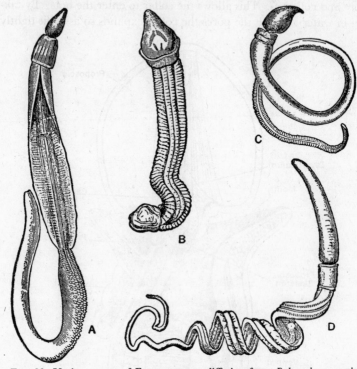

Fig. 33. Various types of Enteropneusta differing from *Balanoglossus* mainly in proportions of body regions. A, *Balanoglossus clavigerus;* B, *Glandiceps;* C, *Schizocardium;* D, *Dolichoglossus.* (From Harmer.)

numbers of small organisms live in marine sand. The sand taken into the mouth also contains much water, which is passed out through the dorsal, more or less separate, part of the alimentary tract that is perforated by numerous paired gill-slits. The gill-slit apparatus thus serves the double function of respiration and food concentrating, or the elimination of excess water from the food supply. In this respect there is a rough analogy between *Balanoglossus* and amphioxus.

In fact, the closest relationship between the Enteropneusta and the true chordates exists in the remarkably close similarity in gill-slits as between *Balanoglossus* and amphioxus. It will be recalled that in amphioxus each primary gill-slit is divided into two slits by a tongue bar that grows down from the dorsal side, and that these tongue bars and the partitions between adjacent gill-slits are supported by skeletal rods. The gill-slits of *Balanoglossus* are very similar indeed to those of amphioxus, but differ in that the tongue bar in *Balanoglossus* does not completely divide the slit. This rather detailed correspondence between the gill-slits of *Balanoglossus* and amphioxus was the first discovery to suggest a phylogenetic relationship between the two. Whether the correspondence is really due to homology or merely to analogy, or con-

vergent evolution, is difficult to decide. Two considerations have a bearing on this question. First, the tunicates, which are certainly more closely related to amphioxus than are the hemichordates, exhibit no such close resemblance to amphioxus in the architecture or development of gill-slits. Second, it is somewhat of a question whether the gill-slits of *Balanoglossus* really are pharyngeal clefts. They actually belong to the trunk, whereas if there is any region in *Balanoglossus* that deserves to be called the head, that region is the

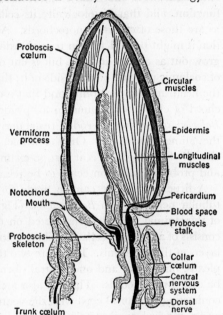

Fig. 34. *Schizocardium braziliense*, sagittal section. (From Harmer, after Spengel.)

collar plus the proboscis. If the branchial region of the alimentary tract is really a pharynx, the latter must be very extensive for in one species of *Balanoglossus* there are as many as 700 pairs of gill-slits, which extend far down into the trunk.

Be that as it may, it was the discovery of the close analogy between the gill-slits in *Balanoglossus* and amphioxus that stimulated a search for additional chordate characters in *Balanoglossus*. Bateson was the first to identify what he regarded as a notochord (Fig. 32). This structure consists of a thick-walled, hollow diverticulum of the dorsal wall of the mouth cavity which extends forward into the hollow of the proboscis. In *Schizocardium* (Fig. 34) the diverticulum is prolonged into a slender tube. The diverticulum itself is not rigid enough to have much of a skeletal function, but beneath it and partly developed from it is a Y-shaped cartilaginous structure which is regarded as the main support of the proboscis stalk. Bateson's identification of this diverticulum as a notochord depends on the fact that the structure is derived from a median dorsal region of the endoderm (as in chordates), that it has some relation to the skeletal function, and that histologically its cells are somewhat vacuolated as are those of chordate notochords. Against Bateson's interpretation it might be said that in true chordates the notochord does not grow out as a diverticulum, but is cut off because of the formation of coelomic pouches on each side of it; that it extends backward from the head, not forward only; and that a closer analogue of the notochord of chordates is found in a "pygochord" in the tail region of *Balanoglossus*, a median rod of tissue derived from the ventral side of the alimentary canal. On the whole, then, the so-called "notochord" of *Balanoglossus* is at best an example of far-fetched homology and probably will soon cease to be regarded as a notochord at all.

A little better case can be made for the existence of a dorsal, tubular nerve cord in *Balanoglossus* (Fig. 32). The nervous system of this animal is really constructed on the nerve-net principle and consists of a plexus of cells and fibers belonging to the basal or deeper layers of the epidermis. There are two thicker portions of this nerve plexus, one dorsal and one ventral, forming what may by courtesy be called nerve cords. There is also a circular tract of nerve fibers connecting the dorsal cord with the ventral cord in the collar region and a marked concentration of nerve cells surrounding the whole proboscis stalk. In the dorsal region of the collar the main nerve tract tends to be folded in to form a tube for a short distance, and in *Dolichoglossus* the nerve cord of the collar is tubular throughout and open to the exterior in front and behind, the openings being called, again by courtesy, anterior and posterior neuropores. On the basis of the conditions described, even so good a morphologist as Harmer allowed himself to say that "*Balanoglossus* is thus typically provided with a dorsal, tubular, central nervous system," a statement that seems hardly justified by the facts of the case.

Thus all three of the alleged chordate characters of *Balanoglossus* (gill-slits, notochord, and dorsal tubular nerve cord) seem to be decidedly questionable. To the same extent the claims of the Enteropneusta to full chordate status are no less so. Nevertheless there are cogent reasons for regarding the hemichordates as at least distantly related to the true chordates, as we shall soon see.

Embryonic and Larval Characters. — *Balanoglossus* has a classic larval stage, known as *Tornaria* (Fig. 35), which is said to be so similar in appearance to the Bipennaria larva of starfishes that Johannes Müller, who first described it, regarded it as the larva of a starfish. The special features of this larva are as follows: In shape it is ovoid with a complexly looped band of cilia traversing two-thirds of the anterior surface; the mouth opens on the ventral side near the equator, and oesophagus, stomach, intestine, and anus are clearly

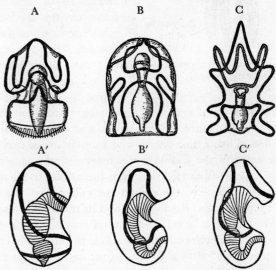

FIG. 35. Comparison of Tornaria larva with larval echinoderms. Main ciliated bands in black, lesser systems cross-lined. Upper row ventral aspect; lower row right lateral aspect. A, A', Tornaria; B, B', Auricularia (sea cucumber); C, C', Bipennaria (starfish). (From Lull, after Wilder.)

differentiated, the latter arising at the blastopore. In front of the anus is a circular ring of cilia, not comparable with anything in the echinoderm larva. Whether the resemblances between the Tornaria larva of *Balanoglossus* and the Bipennaria larva of starfishes constitute evidence that these two groups have descended from a common

ancestor is an open question. A more significant resemblance between *Balanoglossus* and the echinoderms is found in the origin and
arrangement of the coelomic cavities, especially well shown in the
embryo of one of the species of *Balanoglossus* that exhibits direct development (Fig. 36) without a Tornaria larva. It will be seen that
there are five body-cavities, an unpaired anterior one that becomes
the coelom of the proboscis, a middle pair destined to become the
coeloms of the collar, and a posterior pair that become the coeloms

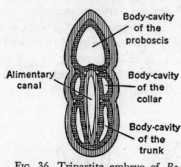

Body-cavity
of the
proboscis

Alimentary
canal

Body-cavity
of the
collar

Body-cavity
of the
trunk

Fig. 36. Tripartite embryo of *Balanoglossus,* showing coelomic cavities.
(From Bateson.)

of the trunk. These five cavities,
constituting the trisegmental condition, are also found in echinoderm larvae, in an embryonic
stage of amphioxus and possibly
in the Actinotrocha larva of
Phoronis.   In all these forms the
coelomic cavities are pinched off
from the archenteron, a method
of coelom formation not found
among most other invertebrates.
These coelomic resemblances of
the groups mentioned are re-
garded by some as of even greater phylogenetic significance than
the external resemblance of their larvae, and possibly than those of
the so-called gill-slits, notochord, and tubular dorsal nerve cord.

On the basis of the fact that the trisegmental character of the
Balanoglossus larva is carried over into the adult (the first segment
becoming the proboscis, the second the collar, and the third the
trunk) we might regard *Balanoglossus* and its relatives as a group that
retains through life a larval organization and never passes the tri-
mental stage of development.   Amphioxus and the vertebrates
may be then regarded as a group that started out with the trisegmental organization, but secondarily introduced metamerism by
segmenting the posterior coeloms to form a long series of polyisomeres.

CLASS II. PTEROBRANCHIA

The members of this class are nearly all sessile deep-sea forms of
minute size. The name of the class means literally wing-like gills.
They occur mainly in the Indian Ocean and adjacent waters. The
Pterobranchia bear about the same relation to *Balanoglossus* and its

kind as do the tunicates to amphioxus: they may be regarded as
degenerate sessile derivatives of free-living ancestors.   As in the

tunicates, the alimentary
tract of the pterobranchiates
is bent around in U-shaped
fashion, mouth and anus
opening in the same direction. The class consists of
but two genera, *Cephalodiscus*
and *Rhabdopleura*, which require separate description.

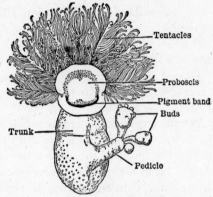

FIG. 37. *Cephalodiscus*, anterior view of
single individual. (From Hegner, after
McIntosh.)

CEPHALODISCUS

A *cephalodiscan* individual
(Fig. 37) is about 2–3 mm.
in length. The animals are
colonial in the sense that
many of them live together
embedded in cavities of a gelatinous apartment house, if we may
use the term. They have in general the appearance of Polyzoa,

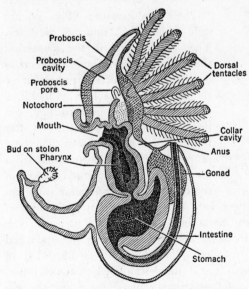

FIG. 38. Sagittal section of an individual *Cephalodiscus*. (Redrawn after Patten.)

to which some biolo-
gists consider them
related.

At first sight there
seems to be little re-
semblance between
Cephalodiscus and *Ba-
lanoglossus*, but care-
ful study shows that
the two possess the
same pattern of or-
ganization. There is
no trouble in recog-
nizing the three body
regions: proboscis,
collar, and trunk
(Fig. 38). Also there
are present coelomic
cavities in these three
regions with pores

opening to the outside. The same structure called a notochord in *Balanoglossus* is also found in *Cephalodiscus*. The chief differences between Enteropneusta and Pterobranchia are as follows: In *Cephalodiscus* there is but one pair of gill-slits; the dorsal nerve plexus of the collar is not sunk beneath the skin; the proboscis is merely a sort of loose upper lip over the mouth; the dorsal side of the collar gives off six tentacular arms covered with numerous hollow, feathery branchiae that contain branches of the collar coelom; and the proboscis coelom opens by two pores instead of one as in *Balanoglossus*.

A rather remarkable characteristic of *Cephalodiscus* is its peculiar method of budding and the fact that this method is somewhat similar to that employed by the nurse generation of the salpians (Urochordata). From the trunk region a process of the body-wall, a stolon, grows out at right angles from the ventral side. From the end of the stolon new individuals are budded off, which become free after they have reached a certain age, and thus add to the population of the colony.

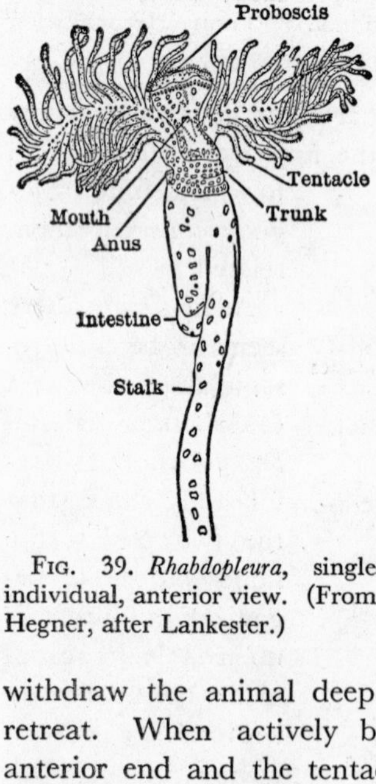

FIG. 39. *Rhabdopleura*, single individual, anterior view. (From Hegner, after Lankester.)

RHABDOPLEURA

These tiny creatures (Fig. 39) are only about 0.12 mm. in diameter. They are colonial in the sense that they are attached in large numbers to a common axis which lies prone against the substratum. Each individual lives in a transparent tube consisting of a linear series of rings secreted one after the other by the proboscis. The base of each individual is attached by a muscular stalk to the common axis of the colony. This muscular stalk can withdraw the animal deep into the tube when there is need of retreat. When actively breathing and feeding, however, the anterior end and the tentacles are protruded from the open end of the tube. While its body-plan (Fig. 40) is like that of *Cephalodiscus*, *Rhabdopleura* is still more simplified than the latter, differing from it in the following particulars: there are no gill-slits at all, there are only two tentacular branches of the collar (each armed with numerous branchiae), and the buds do not break off from the stolon but remain permanently attached to form a colony.

PHORONIDEA

Largely on the basis of investigations by Masterman, which as yet are unconfirmed, the genus *Phoronis* is ranked by some authors as an order of Hemichordata. *Phoronis* is a small tube-dwelling form of colonial habits, and is more commonly classified as a relative of the Gephyrea, which are, in turn, sometimes regarded as aberrant relatives of annelids.

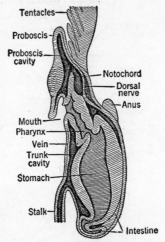

The main reason for including *Phoronis* among the chordates is that its so-called Actinotrocha larva is said to resemble in many ways the adult of *Cephalodiscus*. This larva is described incorrectly as having a pre-oral lobe with a body cavity, corresponding to the hemichordate proboscis, a region back of this and separated from the trunk by a diagonal partition is called the "collar," and the "trunk" ends in an anus that is surrounded by

Fig. 40. *Rhabdopleura*, sagittal section. (After Schepotieff.)

a ring of cilia, like that of the Tornaria larva of *Balanoglossus*. "Collar" and "trunk" have body cavities like those of the late larva of *Balanoglossus* and the number and mode of formation of these body cavities is said to be the same. The "collar" is, like that of *Cephalodiscus*, provided with respiratory tentacles or branchiae, enhancing the resemblance to *Cephalodiscus*.

Masterman goes so far as to find a "notochord" in this larva in the form of a median diverticulum of the alimentary canal, and a central nervous system superficially placed in the dorsal epidermis, but he makes no claim for gill-slits.

The present writer is inclined to regard the inclusion of *Phoronis* among chordates, or even hemichordates, as stretching phylogeny a little too far. If such linkages as this are permitted it would be difficult to avoid linking the whole animal kingdom together on similar grounds, for there are almost equally good grounds for linking up the ectoproctous Polyzoa with *Phoronis* and the Brachiopoda with the Polyzoa.

PHYLOGENETIC SPECULATIONS

Perhaps the soundest view as to the relationships of true chordates, hemichordates, Echinodermata, and possibly Phoronidea, Brachio-

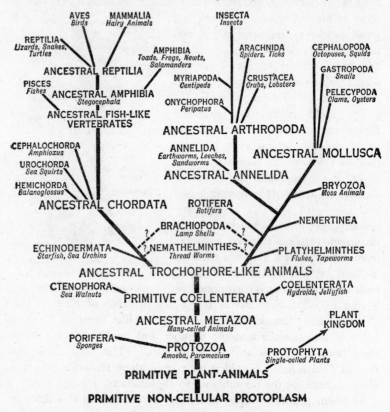

GENEALOGICAL TREE
SHOWING PROBABLE RELATIONSHIPS OF PRINCIPAL GROUPS OF THE
ANIMAL KINGDOM

Fig. 41. Genealogical Tree of the Animal Kingdom. (Designed by Sigerfoos, after Allee.)

poda and some Polyzoa, is that they all belong to the general chordate-echinoderm trunk of the two-branched (diphyletic) ancestral tree (Fig. 41), that each represents a mere side branch, none being ancestral to the others, but all derived from the same very ancient general ancestral stem stock.

All these forms, so far as they have been investigated, correspond in deriving the coeloms by means of outpouchings of the archenteron, and commonly there are but three pairs of such coeloms (additional coelomic cavities in amphioxus and vertebrates being produced in a different way); the larvae (when such exist) tend to have longitudinal bands of cilia that pass behind the mouth (the dipleurula type of larva); and the anus is usually derived from the blastopore region.

In these respects the group of animals under consideration differs markedly from annelids, mollusks, and arthropods. For this reason it is futile to attempt to derive vertebrates from either annelids or arthropods, as has so often been attempted, for these animals differ fundamentally in their development and in their general morphology.

It is necessary to look for the immediate ancestors of the vertebrates among those forms most closely allied to vertebrates. Amphioxus is so much closer to vertebrates than any other animal that Goodrich has included it among the vertebrates themselves. The present writer finds it difficult to accept this somewhat arbitrary classification, but must agree that amphioxus is the vertebrates' closest of kin. We regard amphioxus as a semi-sedentary degenerate, whose ancestor had a good head that was better developed and possessed even better sense organs than has the tunicate "tadpole" larva. From this amphioxus-with-a-head ancestor were probably derived the first true vertebrates, which worked their way up from estuaries into the large rivers. Another branch of this stock we picture as migrating along the shores and taking on sand-burrowing habits, giving rise to the present amphioxus group. Still another branch became fully sessile, giving rise to the degenerate tunicates. Some descendants of the tunicates seem to have become secondarily free swimmers and from these came the salpians; while the appendicularians may be regarded as permanent larvae, or neotenic degenerates.

If a still earlier ancestral form be sought, we might enter the realm of pure speculation and look for some form that could be ancestral to all those groups placed in the chordate-echinoderm branch of the diphyletic tree. Such a form could be pictured as a very small non-metameric plankton form, with bands of cilia like those of the echinoderm and Tornaria larvae, and with three pairs of primary coelomic pouches. Such an early ancestor would not be very far removed from the coelenterate condition and might be called the dipleurula ancestor.

CHAPTER VI

THE MOST PRIMITIVE VERTEBRATES MONORHINA (AGNATHA)

INTRODUCTORY STATEMENT

In Chapter I the chief distinguishing characters of the Subphylum Craniata (vertebrates) have already been listed and briefly discussed. These need not be repeated here, but should be well in mind as a background for an understanding of what is to come.

A subphylum is usually divided into a number of classes. The Subphylum Craniata comprises seven classes: Ostracodermi, Cyclostomata, Pisces, Amphibia, Reptilia, Aves, and Mammalia. In general this order corresponds to the evolutionary sequence of these classes, the most primitive classes first and the most specialized last. In such a large and highly diversified assemblage as the vertebrates further groupings of the classes are necessary in order to bring out the more fundamental evolutionary advances that come in from level to level. Thus as the first step in further classification, the Subphylum Craniata is divided into two very unequal groups called Branches. Branch I, Monorhina, comprises the most primitive known vertebrates belonging to two classes, Cyclostomata and Ostracodermi; while Branch II, Gnathostomata, includes all the other classes. Branch II, Gnathostomata, is then divided into two Grades of unequal size. Grade I, Ichthyopterygii, consists of one class, Pisces, as over against Grade II, Tetrapoda, including all higher classes. Grade II, Tetrapoda, is then divided into two Subgrades, Anamnia and Amniota. Subgrade I is represented by but one class, Amphibia, as over against Subgrade II, which includes all of the three highest classes, Reptilia, Aves, and Mammalia.

This branching-by-two, or dichotomy, is an expression of what appears to be the mode of evolution in this, as in other groups. Starting in with the lowest known types we find that some representatives retain the ancestral pattern of organization while others add some one or more important improvements. The conservatives and the progressives constitute the first dichotomy. The progressives of the first dichotomy then repeat the story, some remaining relatively little changed and others adding improvements, and we have a second dichotomy. A further dichotomy of the more progressive branch then occurs, and so on. Of course, minor dichotomies occur in the more conservative branches but these are less significant than those in question, for they are merely subdivisions of the classes themselves. This system of dichotomies is a sort of formalized expression of the main outlines of progressive evolution in the Craniata, but the whole history needs to be told chapter by chapter. The present chapter concerns itself from here on with the vertebrates belonging to the lower Branch, Monorhina (Agnatha). These are fish-like vertebrates with a single median nostril (all higher forms having paired nostrils); with a mouth consisting of a round opening without hinged jaws; without paired fins; and with relatively primitive brain, heart, kidneys, and many other structures. They are regarded as closer to the ancestral vertebrate than are members of other classes, but are already well along in specialization as compared with the unknown earliest vertebrates of which we have as yet no fossil remains.

We shall first attempt to find out what the earliest known vertebrates (Ostracodermi) were like and then describe the modern survivors of this earliest level of vertebrate types, the Cyclostomata.

CLASS OSTRACODERMI
(The Oldest Vertebrate Fossils)

In Ordovician rocks, deposited as long as 450,000,000 years ago, have been found small fragments of bone that are regarded as having belonged to some kind of vertebrate. These bony plates and scales are embedded in rocks of marine origin, but there is good reason to believe that the vertebrates from which they came lived in fresh waters and that the fossil fragments had been carried in rivers and deposited with silt in shallow seas.

Not until late Silurian, approximately 100,000,000 years later, do we find complete fossil remains of vertebrates. These early vertebrates, many of which are very well preserved, were queer looking aquatic vertebrates with heavily armored heads and with fish-like bodies and tails. The heavy head armature has given the name of Ostracodermi to the group, a name which means literally, shell-skinned. When we get our first glimpse of the ostracoderms they had already split up into a number of diversely specialized groups that have been classed as four orders, each with several suborders, families, genera, and species. Hence they must have been in existence for a very long time before they began to leave good fossil remains. It is probable that the ancestors of these forms had little or no bony parts and hence were not well adapted to fossilization.

It is not our purpose to deal at all extensively with the ostracoderms, but merely to note a few of their salient features. Perhaps

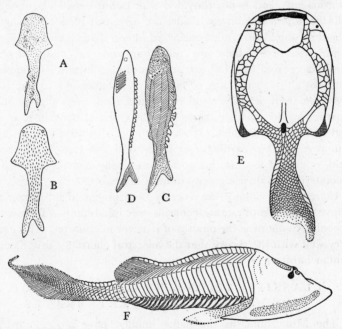

Fig. 42. A group of ostracoderms. F, directly after Patten; the rest from Patten, after Traquair. A, *Theolodus;* B, *Lanarkia;* C, *Birkenia;* D, *Lasanius;* E, *Drepanaspis;* F, *Cephalaspis.* (Redrawn after Patten.)

Cephalaspis, so adequately studied by Stensiö, is the best-known type and will serve to illustrate the characteristics of the group.

Cephalaspis. — Seen from the side this animal is strikingly fish-like (Fig. 42, F). The trunk and tail are, in general appearance, very much like those of a fish. The dorsal and caudal fins are comparable with those of a shark. The forward part of the trunk is covered with transverse band-like scales, which grade off into more typical scales toward the tail region. The head is covered with a heavy, continuous bony shield. The paired eyes are rather close together on top of the head, and apparently could look only upward, a fact that has led *Cephalaspis* and its relatives to be regarded as bottom feeders. Between the paired eyes is the socket of a small median pineal eye. A striking peculiarity, common to all members of the Monorhina, is the single median nostril, which in *Cephalaspis* is on top of the head. The head, when viewed from the under side, does not look much like that of a fish. The mouth is a roundish opening at the anterior end, and is not provided with biting jaws. The roundish gill-slits, about ten on each side, are arranged in two semicircles. The head-shield protrudes backward in two sharp lateral prolongations. Attached to these are paired "appendages" that look something like paired fins, but are not regarded as in any way homologous with the paired fins of fishes. It is important to note that *Cephalaspis* and other ostracoderms had a good internal skeleton, at least moderately ossified, as well as the external bony head armor and many dermal scales. If such forms as these were ancestral to lampreys and the cartilaginous fishes, and this view is commonly held, one must assume that these present-day boneless forms have secondarily lost their capacity to form bones.

Convincing evidence has recently been presented by Romer and Grove to the effect that ostracoderms were inhabitants of fresh water, probably living near the mouths of rivers or in estuaries. This agrees very well with the theory that the ancestral chordates originated in similar habitats.

CLASSIFICATION AND AFFINITIES OF JAWLESS, LIMBLESS VERTEBRATES

The Monorhina, as the name implies, have a single median nostril. The same group is sometimes called Agnatha, which means jawless. The Monorhina are classified as follows:

Class I.   Cyclostomata (Marsipobranchii)
   Subclass 1.   Myxinoidea (Hag-fishes)
   Subclass 2.   Petromyzontia (Lampreys)

Class II.   Ostracodermi
  Order 1.   Anaspida (4 genera)
  Order 2.   Cephalaspidomorphi (5 genera)
  Order 3.   Pteraspidomorphi (5 genera)
  Order 4.   Pterichthyomorphi (3 genera)

The question arises as to whether the ostracoderms themselves are to be regarded as ancestral to any of the surviving vertebrates. A great deal of recent study of the group has led to the belief that some of them, Anaspida, Pteraspidomorphi, and Cephalaspidomorphi, are not far from the lines of descent of respectively true fishes, hag-fishes, and lampreys. *Cephalaspis* and its relatives show many internal as well as external resemblances to the lampreys, and may have come from the same ancestral stock as the latter. The anaspids, however, were small-headed, fish-like forms with long sinuous bodies, relatively large eyes on the sides of the head, and with plates on top of the head somewhat suggestive of those of the fish skull (Fig. 42, C, D). They are believed to have been swift-swimming, predaceous forms like the earliest fishes, but, lacking jaws. They could not have captured anything but small prey that could be taken in by the round, jawless mouth. It seems not improbable then that the first true fishes were derived from the general anaspid stem.

Gregory has recently offered a new interpretation of amphioxus, which may be somewhat far-fetched. "Amphioxus," he says, "may be regarded as a greatly degraded anaspid ostracoderm which has completely lost its head shield and suffered marked anisomerous growth of the notochord, with secondary polyisomerism of the branchial basket. The brain has become extremely small. Its nakedness is to be expected in a specialized derivative of primitively armored forms." This view leaves the atrium and atriopore unaccounted for.

For a more detailed study of the characteristics of the limbless-jawless level of vertebrate evolution we shall now proceed to an examination of the existing cyclostomes.

CLASS CYCLOSTOMATA

The cyclostomes are surviving limbless, jawless vertebrates, sometimes called "round-mouth eels." The class consists of two subclasses that are not at all closely related, but are doubtless end products of two lines of evolution going back to two different orders of ostracoderms. The subclass Myxinoidea is regarded as a degenerate offshoot of the Pteraspidomorphi and the subclass Petromyzontia as a slightly less degenerate descendant of the Cephalispidomorphi. Both hag-fishes and lampreys may be viewed as exhibiting the eel-type of racial senescence, many other instances of which we shall encounter in various vertebrate classes. Just how many of the apparently primitive features of the cyclostomes are to be regarded as having been persistently retained from their ancestors and how many are to be interpreted as the results of developmental arrest, or as degenerate, it is very difficult to decide. When all is said, however, there is no question but that the cyclostomes are the most primitive of surviving vertebrates.

SUBCLASS I. MYXINOIDEA (HAG-FISHES)

Habits and Distribution

The myxinoids are commonly called "hag-fishes" or "borers." The first of these appellations suggests their ugly, wrinkled appearance; the second, their method of entering and feeding upon the bodies of their prey. The animals have been described as parasitic, or quasi-parasitic, because they are sometimes found within the bodies of their prey, which are fishes of various sorts. It seems more reasonable, however, to regard them as truly predaceous, for they actually attack, kill, and devour their prey. They usually attack their prey by attaching themselves to the gills of fishes and then boring their way into the body by means of a special drilling apparatus described below, devouring the viscera and muscles and leaving only a shell of skin, bone, and scales. Because of the fact that the hags seem to feed largely on fishes caught on lines and in gill-nets it is believed by some that they attack only disabled or dead fishes, but this does not seem probable for the reason that hags must have been abundant long before man had appeared to help them capture their prey. In regions where men depend on fishing for a livelihood hag-fishes are extremely unpopular, for frequently when a fisherman hauls in his night lines he finds nothing but the empty hulks of his captives, with sometimes hags still inside.

Hag-fishes are nocturnal feeders, as might be assumed from the fact that they are blind. During the daytime they live buried in the sea-bottom mud, at depths of over 2000 feet. They are somewhat peculiar among vertebrates in being hermaphrodites, each individual being either predominantly a male or female. It is said that most of them function as males when young and as females when old.

There are two families of hag-fishes, the Myxinidae and the Bdellostomatidae. The first family consists of a number of species of one genus, *Myxine*. This genus has a very wide distribution, being present along most sea coasts of both the Atlantic and Pacific Oceans, occurring in the waters of northern Europe, North Atlantic America, Chili, Japan, etc. The second family, represented by the genus *Bdellostoma*, occurs off the Pacific coasts of both North and South America, South Africa, and New Zealand. The very wide distribution of these forms argues for their great antiquity and their relative evolutionary stability.

General Anatomy

External Characters. — The long, eel-like body has a soft integument without scales of any sort. In *Myxine* (Fig. 43, A) a low, continuous median fin runs from about the middle of the dorsal surface, around the tail and well forward on the ventral surface as far as the cloacal pit. In *Bdellostoma* (Fig. 44, A) the fin-fold is confined to the caudal region. The whole fin-fold is supported by cartilaginous rays, which have no muscles attached to them. The caudal fin is of the most primitive type, known as diphycercal, in which rays above and below the notochord are equally developed. The mouth is terminal, in contrast with that of the lampreys, and is surrounded by soft lips with a puckered appearance like those of an old hag. Hagfishes lack the buccal funnel (or vacuum cup) of the lamprey, and of course have no jaws. Lateral to the mouth are four pairs of short tentacles, supported by skeletal rods, that have been plausibly compared with the buccal tentacles of amphioxus. The single nostril lies very close to the mouth and opens terminally, in contrast with the dorsal position of this opening in lampreys and many ostracoderms. In this respect the hags resemble certain ostracoderms (Pteraspidomorphi) that may be ancestral to them. The blind look of the head is due to the fact that the degenerate paired eyes do not reach the surface. On top of the head is visible the unpaired pineal eye, which is probably the only functional visual organ. Other external features are the openings of the gill-pouches, the large mucous glands, the rudimentary, scarcely visible pits on the head that are regarded as primitive lateral-line organs, and the opening of the cloaca. The latter is a shallow invaginated pouch of the body-wall into which open the anus, the excretory ducts, and the genital pores. Running lengthwise along the side of the body, almost from end to end, are numerous mucous sacs or glands. From these so much slimy mucus exudes that the animal is too slippery to hold, if captured. This seems to be almost the only defensive adaptation the animals possess, except that they are nocturnal and therefore less exposed to view.

Brain, Spinal Nerves, and Sense Organs. — In contrast with amphioxus, these lowest vertebrates have a true head with a relatively complex brain, a cranium of a simple sort, and characteristic vertebrate sense organs. The brain is surprisingly small for the size of the animal, is rather thick-walled, and has a very small central cavity. Fore-, mid-, and hind-brains are easily recognizable but neither cerebral hemispheres nor cerebellum can be distinguished. The fore-brain consists mainly of rather ill-defined olfactory lobes, the mid-brain consists chiefly of the optic lobes, and the hind-brain consists of the large, thin-roofed medulla oblongata. This is the simplest vertebrate brain known, even simpler than those so well described by Stensiö for the ostracoderms. We suspect that the brain of hag-fishes is somewhat degenerate.

Only the first eight pairs of cranial nerves emerge from the cranium, the ninth and tenth (glossopharyngeal and vagus) being post-cranial, therefore not belonging to the brain proper. This indicates a grade of cephalization lower than that in higher vertebrates.

The dorsal and ventral spinal roots fuse to form a common nerve. This situation is rather odd in view of the fact that the lampreys, regarded as a little higher in the evolutionary scale than the hags, still retain the primitive unfused nerve roots, as in amphioxus. The spinal nerves are also very primitive in that they are naked, without medullary sheaths.

The paired eyes, although apparently functional in the larvae, are in the adult sunk deep below the surface of the head and are without muscles or nerves. They are undoubtedly secondarily degenerate. The median dorsal pineal eye comes close to the surface and is doubtless an aid in determining when daylight comes and it is time to go into hiding.

The olfactory organ consists of a median nasal sac that opens to the exterior by means of a single nostril, which is placed in an anterior position just above the mouth. The nasal sac is innervated by nerves from the olfactory lobes. There are no true "ears," if by this we mean auditory organs, but the forerunner of an auditory organ is present in the form of a single semicircular canal on each side of the head (Fig. 43, C). This is in contrast with the two semicircular canals in lampreys and three in all higher vertebrates. This is, therefore, the most primitive "ear" among vertebrates.

One of the really striking features of hag-fish anatomy is the fact that a duct, hypophysial duct, into which the nasal sac opens, leads from the single nostril at the tip of the snout into an enlarged passage that opens into the roof of the pharynx. This structure is regarded as homologous with the hypophysial duct of tunicates and with the hypophysial part of the pituitary gland of vertebrates. In the hag-fishes this duct admits a stream of water into the pharynx and thus permits respiration while they are buried in mud up to the nose dur-

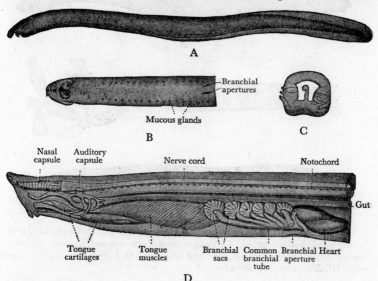

FIG. 43. *Myxine*. A. External view of entire animal; the rows of pores are openings of mucous glands; no eyes. B. Ventral view of anterior end, showing terminal nostril, oral hood with buccal tentacles. C. Inner ear showing single semicircular canal. D. Internal anatomy. (Redrawn after Parker and Haswell.)

ing the daytime. This is in contrast with the lampreys in which the hypophysis is a closed sac.

Skeletal System. — The main body support is the notochord (Fig. 43, D) which exists in a primitive condition much like that of amphioxus except that it has added an additional tough, elastic sheath to the surface. It extends from the floor of the brain in the region of the infundibulum to the end of the tail. No true vertebral elements are present, not even in the rudimentary form found in lampreys. This condition may well be regarded as degenerate. The cranium (Fig. 43, D) consists of several flat cartilages forming a floor beneath the brain and acting as a general support to the head. The true brain case, however, is probably the membranous sheath that covers the whole brain. It is very doubtful indeed whether the cartilaginous bars commonly considered as constituting the cranium of cyclostomes are in any sense homologous with any parts of the

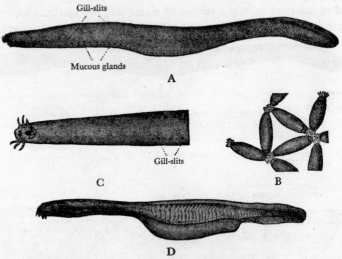

FIG. 44. *Bdellostoma*. A. External view of whole animal. B. Group of eggs adhering by anchor-like hooks. C. Ventral view of anterior end, showing somewhat ventral nostril, ventral mouth, and oral tentacles. D. Larva, showing functional eye. (Redrawn mainly after Dean.)

cranium of higher vertebrates, while the membranous sheath may be the true precursor of the cranium of fishes. The nasal sac is well covered with a fenestrated cartilaginous capsule attached to the cranial cartilages by membranous connections; the "ear" is enclosed in a cartilaginous capsule which is fused solidly with the cranial cartilages. The branchial region of the pharynx is supported only anteriorly by a few cartilages, in contrast with the complete branchial basket of lampreys.

Branchial Apparatus and Alimentary Tract. — The number of pharyngeal pouches and gill-slits varies considerably among hagfishes. In *Myxine* there are, as a rule, only six pairs, which do not open separately to the outside, but have long exit canals that pass backwards, unite to form a common canal, and open by a single branchial pore on each side (Fig. 43, D). In *Bdellostoma*, however, the number of gill-slits may be as many as fourteen pairs, which all open independently by round pores (Fig. 44, A, B). In all the hag-fishes the branchial region proper is restricted to the spherical pouch-like enlargements of the gill passages, a character that has given the group the name Marsipobranchii (pouch gills). While *Myxine* has no more gill-slits than some of the true fishes, the much larger number in *Bdellostoma* may be regarded as a more primitive condition.

The alimentary tract is straight, without loops, and rather slender, with but little regional specialization. Associated with the mouth cavity is the elaborate "tongue," or boring apparatus (Fig. 43, D), composed of several cartilages forming a fulcrum for the opera-tion of the massive tongue musculature. The tip of the "tongue" is armed with rows of horny teeth that shred up the flesh of the prey before it is swallowed. This tongue may be regarded as a specializa-tion and is probably not homologous with the tongue or any other structure of true fishes. The stomach is scarcely enlarged and the in-testine has no spiral valve. The liver is large and bilobed, with a gall bladder, but the pancreas, if really present, is represented merely by certain small glandular tubules embedded in the liver.

Muscular System. — The segmental musculature of the hags is almost as generalized as in amphioxus. Regular segmental myo-tomes run uniformly from head to tail with no regional specializa-tions except where they are interrupted by gill-slits and eyes. Back of the head each myotome has a W-shape instead of the V-shape seen in amphioxus. No horizontal septum divides the myotome into dor-sal and ventral halves, as in true fishes. The muscular system of the "tongue" is a rather intricate system of muscle bands that need not be described in detail.

The **Circulatory System,** though somewhat advanced over that of the amphioxus, is very primitive. The heart is a single tube, bent rather loosely within the pericardium into an S-shaped structure. It has a sinus venosus, a thin-walled atrium (auricle), and a thick-walled muscular ventricle. The ventricle continues forward into a ventral aorta which sends paired afferent branchial arteries to each of the gill-pouches. Efferent branchial arteries leave the gill-pouches and collect to form the paired dorsal aortae which begin very far for-ward, run backward, and then unite to form the single dorsal aorta which gives off many branches to the myotomes and the viscera.

Excretory System. — There are no true nephridia in hag-fishes: in fact there are none in any craniate. Instead there is a series of coelomoducts. The excretory system is derived from the segmented mesoderm, a part of which (nephrotome) is given over to the formation of kidney tubules. In the hag-fishes a pronephros, composed of a few segmental nephric tubules with funnels opening into the pericardial coelom, is functional in the adult, although no pronephric duct is present. This is the most anterior and most primitive part of the nephric system existing in any adult vertebrate. This is significant in view of the fact that in lampreys and in all higher vertebrates the pronephros appears only in embryos and is later reduced to a vestige. The more important kidney of the hags is the long mesonephros composed of metamerically arranged tubules, without openings into the coelom, but with renal capsules (glomeruli) as in other vertebrates. The mesonephric tubules of each side connect with a single mesonephric duct, purely excretory in function, that empties into a common urogenital sinus. This, in turn, opens to the cloaca by a median hollow papilla.

Reproductive System and Development. — The hag-fishes are hermaphroditic with a single ovotestis, the anterior part being ovary and the posterior, testis. The eggs and sperms are released directly into the coelom and pass without ducts to the exterior through paired genital pores opening between the anus and the urinary pore. Thus there is no communication between gonads and kidneys as in fishes and higher forms, and hence no use of kidney ducts by genital products. The whole urogenital system is doubtless primitive.

The eggs of some hags are large and enclosed in horny egg cases with hooks on the ends by means of which they are attached together in groups (Fig. 44, B). In shape the eggs are long ovals varying in length from about 10–29 mm. and in width from 7–14 mm. On account of the large amount of yolk present, cleavage is meroblastic, as in teleost fishes, and there is probably no larval period. This is in contrast with the prolonged larval life of the lampreys.

SUBCLASS II. PETROMYZONTIA (LAMPREYS)

Distribution. — These animals, known variously as lampreys "lamper eels," "lamperns," "sand-pride," etc., belong to a single family, Petromyzontidae, consisting of eight or more genera of which the genus *Petromyzon* is the best known. The family has an almost world-wide distribution, being present in both salt and fresh waters of North America, Europe, West Africa, Japan, Chili, Australia, New Zealand, and Tasmania. This very wide distribution, together with the fact that all lampreys are fundamentally similar, argues for the antiquity and relative primitiveness of the group and that they have not changed much since Palaeozoic times.

Habits and Habitats. — The lampreys are all carnivores, and although they are sometimes spoken of as quasi-parasitic, they should

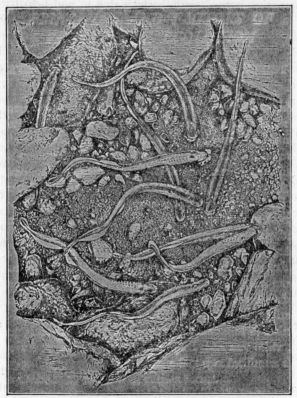

FIG. 45. Spawning of the Brook-Lamprey (*Petromyzon wilderi*). On the right of the figure a male is attached to the head of a female. (From Cambridge Nat. Hist., after Dean and Summer.)

properly be regarded as true predators, for they actually catch and eat their prey, albeit the prey is not at once killed as is the custom with more typical predators. The method of feeding is peculiar and quite specialized. Lampreys are swift swimmers, capable of overtaking slower prey. The animal attacks fishes, turtles, etc., of many sorts, usually larger than itself. It attaches itself by means of its circular mouth (a character that has given the name Cyclostomata to the whole group). This mouth operates as a sucker or vacuum cup and has very tenacious holding power. While thus attached it rasps or shreds the flesh of the prey with its "tongue" apparatus, which is similar to that of the hag-fish. The round mouth is armed with inpointing horny "teeth," which sink in and help it to hold firmly. The "teeth" should be carefully distinguished from the true teeth of fishes, for they are in no sense homologous with the latter.

Brook lampreys spend a great deal of their time resting. They attach themselves to rocks in rapid streams, using the vacuum cup for attachment, and breathing in a manner to be described later. It is a familiar sight to see quite a number of lampreys thus resting close together with their limp bodies undulating like streamers in the current. It is a curious fact some species of brook lampreys do not feed as adults. The alimentary canal back of the pharynx is in these species degenerate. The sucker-mouth is also used during mating, the male fastening himself to the head of the female who is attached to a rock, and wrapping his body about her in such a way as to fertilize the eggs as they exude from the genital pore. The eggs are laid in a sort of prepared "nest" on the stream bottom. A space between larger rocks is cleared of smaller stones, members of both sexes lifting and carrying off stones with the sucker (Fig. 45). The story of embryonic and larval development will be told in another place.

General Anatomy

External Characteristics. — The surface of the body is smooth and slimy, and generally heavily pigmented, with sometimes a mottled pattern. The epidermis, in contrast to amphioxus, is about a dozen cell-layers thick and contains numerous mucous glands. The median fin system (Fig. 46, A) is more specialized than that of the hags in that it is differentiated into two dorsal and a caudal fin, all supported by cartilaginous rays, longer than in hag-fishes. These rays are fused together at their bases to the membranous sheath that surrounds the notochord and neural tube and help to strengthen the latter. The head region is characterized by the great forward development of the upper-lip region, involved in the formation of the buccal funnel (Fig. 46, B). The intercalation of this structure between the mouth and the median nostril has, as in *Cephalaspis*, pushed back the nostril to a dorsal position far back from the anterior end (Fig. 46, C). The head has a much more normal appearance than

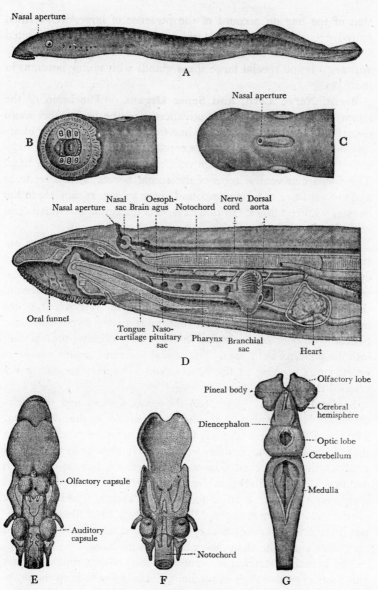

FIG. 46. *Petromyzon*. A. External view of entire animal. B. Ventral view of head showing funnel-like oral sucker armed with chitinous teeth; end of "tongue" in mouth opening. C. Dorsal view of head, showing median nostril. D. Internal anatomy. E. Ventral view of cranium. F. Dorsal view of cranium. G. Dorsal view of brain. (Redrawn after Parker and Haswell.)

that of the hag on account of the presence of large, well-formed paired eyes. There are regularly seven pairs of gill-slits situated farther forward in the head than is the case in hag-fishes. There appear to be no special large slime glands with visible pores, as in the hags.

Brain, Nerve Cord, and Sense Organs. — The brain of the lamprey (Fig. 46, G) is more advanced and the brain lobes more clearly differentiated than in the hag-fish. It has well-defined olfactory lobes, small but recognizable cerebral hemispheres, and a rudimentary cerebellum. The brain vesicles are larger than in the hags. The dorsal and ventral roots of the spinal nerves remain separate and are not fused to form compound nerve trunks, as they are in the hags and in true fishes. In other respects the brain and nerve cord resemble those of the hags.

The paired eyes are relatively large and functional. There are two small median eyes on top of the brain, the pineal and parietal eyes, the latter beneath the former and rudimentary. The ears possess two semicircular canals, a number intermediate between that of the hags and that of true fishes. The olfactory sac (Fig. 46, D) opens into the nasal canal, the latter continuing as the hypophysial sac beneath the floor of the brain, where it ends blindly, not opening into the pharynx as in hags. The lateral line sense organs consist of isolated pits opening at the surface and are somewhat better developed than in the hags.

Skeletal System. — Except in the respects mentioned, the skeleton of the lamprey may be assumed to be similar to that of the hag. The so-called cranium (Fig. 46, E, F) is a little better developed than that of the hag. Rudimentary vertebrae are present in the form of small cartilages on each side of the notochord, two pairs to each metamere. In the tail region the paired cartilages unite dorsally and arch over the nerve cord to form neural arches, which of course partly enclose the nerve cord. The presence of even these rudimentary vertebral components may be regarded as a more advanced vertebrate condition than their absence in the hags.

The branchial skeleton is a true branchial basket, much stronger and more extensive than in the hags. This serves to keep the branchial sacs widely open, and thus makes possible the peculiar mode of respiration soon to be described. This branchial skeleton is regarded by some writers as roughly homologous with the visceral skeleton of higher vertebrates.

Branchial Apparatus and Alimentary Tract. — In the lampreys there are seven pairs of branchial pouches (Fig. 46, D) and the same number of gill-slits that open separately closer to the head than in the hags. The number of gill-slits is one higher than in *Myxine*, but only about half that of *Bdellostoma*. In the adult lamprey (but not in the larva, as will be seen later) the respiratory part of the pharynx is cut off from the rest of the alimentary tract as a voluminous sac, ending blindly posteriorly but communicating anteriorly with the front part of the pharynx by a small opening guarded by a valve, which closes when the animal is attached by the sucker-mouth. The hypophysial sac is closed and no water can enter the pharynx through the nostril or through the attached mouth. Hence water must be breathed both in and out through the gill-slits. This is accomplished by alternate contraction and expansion of the body musculature in the branchial region. This whole condition is regarded as a distinct specialization associated with the peculiar mode of attachment while feeding and resting, and is very efficient.

The oesophagus, which is quite slender, comes forward and opens directly into the buccal cavity. The straight alimentary canal, without stomach enlargement, possesses a rudimentary spiral valve, absent in hags but extensively developed in many fishes. The epithelial cells of the gut are ciliated, as in amphioxus, a primitive character. The liver in the adult is rather degenerate and the bile duct does not empty into the intestine, so that the liver becomes an endocrine gland in the sense that its secretion is poured into the blood. The pancreas is separate from the liver and occurs as small isolated glands along the intestine.

The **Muscular, Circulatory,** and **Reproductive Systems** are essentially the same as in the hags.

The **Excretory System** differs from that of the hags in that the pronephros is functional only in the larva, the adult using only the mesonephros.

Embryonic and Larval Development

In contrast with hag-fishes, the eggs of the lamprey are comparatively small, about one millimeter in diameter, with little yolk and without shell or hooks. Cleavage is holoblastic. In these respects lampreys are more primitive than hags and closer to amphioxus. The embryo hatches as a larva known as the "Ammocoetes," which is very important phylogenetically in that it is in many respects a

connecting link between amphioxus and the cyclostomes. The
mouth of this larva (Fig. 47) is bounded above by an oral hood much
like that of amphioxus, and below by a short transverse lower lip.
The mouth opening is guarded by a velum, as in amphioxus. The
pharynx is ciliated and the method of feeding essentially like that of
amphioxus. In the floor of the pharynx is an open glandular and
ciliated groove, a true endostyle, that functions for a time as does
that structure in amphioxus. In Ammocoetes this groove runs for
only a fraction of the length of the pharynx, but in the embryo of the
hag-fish, *Bdellostoma*, the groove runs the full length of the pharynx
as in amphioxus. There is a hyperpharyngeal groove and a peripharyngeal groove carrying the mucous rope. The fact that the
larva lives with all but the head buried in mud, and feeds exactly
like amphioxus, is, of course, highly suggestive. The larva differs
from the adult also in other important ways. The branchial region

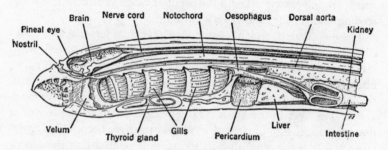

FIG. 47. Ammocoetes larva of lamprey. (From Goodrich.)

of the pharynx is not cut off but opens directly into the intestine.
The liver empties through the bile duct into the intestine. The paired
eyes are deeply sunk and not yet functional, but the pineal eye is well
developed. The median fin is continuous and not broken up into
separate fins. The branchial basket is very poorly developed.

The Ammocoetes has a larval career of three, four, or more years,
and then during a few weeks in the winter undergoes a profound
metamorphosis, changing all its larval structures and habits to those
of the adult. The oral hood becomes rounded out into a buccal
funnel with horny teeth. The paired eyes grow out to the surface and
become functional. The pharynx becomes subdivided: the endostyle becoming pinched off to form the thyroid gland, the branchial
sac becoming cut off ventrally, and the oesophagus being pinched

off dorsally. The velum disappears except for a rudiment, and the branchial basket develops. The continuous median fin becomes interrupted to form separate fins. The gall bladder disappears and the liver is cut off from connection with the intestine.

It is suspected by some writers that the Ammocoetes larva of the lamprey approaches rather close to the condition of the ancestral chordate. Some have gone so far as to suggest that amphioxus, as we find it today, may be a permanent (neotenic) larva of some vertebrate related rather closely to the cyclostomes. This view is supported to some extent by the fact that amphioxus is so obviously degenerate in other respects. It would be too bad, however, to demote the classic Adam and Eve of the vertebrates from its present highly respected status to that of merely a degenerate larva of some run-down cyclostome.

SUMMARY

The significant characteristics of the cyclostomes may be conveniently summarized by listing those in which the whole group is primitive (in retaining characters like those of amphioxus or in lacking or showing in less advanced condition the characters of true fishes), specialized characters, and degenerate characters. Also the hags and lampreys may be compared as to their relative primitiveness or specialization in various systems.

I. Primitive Characters of Cyclostomes in General.

A. *Characters resembling those of amphioxus:*
    Continuous notochord (but with an added sheath).
    Segmental musculature but little modified from head to tail.
    Relatively large numbers of gill-slits (in some hag-fishes).
    Gonads without ducts.
    Alimentary tract straight and without much regional specialization.
    Endostyle in lamprey larva.
    Ciliated alimentary tract.

B. *Characters more primitive than in fishes:*
    No hinged jaws.
    No paired limbs.
    No true teeth.

Continuous or nearly continuous median fin-fold (in hag-fishes).

Diphycercal caudal fin.

Fin-rays without muscular attachments and probably con-tinuations of neural spines.

Cranium incomplete.

No vertebrae, or poorly developed vertebrae.

Rudimentary pancreas.

No spiral valve, or only slightly developed spiral valve, in intestine.

Single median nostril.

Brain relatively small and generalized.

Heart a rather loosely twisted S-shaped tube.

Lateral-line organs poorly developed and in isolated pits.

Hypophysial duct rather large, open to the exterior, and not connected with the pituitary body.

Ninth and tenth "cranial nerves" not enclosed in cranium.

Absence of medullated nerves.

Sympathetic nervous system very primitive and poorly developed.

C. *Characters more primitive in hags than in lampreys:*

Median fin regionally undifferentiated and continuous.

Terminal nostril.

Less specialized brain without cerebral hemispheres or cerebellum.

Cranium less developed.

Only one semicircular canal.

Functional pronephros in adult.

No spiral valve.

No vertebrae.

Hypophysial duct opening into mouth.

Less well-developed lateral-line organs.

Functional liver and bile duct in adult.

Relatively large number of gill-slits (*Bdellostoma*).

D. *Characters more primitive in lamprey than in hags:*

Separate dorsal and ventral spinal nerves.

Small egg with little yolk.

Holoblastic cleavage.

Larval stage showing many resemblances to amphioxus.

II. Specialized Characters.

A. *Characters of cyclostomes showing an advance over amphioxus:*

A distinct head (lack of head in amphioxus, however, may be secondary).

A so-called cranium.

A more advanced brain.

Pro- and mesonephric kidneys.

Epidermis several layers thick.

A second sheath on notochord.

Dorsal spinal nerves with ganglia.

Vertebrae introduced (lampreys).

Myotomes W-shaped.

A slightly developed sympathetic nervous system.

Well-developed external eyes and inner ears.

B. *Particular specializations:*

"Tongue" apparatus.

Sucking mouth and horny teenth (in lampreys).

Sac-like gill pouches.

Separate branchial sac with branchial basket (in lampreys).

The dorsal position of nostril in lampreys.

Large, heavy-yolked egg, with meroblastic cleavage and no larval stage in hags.

The large slime glands, especially in hags.

III. Degenerate Characters.

The greatly elongated eel-like body, more marked in hags.

Rudimentary paired eyes in hags.

Reduced liver and lack of gall bladder and bile duct in adult lamprey.

Lack of exoskeleton.

Lack of ossification of endoskeleton.

CHAPTER VII

INTRODUCTION TO THE CLASS PISCES
(*GNATHOSTOME FISHES*)

GENERAL CHARACTERISTICS OF FISHES

Everyone knows a fish when he sees it, but not everyone could say offhand just what are the distinguishing characters of a fish. One thinks at once of fins, scales, and gills as fish characters, but many animals other than fishes possess one or all of these at some time or other. It may be interesting therefore to list a score or so of characters that will at least distinguish fishes from their nearest of kin, the cyclostomes:

1. Hinged jaws.
2. Paired fins.
3. Paired nostrils. These do not open into pharynx except in lung fishes and lobe-finned fishes.
4. Pharynx greatly shortened up and without at any time having a food-concentrating apparatus.
5. Gill-slits without gill-pouches.
6. Number of gill-slits never more than seven pairs, usually only five pairs.
7. The cranium completely enveloping the brain.
8. Vertebrae always more or less replacing the notochord.
9. Some kind of exoskeleton composed of dermal denticles, scales, or bony plates, usually present.
10. True teeth derived from dermal denticles.
11. The cranium enclosing the ninth and tenth cranial nerves. Hence the fishes are more highly cephalized.
12. The lateral-line organ system is more extensive and the organs are enclosed in closed canals sunk beneath the surface, with open pores.
13. There are always three semicircular canals in the membranous labyrinth.
14. The dorsal and ventral spinal nerves always unite to form mixed nerves.

126

15. All nerves except those of the sympathetic nervous system are medullated.
16. The alimentary tract shows more specialization, a definite stomach and a well-defined pancreas being present.
17. The functional kidney of the adult is always the mesonephros.
18. The gonads possess true ducts, oviduct and vas deferens, the origin of which will be explained later.
19. Ribs of some sort are always present.
20. Myotomes are separated into dorsal and ventral portions.
21. Dermal fin-rays, structures in some respects related to dermal scales, are furnished with muscles.
22. The pituitary body, is in the form of a compound endocrine gland of small size and attached to the floor of the 'tween-brain.

Of all these characters perhaps the ones that are most distinctively fish-like are the fins, the gills, and the scales and we shall go into some detail regarding these peculiarly piscine features.

FINS

The median fin system of fishes is found in very many specialized forms among the different groups of fishes. In general, it appears to have originated as a continuous flange-like fold running from just back of the head and continuing around the tail to the anal region. In the course of evolution this generalized fold has been broken up into a varying number of dorsal fins (sometimes lacking), several types of caudal fins, and an anal fin on the ventral side. All derivatives of the primitive fin-fold are supported by cartilaginous or bony rays. The paired fins are a contribution to vertebrate evolution introduced by gnathostome fishes. Some anatomists consider that the paired fins are derived from gill septa, but this view has very little evidence in its support. The prevailing view at present is that the paired fins are essentially parts of the same system as the median fins which branched around the anus and continued forward as ventrolateral folds. This theory will be discussed in connection with an account of the primitive "sharks" and their contributions to vertebrate evolution.

Varieties of Caudal Fins. — The most primitive type of caudal fin is known as *diphycercal* (Fig. 48, A), in which the blade of the fin above and below the notochord is about equally developed and with epichordal (above the notochord) and hypochordal (below the notochord) supporting rays both well developed. Such fins as this are present in hag-fishes, chimaeras, and modified forms of the diphycercal fin are found among some bony fishes (Fig. 48, C). A modified type of diphycercal fin in which the tail blade is drawn out to a point is known as *gephyrocercal*. A very common type of caudal fin found in most "sharks" and in many primitive bony fishes is the *heterocercal* fin (Fig. 48, B, D) characterized by much

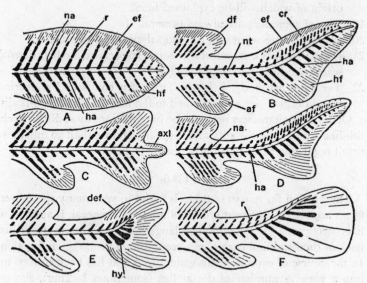

Fig. 48. Types of Caudal Fins. A. Diphycercal, with equal dorsal and ventral lobes. B. Heterocercal (Selachii). C. Modified diphycercal (some teleosts). D. Heterocercal (Chondrostei). E. Homocercal (teleosts). F. Abbreviated heterocercal (some Holostei). af, anal fin; axl, axillary process; cr, caudal fin rays; def, dorsal lobe of caudal fin; df, dorsal fin; ef, epicaudal lobe of caudal fin; ha, haemal arches; hf, hypocaudal lobe of caudal fin; na, neural arches; nt, notochord; r, dermal fin rays. (From Lankester, *Treatise on Zoölogy*, Vol. IX, A & C. Black.)

greater development of the hypochordal than the epichordal rays. The heterocercal is sometimes called the shark-tail type of caudal fin. Modified heterocercal fins (Fig. 48, F) are rather common among primitive bony fishes. These fins give the impression of being symmetrically developed above and below, and thus appear to be homocercal, but an examination of the skeleton shows that they are only disguised heterocercal fins. The *homocercal* tail fin (Fig. 48, E) is characteristic of most teleosts. Usually the rays of these fins are longer above and below and shorter in the middle, giving the forked, or conventional fish-tail shape. Examination of the skeletal parts, however, and especially studies of the fin development, reveal that even the typical homocercal fin is only a specialization of the hetero-cercal type, for the end of the vertebral column is turned up dorsal-ward and all of the rays supporting the fin blade come from the ventral side of the tail, and thus are hypochordal. In evolution the tail fin seems to have been at first diphycercal, then heterocercal, and finally in the most modernized fishes it has taken on the homo-cercal condition. In the development of a teleost larva one can see

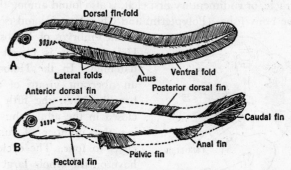

Fig. 49. Diagram illustrating the fin-fold theory of the origin of paired fins in fishes. A. The undifferentiated condition with continuous fin-fold. B. After parts of the continuous fold have been lost, leaving the fins characteristic of the typical fish. (From Messer, after Wiedersheim.)

the individual go through these three stages and apparently repeat in its ontogeny the phylogeny of the tail fin.

The **Paired Fins** are usually regarded as having arisen through the specialization of two regions of a continuous pair of fin-folds with parallel rays (Fig. 49). As these fins become more elongated and paddle-shaped there is a tendency for the basal parts of the jointed rays to converge, fuse together into a few larger bones, and to be in other ways reduced in number, while the distal rays tend to remain separate and to diverge fan-fashion. For a more complete account of the structure of the paired fins of a fish the student may turn to Chapter IX, where a rather full account of the anatomy of the dogfish is given.

THE RESPIRATORY ORGANS OF FISHES

The characteristic respiratory organs of aquatic vertebrates are gills, or branchiae. These structures are finely divided outgrowths of the ectodermal or endodermal epithelium of the branchial clefts. The number of clefts or gill-slits in gnathostome fishes varies from four to seven in number, each cleft being separated from its neighbors by branchial septa. The most primitive fishes have the larger number of branchial clefts and the more modern types have regularly five. *Heptanchus*, sometimes mentioned as the most primitive living species of shark, has seven clefts, *Hexanchus*, another primitive shark, has six, while the elasmobranchs in general have five fully developed clefts and a vestigial anterior first cleft called a spiracle. The spiracle, or rudimentary first cleft, is also found among the most primitive bony fishes (Polypterini and Chondrostei), and is present

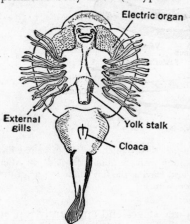

in the embryos of Teleostei and Holostei, but is closed before hatching. In the Holocephali, an aberrant group of elasmobranch fishes, the fifth cleft is closed in the adult, thus reducing the number of functional clefts to four. The cyclostomes have on the whole larger numbers of clefts than the true fishes. Though the hag-fishes of the family *Myxinidae* have no more than six pairs, those of the family *Bdellostomatidae* have from six to fourteen pairs, while the lampreys all have seven pairs. The direction of evolution appears to

Fig. 50. External gills in embryo torpedo. (From Bridge, Cambridge Nat. Hist., Vol. VII.)

be one of reduction in number of pairs of clefts from possibly ten or so in the ancestral vertebrate, fourteen to six in the cyclostomes, and seven to four in the true fishes.

The openings of the clefts to the exterior differ in different groups of fishes. Among the elasmobranchs the usual situation is that each cleft opens separately and is not covered by any flap or operculum; though in *Chlamydoselachus* the primitive "frilled shark" (Fig. 60, A) each cleft has a backwardly directed flap or gill-cover. In the Holocephali the first three clefts are covered by an operculum and only the fourth, or last functional cleft, opens freely to the outside. In the great majority of bony fishes the five clefts are covered with a flap-like operculum, capable of opening and closing and thus effectively protecting the branchial filaments from injury. In some of the eels and in other specialized types of teleosts the gills are completely

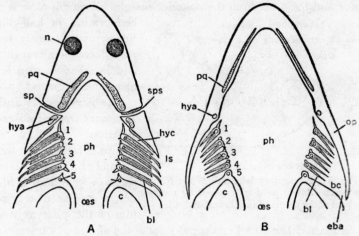

FIG. 51. Diagram of gills of fishes. A. Horizontal section through the head of an Elasmobranch. B. Similar section of a Teleost. bc, branchial cavity; bl, branchial lamellae; c, coelom; eba, external branchial aperture; hya, hyoid arch; hyc, hyo-branchial cleft; ls, interbranchial septum; n, nasal organ; oes, oesophagus; op, operculum; pq, palatoquadrate cartilage; ph, pharynx; sp, spiracle; sps, spiracular pseudobranch; 1–5, 1st to 5th branchial arches. (From Bridge, after Boas.)

covered with a fold of skin and the only exit is through one or a pair of small water-pores.

Two quite different and distinct kinds of gills are found among fishes: external and internal gills.

External gills are purely larval or embryonic organs and are not functional in any adult fish, though their homologues are found in some adult tailed Amphibia, believed to be neotenic or permanent larval types. External gills are finely branched processes of the ectodermal epithelium of the body surface near the gill-slits. They are found in the embryos of many elasmobranchs (Fig. 50) and in some teleosts. A notable case of larval gills is seen in the advanced larva of *Polypterus* (Fig. 79, C).

Internal gills (Fig. 51) are the true functional gills of adult fishes. There is still some controversy as to whether they are covered with ectoderm or endoderm, but there is strong evidence that they, like the external gills, are ectodermal. In fact, some authorities hold that external gills are merely precociously developed portions of the same primordia that later produce the internal gills. The gills are out-growths from the outer margins of the gill-bars, one from the anterior and the other from the posterior margin. Each gill-plate is a hemibranch, or half-gill. Filaments in closely set rows form hemibranchs, and lamellae in turn lie along the filaments.

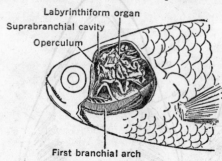

Labyrinthiform organ
Suprabranchial cavity
Operculum

First branchial arch

FIG. 52. Respiratory labyrinth of the climb-ing perch (*Anabas scandens*) exposed by remov-ing part of the operculum. (From Bridge.)

The Air-bladder and Accessory Organs of Res-piration.

— In all of the groups of fishes above the elasmobranchs there is a single or paired air-blad-der, a sac-like diverticu-lum of the pharynx de-rived from either dorsal or ventral sides of the alimentary tract. It is in all cases supplied with blood from the "pulmonary artery" and, primitively at least, subserves two functions: that of a hydrostatic

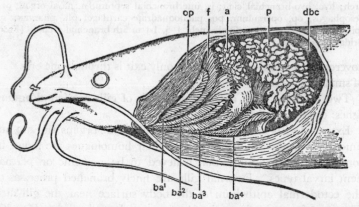

op   f   a   p   dbc

ba¹ ba² ba³ ba⁴

FIG. 53. Accessory respiratory organs of the cat-fish (*Clarias*) as seen after re-moval of operculum. a, anterior arborescent organ; ba¹⁻⁴, first four branchial arches; dbc, dorsal extension of left branchial cavity; f, modified gill-filaments; op, base of operculum; p, posterior arborescent organ. (From Bridge.)

or buoyancy organ and that of an accessory respiratory organ or primitive lung. In the most primitive surviving bony fishes such as *Polypterus*, it is used as a lung when the water is foul; in *Amia* it is constantly functional as an air-breathing apparatus; while in the

Dipnoi (lung-fishes) it is an elaborately pouched lung, used to tide the fish over a period of drought.

In certain other fishes that have acquired terrestrial habits, such as the climbing perch, *Anabas* (Fig. 52), and in the air-breathing eel, *Clarias* (Fig. 53), there is an extensive postbranchial chamber provided with labyrinthine or arborescent elaborations of the epithelium that are highly vascular and play a pulmonary role.

TYPES OF SCALES IN FISHES

Scales appear to be the primitive and fundamental units of the exoskeleton of fish-like vertebrates. So far as may be judged, the body scales of ostracoderms are the same sort of thing as those of various kinds of gnathostome fishes. Some ostracoderms, notably *Lanarkia* and *Thelodus*, had the whole body, including the head, covered with isolated or rather closely packed denticles resembling those of the sharks. It has been urged that this fact might be taken as evidence of a phylogenetic relationship between these ostracoderms and the earliest sharks. These denticles, however, are composed of dentine with only a trace of enamel on the surface and are merely hollow cones without a basal plate. In other ostracoderms the closely fitting denticles are fused in groups to underlying bone-like plates. The inner layer of these plates is strengthened by many layers of denser substance similar to the cosmine of the scales of some of the Crossopterygii. The reason for recalling the ostracoderms in this connection is to avoid the error of assuming that the scales of gnathostome fishes are innovations. Scales are far older than gnathostome fishes.

Agassiz classified fishes on the basis of their scale characters into Placoidei, Ganoidei, Cycloidei, and Ctenoidei, reflecting the common practice of classifying scales into four types: placoid, ganoid, cycloid, and ctenoid. The placoid scale is the typical dermal denticle of the elasmobranchs with the hollow cone and an expanded basal plate. Such scales and their relation to teeth will be more adequately described in Chapter VIII. Some authors distinguish between denticles and "true scales," for it is common to find both present at the same time, the former attached to the latter. The true scale is then a distinct entity and may or may not be combined with denticles.

Among bony fishes apparently the most primitive type of scale is the **cosmoid** scale. It is confined to the Osteolepidoti (crossopterygian fishes believed to be ancestral to Amphibia) and to the lung-fishes (Dipnoi), now regarded as coming from the same stock as Crossopterygii. The cosmoid scale is formed of three layers: a middle bone layer of spongy consistency, an inner layer composed of several lamellae of hard bone with cells between the layers, and an outer layer of cosmine.

There are several types of **ganoid** scales but they all agree in having layers of a hard, glistening substance, ganoin, both above and below and in having no cosmine layer. It is believed that the ganoid type of scale has been derived from the cosmoid type. Ganoin is found in the scales of all ganoid fishes and in those of some of the relatively primitive teleosts.

Cycloid and **ctenoid** scales are closely allied types derived from an ancestral ganoid type, through the loss of the ganoin and cosmine layers and an accentuation of the bony layers of the scale. They are found only in teleost fishes. The cycloid type is roundish in outline and is more primitive; the ctenoid type has an elaborate series of tooth-like processes at the free edge, giving that edge a comb-like appearance.

Closely allied to scales, if not strictly homologous with them, are the jointed dermal fin-rays (**lepidotrichia**) of bony fishes. These may be of compound nature, having sometimes a ganoin layer and denticles attached to the outer surface.

The dermal bony plates of the skull and limb girdles are regarded either as enlarged scales or as products of fusion of several adjacent scales. It should be emphasized that, except for the enamel layer of the placoid denticle, which is epidermal in origin, the rest of the scale of fishes is composed of materials derived from the dermis. The epidermis of fishes is thin and soft, not cornified as in reptiles and higher forms.

* * *

For a classification of gnathostome fishes the reader is referred to the general classification at the end of Chapter I.

CHAPTER VIII

CHONDRICHTHYES (SHARK-LIKE FISHES)

INTRODUCTORY STATEMENT

"There lives today," says Daniel, "a vast group of fishes, some of which are littoral, keeping close to the shore; others are the nomads of the ocean, roaming vast expanses of its waters; others there are which are pelagic, living near its surface; and still others are the inhabitants of the profound depths into which light never penetrates — these are the sharks, to man with nets the most worthless, to the naturalist among the most interesting of living things."

While the sharks and their allies are still to a large extent kings of the seas and exist in a great variety of sizes and forms, those of the present are few as compared with the hordes that once lived and are now extinct. Since sharks have during most of their career been cartilaginous, and since cartilage does not make good fossils, the only parts preserved of hundreds of species of ancient sharks are the teeth, which are among the commonest of fossil remains. Some of the most primitive sharks, however, had a partially ossified internal skeleton.

Some of the most ancient of the shark-like fishes have been excellently preserved. Among the most significant of the well-preserved primitive sharks are *Cladoselache*, *Climatius*, and *Pleuracanthus*, each of which exhibit certain highly instructive characteristics with which we now propose to deal.

The word shark or shark-like fishes is used here for the whole subgrade Chondrichthyes of the class Pisces. A common substitute for Chondrichthyes is "cartilaginous fishes" in contradistinction to subgrade Osteichthyes, "bony fishes."

PRIMITIVE "SHARKS" AND THE ORIGIN OF JAWS, TEETH, AND PAIRED FINS

The earliest shark-like fishes were the primitive spiny-finned sharks (Acanthodii), which, judging by the character of associated

135

fossils and the rocks in which they are found, must have lived in the rivers and have been contemporaries of the still abundant ostracoderms. These primitive "sharks" are rather well armored, being covered with plates and scales of bony material. Each fin was supported along its forward edge by a stiff spine, resembling a mast supporting a triangular sail (Fig. 54), a character retained by the present-day chimaeras, an aberrant branch of elasmobranch fishes.

A striking feature of the spiny-finned sharks is the variability in the numbers of paired fins. While some of them had only the two pairs, pectoral and pelvic, others had as many as seven pairs, as

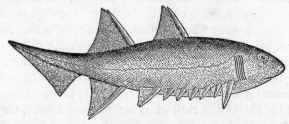

FIG. 54. *Climatius*, a spiny-rayed shark, about three inches long, from the Lower Devonian, showing five extra pairs of fins in series with the pectoral and pelvic fins. (From Traquair.)

in *Climatius* (Fig. 54). It appears therefore that there was a period of experimentation with numbers of paired fins before the fishes settled down upon the condition of just two pairs of appendages and decided the question for all posterity. In those forms with many pairs of fins it is worth noting that the series is almost continuous, a fact that supports the continuous fin-fold theory of the origin of paired fins. Several other shark-like features are well illustrated by these earliest river-dwelling sharks. The gill-slits are few in number, usually five pairs, and they open close together and separately without a gill-flap, or operculum. The caudal fin has the extreme heterocercal form, the fin-rays being entirely beneath the notochord (hypochordal). The mouth is usually ventrally placed, as in most modern sharks.

Before the end of the Devonian the shark-like fishes had begun an extensive migration from the rivers into the sea. A few of the earlier types continued as river dwellers up till the end of the Palaeozoic, but the shark tribe as a whole became strictly marine at a relatively early time and have remained so ever since. There are no fresh-water sharks at present.

Among the most interesting of the early marine sharks is *Clado-selache*, a Devonian type that has lost most of its body armor and, judging by its form, must have been a swift-swimming, preda-ceous creature. *Cladoselache* illustrates perhaps better than any other type three important evolutionary contributions of the early true fishes: the origin of biting jaws, the origin of teeth, and the origin of paired fins.

The Origin of Jaws. — *Cladoselache* (Fig. 55) has a less typically shark-like head than has *Climatius*, for the mouth is nearly terminal. A ventral view of this head (Fig. 56), with skeletal parts exposed, shows the seven pairs of gill-bars that support the gill-slits. The

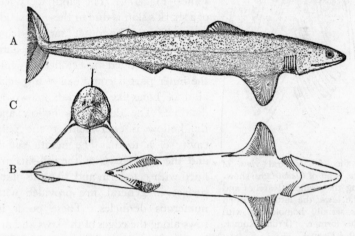

Fig. 55. *Cladoselache*, a primitive shark-like fish from late Devonian. A. Right side view. B. Ventral view. C. Front view. The parallel rays of the paired fins suggest their derivation from a continuous fin-fold. (From Lankester, after Woodward.)

posterior gill-bars are the smallest and there is a steady increase in the size of these bars as one proceeds forward, the most anterior pair being much the largest. This most anterior pair of bars, which seems to belong definitely to the series of gill-bars and is therefore regarded as homologous with the others, is in reality the skeleton of the jaws. Hence, if this reasoning is valid, the jaw cartilages are derived by a modification of the first pair of gill-bars. A study of the embryonic development of modern sharks supports this conclusion. Hence the origin of jaws in the gnathostome fishes does not in-volve the appearance of an entirely new structure, but merely a change in function of an old structure. Most important evolutionary changes are of this sort.

The Origin of Teeth. — In the marine sharks, in which armor plates had largely disappeared, the body remained more or less completely covered with dermal denticles (meaning literally, little teeth). These denticles have a base, somewhat like the head of a tack, embedded in the skin; and a spine, like the point of a bent tack, protruding from the skin. In some sharks the denticle has three spines (Fig. 57). The sandpapery feel of a shark's skin is due to these protruding points. The outer surface of a denticle is covered with enamel, a hard substance secreted by ectoderm, while the inner part is composed of a special kind of bone-like material, known as dentine. The denticle is hollow and the hollow is equivalent to the pulp cavity of a tooth. The mouth cavity and the outer parts of the gill-slits are lined with ectoderm and, like the outer surface in general, are provided with numerous denticles. These occur in rows along the edges of the jaws and are larger there than elsewhere (Fig. 56).

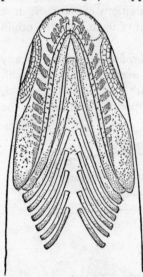

Fig. 56. Ventral view of the head of *Cladoselache*, showing the branchial arches and the jaws, the latter regarded as serially homologous with the former. (From Romer, after Dean.)

They are the first true vertebrate teeth. There can be no doubt then that teeth originated either from single denticles or from two or more denticles fused together, and that the teeth of higher vertebrates, which are structurally similar to denticles, have been derived from the denticles of the shark-like ancestors of all higher vertebrates.

The Origin of Paired Fins. — Two theories of the origin of the limbs of vertebrates have been proposed: the "gill-arch theory" of Gegenbaur, according to which the skeletal elements of the paired fins have been derived from gill-arches, and the continuous fin-fold theory of Balfour and others. The former theory has very few advocates today, while the latter is almost universally accepted as the most probable and is supported by better evidences.

According to the continuous fin-fold theory the paired fins are of essentially the same nature as the median fins. They follow the same course of embryonic development and have the same relation to muscle buds and other structures. A theoretical picture of the earliest condition of paired fins is shown in Figure 49, A. According to this view, the ancestors of the true fishes, instead of having the median fin system as a continuous dorsal and ventral flange terminating back of the vent, had this system bifurcated around the vent and continued forward as paired ventro-lateral flanges almost up to the gill region. From this continuous pair of lateral folds, at first several pairs of separate fins were specialized as in Figure 54 and later only two such pairs were formed as in Figure 55.

Supporting evidences for this theory are the facts that: *a*, in amphioxus the metapleural folds, which are sometimes regarded as the precursors of paired fins, are continuous with the median fin of the ventral region; *b*, in some primitive sharks such as *Climatius* (Fig. 54) the seven pairs of fins form practically a continuous series; and *c*, that in *Cladoselache* (Fig. 55, B) the pectoral and pelvic fins are essentially lateral folds unconstricted at the base and supported by rays that are nearly parallel. In the pelvic fins of *Cladoselache* the fin-rays form a series of parallel supports almost identical with those of a dorsal fin, while the pectoral fin-rays seem to be condensed at the base and to have to some extent lost their parallelism through a process of condensation of a formerly much longer part of the fin-fold.

Fig. 57. Three-spined dermal denticles of the shark, *Centrophorus*, which closely resemble the teeth in such forms as *Cladoselache*. Compare with Fig. 56. (From Gegenbaur.)

It should also be said that in the embryonic development of some sharks, such as *Scyllium*, skin-folds appear as precursors of the fins and that the median fold along the back and over the tail is essentially the same in character as the pair of lateral folds running forward from the vent to the pectoral region.

In another primitive extinct shark-like form, *Pleuracanthus* (Fig. 58) one finds the tail fin in its most primitive form, the so-called diphy-cercal type already seen in amphioxus, in the hag-fishes, and in a slightly modified form in the lampreys. Moreover, the caudal fin is practically continuous with the very long dorsal fin. The paired fins, especially the pectorals, have a peculiar skeletal pattern, with

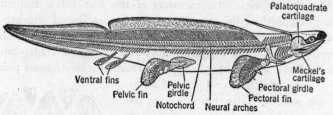

FIG. 58. Restoration of the primitive shark-like fish, *Pleuracanthus*. (From Parker and Haswell, after Dean.)

a central axis and with rays branching off on both sides. This type of fin is thought by some writers to foreshadow the fin architecture of some of the lung-fishes, suggesting the derivation of the latter from a shark ancestry.

MODERN SHARK-LIKE FISHES

As was stated earlier, most of the subclasses of shark-like fishes have become extinct, only one subclass, Elasmobranchii, having surviving representatives. Two orders of Elasmobranchii are still living: order 1, Selachii (sharks, skates, and rays); and order 2, Holocephali (chimaeras).

ORDER 1. SELACHII

Many modern sharks, though they have come through many millions of years of evolution, have retained in large measure a

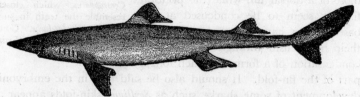

FIG. 59. The dogfish shark, *Squalus acantheus*. (After Dean.)

remarkably generalized organization, probably not very different from the ancestral condition. Such conservative forms are the dog-fish sharks and the Notodanidae. The latter are more primitive than the former, but are rare types seldom available for laboratory study. Because the dogfishes (Fig. 59) are decidedly generalized and offer a good starting point for introducing vertebrate anatomy, a separate chapter following this is devoted to the morphology of the dogfish. In the remaining part of the present chapter will be presented a brief survey of some of the more unusual or more specialized surviving elasmobranchs, beginning with the true sharks and their

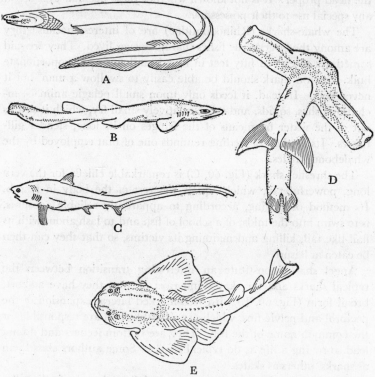

Fig. 60. Group of Modern Sharks. A. Frilled shark, *Chlameidoselachus angui-neus* (after Günther). B. Female dogfish, *Scyllium canesens* (after Günther). C. Thresher shark, *Alopecias vulpes* (after Jordan and Evermann). D. Hammerhead shark, *Sphyrna zygoena*, male (after Bridge). E. Angel shark, *Rhina squatina* (after Bridge).

relatives, the skates and rays, which we shall not separate very sharply, for there is no very sharp distinction between some of the sharks and some of the rays.

For the most part the typical sharks are active, free-swimming, predaceous creatures playing the same role in the sea as do beasts of prey on land and birds of prey in the air. We shall deal with only a few of the more remarkable sharks.

Hammer-headed sharks are characterized by the lateral protrusion of the eyes on thick, flat stalks (Fig. 60, D). There are all gradations between only slightly protruding eyes and those in which the eyes extend so far as to be five times as far apart as the width of the head proper. It is not known whether these peculiar eyes are of any special use to their possessors.

The whale-sharks (Rhinodontidae) are of interest because they are among the largest true fishes that have ever lived. They are said sometimes to exceed fifty feet in length and to be of proportionate bulk. Such a shark should be able easily to swallow a man, but it never does. Instead, it feeds only upon small pelagic animals, including fishes, squids, and other relatively small fry, which it strains out of the water by means of the fringes on its long, slender gill-rakers. Its method of feeding reminds one of that employed by the whalebone whales.

The thresher shark (Fig. 60, C) is remarkable chiefly for the very long, powerful tail, which equals the rest of the body in length. Its method of feeding, according to apparently reliable accounts, is to swim into the midst of a school of fish and to lash about with its flail-like tail, killing and maiming its victims, so that they can then be eaten at leisure.

Angel sharks constitute an interesting transition between the typical sharks and the skates and rays, in that they have a short, broad form (Fig. 60, E) with well-marked lateral expansion of the pectoral and pelvic fins, which are wing-like and are responsible for the common name of the fish. They are bottom feeders and do not lead so roving a life as do typical sharks. Some authors class them as sharks, others as skates.

The skates and rays proper are specialized bottom-feeding Selachii, with body depressed dorso-ventrally and with an excessive lateral extension of the anterior parts of the body, especially of the pectoral fin region, and a relatively slight development of posterior parts of the body, accompanied by a thinning out and prolongation of the tail into a whip-like appendage. For the most part they are sluggish forms feeding along the bottom at various depths, some of them living at great depths. They use the pectoral fins as propellers, and these act like water-wings, for waves of propulsion pass from in front and proceed to the rear. They are usually protectively colored on top so as to resemble the sea bottom, but are white or faintly pinkish below. The best known of these curious fishes are the common skates (Fig. 61, A), which are almost perfectly rhomboidal in

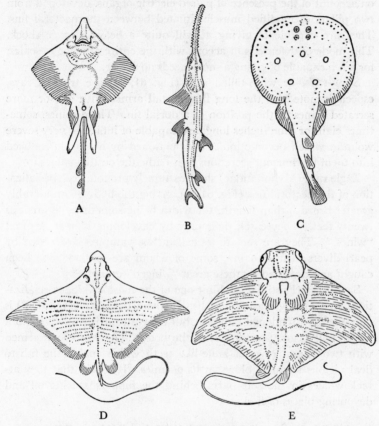

FIG. 61. Group of Skates and Rays. A. Skate, *Raia batis*, male, ventral view after Hertwig). B. Saw-fish, *Pristis antiquorum* (after Cuvier). C. Electric ray, *Torpedo ocellata* (after Bridge). D. Sting-ray, *Stoasodon narinari* (after Jordan and Evermann). E. Eagle ray, *Myliobatis aquila* (after Bridge).

outline, resembling a broad kite with a short tail. They catch their prey (fishes, crustaceans, etc.) by dropping down over them and blanketing them with the broad body and fins. The mouth is on the under side and is armed with numerous sharp, rasping teeth, with which they tear up their prey. Some of the largest of the skates reach a diameter of seven or eight feet. A few of the more remarkable of the rays deserve comment.

The electric rays (Torpedinidae) are more nearly circular in body outline (Fig. 61, C) than the skates. They are especially noteworthy on account of the presence of paired electric organs, developed from two pillars of modified muscle situated between the pectoral fins. They are capable of giving at will quite a heavy electric shock. This mode of defense is in accord with the entire absence of scales, for a fish capable of giving a shock needs no armor.

Sting-rays, or whip-tailed rays (Fig. 61, D) are tropical rays, especially noted for the long flexible tail armed with one or more serrated spines in the position of a dorsal fin. These spines, sometimes eight or nine inches long, are capable of inflicting very severe wounds, which become infected or poisoned by having introduced into them the mucous secretions that bathe the cutting spines.

Eagle rays (Myliobatidae) show extremely pronounced specialization of the pectoral fins (Fig. 61, E), giving the body a considerably greater breadth than length, the width being sometimes as great as twenty feet. They catch their prey by enveloping it in their great "wings." They are sometimes called "sea-vampires," dreaded by pearl divers near Panama, some of whom are said to have been caught and drowned by these great "winged" creatures.

Saw-fishes (Pristiidae) exhibit one of the most striking specializations seen among elasmobranchs. In them the body (Fig. 61, B) is only slightly broadened laterally, but the rostrum is prolonged to a length half as great as the rest of the body. The rostrum is armed with two lateral rows of knife-like teeth which enable the fish to deal vicious slashing blows at its enemies. It is said that they attack whales in the soft parts behind the flippers, tearing off and devouring pieces of flesh.

ORDER 2. HOLOCEPHALI (CHIMAERAS)

This group is very ancient, evidently having split off from the typical sharks during Devonian times. They were abundant during the Mesozoic period, but of the four known families only one (Chimaeridae) have survived. This family now consists of three genera, *Chimaera*, *Callorhynchus*, and *Harriotta* (Fig. 62).

Chimaeras are by some considered as a divergent order of the subclass Elasmobranchii; by others they are placed in a distinct subclass of co-ordinate value with the whole subclass Elasmobranchii. It is difficult to decide between these two alternatives. There are undoubtedly some characters that relate the Holocephali to the Selachii, but there are also some very fundamental differences. They agree with the Selachii in the following ways: — a wholly cartilagi-

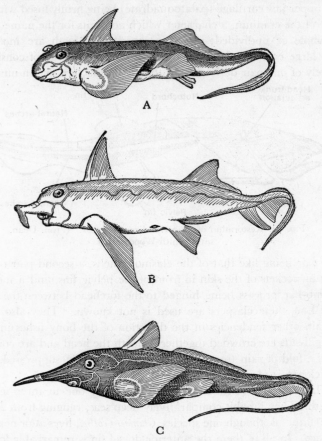

FIG. 62. Group of Holocephali (Chimaeras). A. *Chimaera monstrosa* (after Bridge). B. *Callorhynchus antarcticus*, male (after Parker and Haswell). C. *Harriotta raleighana* (after Goode and Bean).

nous endoskeleton; no cartilage bones or membrane bones; the limb girdles and the limb skeletons essentially selachian in structure; the dermal denticles, present locally in some modern forms and more generally in extinct forms, agree with those of selachians; the brain is very similar; the reproductive system, including clasping organs in the male, and large horny-shelled eggs, remind one strongly of those of some sharks; there is no air-bladder; there is a spiral valve; there is a conus arteriosus; the nostrils are connected with the mouth by oro-nasal grooves. The specialized features are: — The skull is autostylic, the upper jaw cartilage (palatoquadrate) being firmly fused with the base of the cranium, a character which accounts for the name (*holos* — whole or undivided; *cephalos* — head); the teeth are modified into large crushing dental plates; the claspers, instead of consisting merely of one pair derived from the pelvic fins, are five in number,

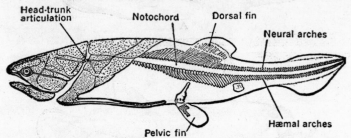

FIG. 63. Restoration of an arthrodire, *Coccosteus*. (From Dean, after Smith-Woodward.)

one pair being like that of the elasmobranchs, a second pair occurring in pockets of the skin in front of the pelvic fins, and a median thumb-like process being hinged to the forehead between the eyes. Just how these claspers are used is not known. They also show certain other tendencies in the direction of the bony fishes in that the gill-slits are crowded together beneath the head and are covered with a fold of skin (operculum), the spiracles are suppressed, and the cloaca is absent.

These curious fishes are of moderate size, one to three feet in length. They inhabit comparatively deep seas, ranging from 200 to 1200 fathoms, though one species, *Chimaera colliei*, lives at or near the surface. In all of them the anterior dorsal fin is remarkable for the presence of a stiff cartilaginous spine, quite like that found in the extinct spiny-finned sharks, such as *Climatius* (Fig. 54). The tail is long and whip-like, reminding one of that in the rays, and the caudal fin is sometimes diphycercal and sometimes weakly heterocercal. Altogether, the chimaeras are biological oddities.

Arthrodires. — An odd side branch of the most primitive shark-like fishes is that of the extinct order, Arthrodira. These strange Devonian fishes are so far out of line with typical fishes of any other group that they are placed in a separate subclass, Coccosteomorphi, co-ordinate with Elasmobranchii. One of the most familiar Arthrodira is *Coccosteus* (Fig. 63). The arthrodires are so different from other fishes that it is not even certain that what appear to be their jaws and paired fins are truly homologous with those of gnathostome fishes. The method of opening the mouth was very unusual, for the lower jaw was held stationary and the upper jaw and skull did the moving up and down, for the skull was loosely hinged. There are structures in what appear to be jaws that look like teeth, but are only bony projections of skull and "jaw."

MODERN SHARK-LIKE FISHES

CHAPTER IX

THE ANATOMY OF THE DOGFISH

(An Example of a Generalized Vertebrate)

Introduction. — The dogfish is almost universally used in zoological laboratories as an introductory type in classes in the comparative anatomy of vertebrates. It is an excellent form for this purpose for several reasons. In the first place, it shows the pattern of organization of the vertebrate body in almost its most generalized condition. In the second place, it is about as near being a median chordate as could well be found. In the third place, the animals are of convenient size and are easily dissected because the skeleton is cartilaginous and even the skull and vertebrae are readily cut away to expose brain, spinal cord, and sense organs. The commonest dogfishes (small sharks) used in America are *Squalus acanthias*, the spiny dogfish, and *Mustelus*, the smooth dogfish. In Europe the favorite genus is *Scyllium*, in most respects not unlike American dogfishes. The following account refers especially to *Scyllium*.

It should perhaps be said here that the student who makes a thorough laboratory dissection following one of the good manuals, will find this chapter useful as a summary and as a comparison with the species used in the laboratory.

External Features. — The body is submarine-shaped, sharp at both ends (Fig. 64). The swimming and balancing devices consist of: *a*, two median dorsal fins; *b*, a single median ventral (anal) fin; *c*, a caudal fin, which is moderately heterocercal in that the longer fin-rays are hypochordal, or ventral to the vertebral column of the tail; *d*, a pair of pectoral fins; and *e*, a pair of pelvic fins, which in the male are specialized in the posterior region to form claspers, copulatory organs used to introduce sperm into the oviducts of the female.

The mouth is ventrally placed some distance from the anterior end of the body, this position being due to a forward extension of a portion of the skull known as the rostrum. The surface of the body feels to the hand like fine sandpaper owing to the presence of dermal

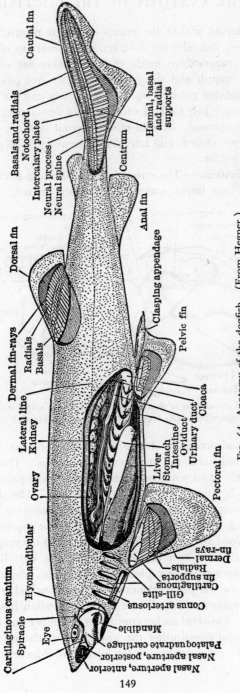

Fig. 64. Anatomy of the dogfish. (From Hegner.)

Caudal fin

Basals and radials
Notochord
Intercalary plate
Neural process
Neural spine

Hæmal, basal
and radial supports

Centrum

Dorsal fin

Anal fin

Dermal fin-rays
Radials
Basals

Clasping appendage

Pelvic fin

Lateral line
Kidney

Cloaca

Stomach
Intestine
Oviduct
Urinary duct

Liver

Ovary

Pectoral fin

Hyomandibular

Dermal fin-rays
Radials
Cartilaginous fin supports
Gill-slits

Cartilaginous cranium

Conus arteriosus

Spiracle

Mandible

Eye

Palatoquadrate cartilage

Nasal aperture, posterior
Nasal aperture, anterior

149

denticles (placoid scales) the points of which protrude from the surface. These denticles are enlarged at the margins of the mouth and become razor-edged teeth, of which there are several rows. Between the mouth and the pectoral fins are five pairs of dorso-ventrally elongated gill-slits, opening separately and not covered by any operculum. Just back of each eye is a small modified gill-slit known as the spiracle. Several other external features, such as the nasal apertures, cloaca, and lateral-line organs will be discussed in another connection.

Skeletal System. — The entire internal skeleton is cartilaginous with only a slight impregnation of calcareous matter. The skull is

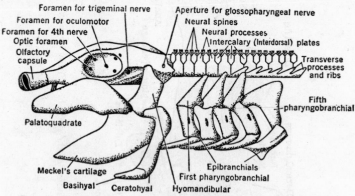

FIG. 65. Lateral view of skull, visceral arches, and spinal column of *Hemiscyllium*. (Redrawn after Parker and Haswell.)

a typical chondrocranium (Fig. 65), a solid, one-piece capsule enclosing the brain and the principal sense organs. The brain-box proper is firmly fused with the paired nasal and the paired auditory capsules and is cupped to form the eye sockets. The skull is perforated posteriorly by the foramen magnum, where the brain joins the spinal cord, and by numerous openings for the passage of cranial nerves and blood vessels. Closely associated with the cranium is the visceral skeleton composed of visceral arches (Fig. 65). Each arch is typically composed of four pieces on each side, which are, from the top downward, pharyngobranchial, epibranchial, ceratobranchial, and hypobranchial. There is also a median basibranchial. The first pair of visceral arches constitutes the upper and lower jaws, the epibranchial constituting the upper jaw (palatoquadrate cartilage) and the ceratobranchial, the lower jaw (Meckel's cartilage).

The pharyngobranchial and hypobranchial have been lost from the jaw skeleton. The upper jaw is not fused with the base of the skull, but is propped to the skull by parts of the second visceral arches, the hyomandibular cartilages. This type of jaw suspension is called hyostylic. The remaining five pairs of visceral arches are true branchial arches.

The *vertebral column* consists of a series of hour-glass-shaped centra (Fig. 66) with lens-shaped pieces of the persistent notochord between adjacent centra. The intervertebral masses of the notochord are interconnected by a continuous strand of notochord that runs through holes in the center of the centra, which resemble the holes

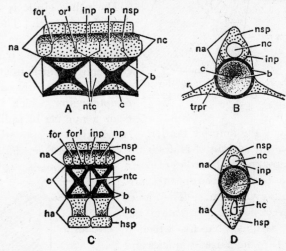

FIG. 66. Portions of vertebral column of *Scyllium;* A and B from trunk, C and D from tail. A and C, two vertebrae in longitudinal section. B and C, single vertebrae seen from one end. (Redrawn after Parker and Haswell.)

through a series of hollow-ended spools. In the trunk region cartilaginous neural arches surrounding the nerve cord lie above each centrum and on each side is a transverse process. In the tail both neural and haemal arches occur, but no transverse processes.

The *appendicular skeleton* is the skeleton of the fins. All the fins have jointed cartilaginous rays, or supports, those of the median fins being originally articulated to neural and haemal arches (vertebral elements). In addition to the purely cartilaginous fin-rays there are terminal horny rays derived from the skin (hence dermal elements) that support the web of the fin.

The skeleton of the paired fins consists of girdles and rays. Both pectoral (shoulder) and pelvic (hip) girdles consist each of a single cartilage supporting both right and left fins. Jointed at sockets in the sides of the pectoral girdle are the main fin skeletal elements: the propterygium, the mesopterygium, and the metapterygium. Intervening between these and the fin-rays are the radial cartilages.

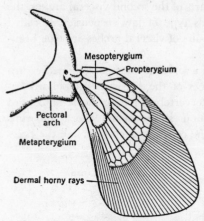

FIG. 67. Pectoral arch and fin of *Hemiscyllium*. (Redrawn after Parker and Haswell.)

The pelvic girdle is simpler than the pectoral. The main pelvic cartilage is an almost straight transverse band, at each end of which is attached a long backwardly directed basipterygium, which in turn bears a number of radial cartilages along the anterior border. Attached to the posterior end of each basipterygium of males is the clasper cartilage. Figures 67 and 68 show the limb girdles of *Hemiscyllium*, a common European shark.

Alimentary System. — The mouth opens directly into the short, but rather capacious pharynx, which is perforated by the paired spiracles and gill-slits. A short oesophagus of rather small caliber leads from the pharynx into a J-shaped stomach, which in turn opens by means of the pyloric valve into the intestine. The latter is composed of two parts: (1) the very short duodenum and (2) the much more

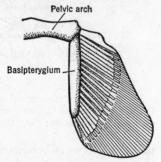

FIG. 68. Pelvic arch and fin of *Hemiscyllium*. (Redrawn after Parker and Haswell.)

extensive ileum, which is provided with a spiral valve (Fig. 64), a fold of the inner wall that runs like a spiral staircase and greatly increases the absorptive surface. The ileum passes into the colon and this into the rectum, which in turn opens through the anus into the cloaca, a sort of common vestibule into which open also the ducts of kidneys and of gonads. The whole alimentary system as found here affords a general pattern for that of the rest of the vertebrates above the cyclostome level. A large trilobed liver with gall bladder and bile duct empties bile into the duodenum. In the U-shaped bend which the stomach makes with the duodenum lies the pancreas, a large and well-defined gland, which gives off a duct into the intestine near the bile duct.

Respiratory System. — Branchial respiration is carried on mainly in the five pairs of branchial clefts (Fig. 64). The branchiae (gills) are the typical respiratory organs of fishes, consisting of elaborately branched extensions of the mucous membrane of the gill-slit walls through which pass the branches of the afferent branchial arteries. As the blood passes near the surface of the thin-walled gill filaments it takes up dissolved oxygen from the surrounding water and gives off carbon dioxide to the water.

Circulatory System. — The blood vascular system of the dogfish (Fig. 69) is not much different from that of the lamprey except for complications introduced by blood vessels running to paired fins. The power center of the system is, of course, the heart, which lies just back of the gill-slits. The heart, still a single tube bent upon itself like a letter S, lies loosely in its pericardium. It consists of four differentiated regions which from posterior to anterior are: sinus venosus, atrium, ventricle, and conus arteriosus. The sinus venosus is a large thin-walled collecting vessel for venous blood, into which open four great veins, the right and left ducts of Cuvier and the hepatic veins, a pair of short trunks coming directly out of the liver. The sinus venosus opens into the single large thin-walled auricle, which in turn leads through a valvular opening into the muscular ventricle. The ventricle passes over into the muscular conus which possesses several valves that prevent backflow into the ventricle. The conus enters the single ventral aorta that runs beneath the pharynx and gives off paired afferent branchial arteries into the four branchial and the hyoid arches. These arteries split up into gill capillaries, which unite above into efferent branchial arteries, and these in turn unite to form the single median dorsal aorta. An anterior extension of the dorsal aorta goes to the brain and is called the internal carotid artery. The posterior extension of the dorsal aorta gives off first vessels to the pectoral fins (subclavian arteries), then sends off into the mesentery that slings the gut a large vessel that gives off branches to the various visceral systems. This vessel is the coeliac artery that branches to form

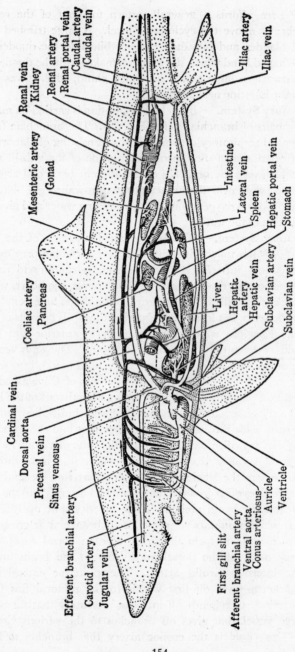

Fig. 69. Circulatory system of a dogfish from the left side. (From Woodruff.)

Renal vein
Kidney
Renal artery
Renal portal vein
Caudal artery
Caudal vein

Iliac artery
Iliac vein

Mesenteric artery
Gonad

Intestine
Lateral vein
Spleen
Hepatic portal vein
Stomach

Coeliac artery
Pancreas

Liver
Hepatic artery
Hepatic vein
Subclavian artery
Subclavian vein

Cardinal vein
Dorsal aorta
Precaval vein
Sinus venosus
Efferent branchial artery
Carotid artery
Jugular vein

First gill slit
Afferent branchial artery
Ventral aorta
Conus arteriosus
Auricle
Ventricle

154

the gastric, the hepatic. Next comes the superior mesenteric artery which gives off branches to the pancreas and spleen and the inferior mesenteric which supplies the gonads. Back of this are the renal artery supplying the kidneys, the iliac running to the pelvic fins, and finally the caudal artery.

The *venous system* consists of a complex series of rather large, thin-walled vessels (veins or venous sinuses), which carry the blood from the capillary systems back to the great sinus venosus. There are fourteen main return channels: four coming back from the head, the paired anterior cardinal sinuses and the paired inferior jugular veins; paired subclavian veins from pectoral fins; and from the posterior region the large paired posterior cardinals, conspicuous paired lateral abdominals, the smaller paired cutaneous, and the short paired hepatic veins. The return course of the blood is complicated by two detours of the blood through the liver and kidneys, called respectively the hepatic portal and renal portal systems, which we shall now describe.

A large subintestinal vein, which takes up digested food from the intestine, runs into the liver, instead of directly back to the heart. This is the hepatic portal system. After passing through the capillaries of the liver the venous blood passes out of the liver through the short hepatic veins, already mentioned. The renal portal system consists of a large median caudal vein which branches at the level of the pelvic fins to form two veins, the renal portals, that enter the outer edges of the paired kidneys. After passing through the kidneys, the blood is collected by the great posterior cardinals, already described, and is carried forward to the heart.

Coelom, Mesenteries, and Myotomes. — The gut is suspended in the peritoneal cavity by the large dorsal mesentery. The coelom of the abdominal region is almost completely cut off from the cavity of the pericardium by the transverse septum, there being only small pericardio-peritoneal canals between the two coeloms. Posteriorly the main body of the coelom opens to the exterior by a pair of small abdominal pores.

The segmental musculature, consisting of W-shaped myotomes is but little modified over the condition in the lamprey. The myotomes, however, are separated into dorsal and ventral portions, an advance over the lamprey condition. The muscles of the paired fins are derived from muscle buds given off from the myotomes and each fin is muscled by several myotomes.

Nervous System. — As in the lamprey, the brain is divisible into fore-, mid-, and hind-brains (Fig. 70). The fore-brain is differentiated into two divisions: the telencephalon and thalamencephalon (diencephalon), which together constitute the prosencephalon. The mid-brain is called the mesencephalon, or 'tween-brain; while the hind-brain is divided into metencephalon and myelencephalon (cerebellum and medulla oblongata).

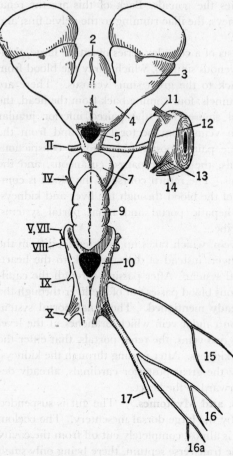

The prosencephalon consists of the very large paired olfactory bulbs, which extend laterally and forward to the olfactory capsules, and a median region on the floor of which is the optic chiasma, where the optic nerves cross from one side to the other. The thickened portion of the side walls constitute the corpora striata. From the floor of the thalamencephalon is a median downward outgrowth, the infundibulum,

Fig. 70. Brain of a dogfish shark, *Scyllium catulus*, dorsal view. 2, pineal stalk; 3, olfactory lobe; 4, cerebral hemisphere; 5, thalamencephalon; 7, optic lobes; 9, cerebellum; 10, roof of hind-brain; 11, 12, 13, 14, muscles that move the eyeball; 15, ninth nerve; 16, 16a, branches of vagus nerve; 17, main trunk of vagus nerve; II–X, roots of the cranial nerves. (From Hegner, after Shipley and MacBride.)

which contributes part of the pituitary gland. From the roof of thalamencephalon extends upward the pineal body, a vestige of the ancestral pineal eye. The cavity of the fore-brain is called the third ventricle. The mesencephalon is relatively small, the roof consisting of the paired optic vesicles. Its cavity is called the aqueduct of Silvius. The metencephalon, or cerebellum, is rather large and partly overlaps the 'tween-brain anteriorly and the medulla posteriorly. The myelencephalon, or medulla, is very thin-roofed, has a large cavity (the fourth ventricle), and passes over gradually into the spinal cord.

The outstanding features of the dogfish brain are: a, the very large olfactory lobes, which are associated with the importance of the sense of smell; b, the relatively large and complex cerebellum, associated with co-ordinated muscular activities and with equilibrium.

The spinal cord back of the medulla and continuing into the tail is not regionally specialized, but much the same at all levels. In each segment of the body on each side the spinal cord gives off a ventral (motor) nerve root and a dorsal (sensory) nerve root with a ganglion. The two nerves unite to form a mixed spinal nerve which was not the case in the lamprey. The nerve fibers are medullated except those of the sympathetic system, whereas in the lamprey they are non-medullated.

Cranial Nerves and the Question of Head Segmentation. — There is a vexing problem of vertebrate morphology concerning the metameric character of the head. Extensive investigation tends to show that the head with its brain is a highly modified metameric structure. In the brain the cranial nerves give a clue as to how many metameres are present in the head. Ten cranial nerves are recognized in the dogfish, but this does not mean that each pair comes off from a different metamere of the brain. Rather, some of the nerves are dorsal, others ventral nerve roots of the same metamere, and they never unite to form mixed nerves as in the nerve cord.

The olfactory nerve (No. I) is not a true cranial nerve, but is composed of fibers that grow in from the nerve cells of the olfactory epithelium which is ectodermal in origin. The optic nerves (No. II) are also not segmental nerves, but are parts of the brain itself. The oculomotor nerve (No. III) is the ventral root of the first segment and supplies some of the eye-ball muscles. In some sharks, but not in *Scyllium*, a dorsal root of this segment is recognized and called the profundus. The trochlear nerve (No. IV) is the ventral root of the second metamere and innervates the superior oblique eyeball muscle. The trigeminal nerve (No. V) is the dorsal root of the second segment and supplies sensory cells in the skin of the head, and also the jaw muscles. The abducens nerve (No. VI) is the ventral root of the third segment and supplies the external rectus muscle of the eyeball. The facialis nerve (No. VII) is the dorsal root of the third segment, and branches into five parts supplying the lateral-line organs of the head, taste organs, etc. The auditory nerve (No. VIII), which is really an enlarged and specialized branch of the facialis nerve (No. VII), innervates the ear, and does not count separately as a metamere indicator. The glossopharyngeal nerve (No. IX) is the dorsal root of the fourth segment, and sends off many branches to the first gill-slit, the gut, lateral-line canal, etc. There is no ventral root in the fourth segment. The fifth segment has lost its ventral root, but the dorsal roots of the fifth, sixth, seventh, and eighth segments are joined together to form the very large paired vagi nerves (No. X), which send branches to the heart, the stomach, and some of the lateral-line organs. The hypoglossal nerve (sometimes considered as No. XI) consists of the ventral roots of the sixth and following segments. It innervates the anterior trunk myotomes, and should not be regarded as a true cranial nerve in the dogfish, since it does not emerge from the cranium. All the other nerves, including the vagi, emerge from the skull, in contrast with the lamprey where the glossopharyngeal and vagi nerves emerge behind the skull. The true brain (or head part of the central nervous system) of the dogfish therefore includes two more metameres than that of the lamprey and is therefore more cephalized, showing a distinct evolutionary advance.

Sense Organs. — The *lateral-line system* consists of a lateral-line canal that runs along the side of the body from head to tail. Just in front of the spiracle the single canal gives off a downward branch, which passes beneath the eye and joins the main lateral line in front of the eye. There is also a small, separate hyomandibular canal on the jaw. The canals open at intervals to the surface by pores. At intervals along the canals there are special lateral-line sensory organs. These organs are believed to be sensitive to low frequency vibrations in the water. Scattered through the skin in the neighborhood of the lateral line are little pores opening into slender tubes at the bottom of which are enlargements in which lie tiny sense organs, known as pit-organs, or ampullae of Lorenzini. Their function is not known, but they are regarded as part of the same system as the lateral-line organs and the ear.

The *ear* is essentially a specialized lateral-line organ, which communicates with the exterior by a long tube and a small pore, the endolymphatic duct. It seems probable that, in addition to its function as an organ of equilibrium, it is sensitive to high-frequency vibrations (which may be the same thing as sound waves in water). The so-called ear, or membranous labyrinth, is divided into a dorsal utriculus and a ventral sacculus. The utriculus gives off three semicircular canals with a swelling (ampulla) at the base of each, in which the organs of balance lie. The sacculus is the part that in higher vertebrates gives rise to the cochlea, or true organ of hearing.

The *eyes* (Fig. 70) are hollow spheres, formed as paired cup-like outgrowths from the floor of the fore-brain. The inturned part of the cup is the retina or sensory layer. The lens is derived from the epidermis; the iris is a muscular diaphragm; and the vascular choroid coat of the eyeball is the skeletal capsule surrounding the sense organ. The eyeball is moved by six muscles which are able to rotate the eye in any position.

The *olfactory sense organs* consist of a pair of deep pits invaginated from the surface ectoderm, which in the dogfish open beneath the snout. These are connected by grooves running to the corners of the mouth. The pits are lined with much folded olfactory epithelium.

Urogenital Systems. — It will be recalled that in the lamprey the kidneys (mesonephroi) and the gonads were quite independent, that both male and female possess mesonephric ducts, and that the gonads have no ducts. In the dogfish the situation is entirely different: the two systems (excretory and reproductive) combine and become inseparable, for the gonads appropriate some of the kidney ducts. The condition differs in the two sexes and must be described separately for each sex. But first, it must be stated that in the dogfish the functional kidneys are mesonephroi and that there are two pairs of mesonephric ducts, instead of only one pair as in the lamprey. One pair of ducts receives the name Wolffian ducts, the other, Müllerian ducts. The Wolffian duct seems to be homologous with the mesonephric duct of cyclostomes. The origin of the Müllerian duct is problematical. It seems to be an added duct, derived from the ancestral mesonephric duct, though parts of it may have been derived from the pronephric tubules. The two sexes differ sharply in the uses to which these two pairs of ducts are put.

The Male Urogenital System (Fig. 71). — The testes, or male gonads, are paired, elongated, strap-like bodies with numerous small ducts, vasa efferentia, regarded as modified coelomostomes, leading into the anterior mesonephric tubules. These tubules pass into the Wolffian duct which is a vas deferens, carrying sperms to the swollen terminal portion called the seminal vesicle, which empties into the cloaca by a genital papilla. The posterior part of the mesonephros is purely excretory and its tubules empty into a collect-

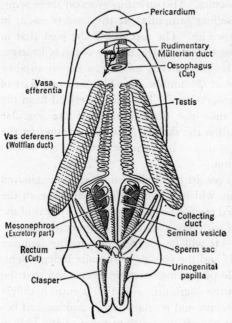

ing duct, ureter, which in turn enters into the Wolffian duct. Thus a short portion of the Wolff-ian duct carries both sperms and urine. The other mesonephric ducts, Müllerian ducts, are much reduced in the male, persisting only as a pair of funnels beneath the oesophagus and as a pair of sperm sacs con-nected with the seminal vesicles.

The Female Urogeni-tal System (Fig. 72). — In the female the Mülle-rian ducts are greatly enlarged to form paired oviducts, which may be enlarged locally to form glands for producing the

FIG. 71. Urogenital system of male dog-fish. (From De Beer.)

shell, etc., of the eggs. In some sharks the eggs have no shell and are incubated in the oviduct. The two oviducts open beneath the oesophagus by means of a single large funnel-shaped opening into the coelom. Eggs given off from the single right ovary into the coelom are collected by this ciliated funnel and carried down the oviducts to the cloaca. Some sharks have paired ovaries. Eggs are fertilized internally high up in the oviduct, sperm being introduced into the oviduct by the claspers of the male. In the female the Wolffian duct is purely an excretory duct, the paired ducts enlarging posteriorly to form urinary sinuses that empty through a urinary papilla into the cloaca. In the female then there is no double function of any part of either Müllerian or Wolffian ducts.

The morphology of a single mesonephric tubule deserves special attention. The single kidney element is an elongated tube (a coelomoduct) with one end blind and the other end opening into the Wolffian duct. At one point in the nephric tubule a cup-like out-pocketing occurs which is the Bowman's capsule, in the hollow of which is a bunch of capillaries called the glomerulus. This organ functions as a filter through which the blood gets rid of various wastes or excesses of dissolved substances.

Endocrine Glands. — Endocrine glands being highly characteristic as chemical regulators in the vertebrates, it is interesting to see what endocrine glands are present in the dogfish. The thyroid gland is present as an elongated gland beneath the pharynx, and, as was shown for the lamprey, is a derivative of the old endostyle of the protochordates, but is never func-

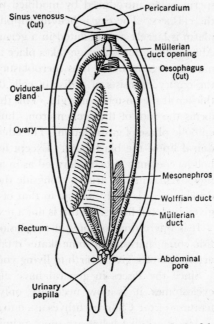

FIG. 72. Urogenital system of female dogfish. (From De Beer.)

tional as a ciliated groove in the dogfish. The pituitary body is fairly large and is derived from the infundibulum and the hypophysis. Suprarenal glands, derived in part from the sympathetic nervous system, are separate from the interrenal bodies derived from the wall of the coelom. In higher forms these two structures are combined to form the compound adrenal glands. Thymus glands, which may not be endocrinal but lymphoid, are found at the top of the gill-slits. The spleen, which is listed by some authors as an endocrine gland, but probably is not, is a large lymphoid organ lying in the mesentery near the stomach. The pineal body, also sometimes considered as an endocrine gland, is a vestige of the pineal eye and has no known function in the dog-fish. A well-defined pancreas is present in the dogfish, in contrast with the diffuse pancreas of cyclostomes, and it doubtless has an endocrine as well as a digestive function, but little is definitely known as to its endocrine function.

Development. — The large eggs are fertilized in the oviduct, sperm being introduced by modified parts of the male pelvic fins, the claspers. The egg is heavily supplied with yolk and the proto-plasm is largely accumulated in a germinal disc at the animal pole. After fertilization cleavage takes place and is confined to the germi-nal-disc region, being thus meroblastic. After cleavage is finished the embryo consists of a disc of cells one or two layers thick, and thicker at the posterior margin. This thicker margin rolls under and forms the roof of the archenteron, thus accomplishing the first, or embolic phase of gastrulation. The edge of the infolded region is the dorsal lip of the blastopore. Except for the fact that there are no hollow coelomic pouches formed as in amphioxus, but instead, solid mesodermal masses arising alongside the archenteron, the rest of the development is fairly similar to that of amphioxus and need not be given in detail here since this is not a textbook of embryology.

It is interesting to note, in conclusion, that some species of dog-fish, some sharks, and some skates retain the eggs in the uterus and are viviparous, giving birth to living young.

Since the Pisces in general have already been contrasted with cyclostomes it is now necessary only to summarize the special features of the Chondrichthyes as contrasted with Osteichthyes.

The shark-like fishes are more primitive than the bony fishes in the following respects:

1. No swim-bladder lung.

2. Gill-slits are not covered with an operculum, but open sepa-rately (except in Holocephali).

3. The upper jaw is not fused with the base of the skull (except Holocephali).

4. The suprarenal and interrenal glands are separate instead of being united into a single adrenal gland.

5. The heart is never more than two-chambered, one auricle (atrium) and one ventricle, whereas in lung-fishes the auricle is divided into two, giving a three-chambered condition.

6. There are no dermal investing bones united with cartilage bones in the skull and other parts.

CHAPTER X

BONY FISHES (OSTEICHTHYES)

INTRODUCTORY STATEMENT

The "bony fishes" are the dominant fishes of today, in some respects *the* dominant vertebrates, for there are said to be about as many species of bony fishes today as of all other vertebrates combined. The term "bony fish" (which is a literal translation of the term, Osteichthyes), is not a very fortunate designation for this group, for it is now clear that bone was an extremely early acquisition of vertebrates and was present in ostracoderms as well as in primitive shark-like fishes. The term "bony fishes" is useful primarily to distinguish this group from the modern shark-like fishes, which are today boneless. It will be shown later that some of the surviving "bony fishes" are also boneless, or better, cartilaginous.

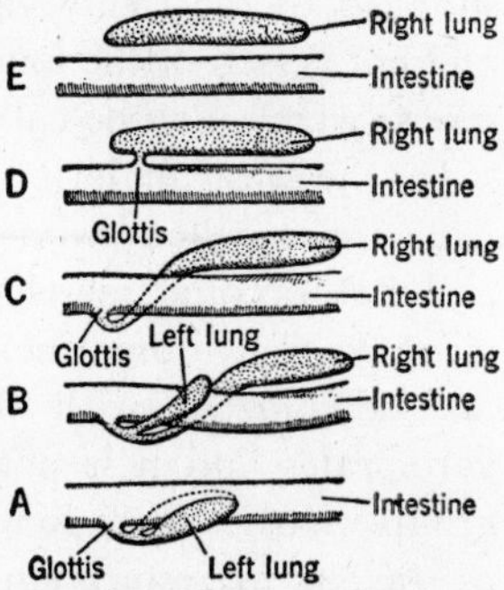

FIG. 73. Diagram illustrating the lungs (air bladders) of fishes. A. Primitive arrangement. B. *Polypterus.* C. *Ceratodus.* D. Physostomatous teleost. E. Physoclistoces teleost. (From Goodrich, after Kerr.)

The bony fishes are, from the standpoint of vertebrate evolution, especially important because they introduced the beginnings of three important characters that all higher vertebrates possess: *a,* lungs; *b,* legs; and *c,* the investing bones of the skull and limb skeletons. We shall discuss these three contributions before proceeding with the historical account of the group.

Lungs. — Remarkably enough, one of the most striking acquisitions of the early bony fishes was an air-bladder, used as an accessory respiratory apparatus supplementing the gills. It will be recalled that the Chondrichthyes never acquired the air-bladder, doubtless because they have always lived in large bodies of water, rivers or seas, where gill respiration was quite adequate at all times. Osteichthyes, on the contrary, seem to have arisen in the swamp waters

163

at the sources of rivers, that are likely to be, at times, unfit for water respiration. The air-bladder (Fig. 73) arises as a single outgrowth of the oesophagus, which may remain single or become bilobed. In some primitive groups of bony fishes (Polypterini and Dipnoi) the air-bladder originates from a ventral outgrowth, while in most Actinopterygii it originates from a dorsal outgrowth. The air-bladder itself, however, always lies dorsal to the alimentary canal no matter whether it originates as a dorsal or a ventral outgrowth. Were it to lie ventrally it would tend to make the fish float belly up. In primitive bony fishes, living as well as extinct, the air-bladder was used as a lung and air was taken into and expelled from it by means of a tube communicating with the anterior part of the oesophagus. In surviving fishes with an air-bladder lung blood is supplied to the richly vascular lining of the sac by means of the afferent vessels of the fourth branchial arch (sixth of the embryonic series) which may be called the pulmonary arch.

In the vast majority of modern bony fishes the air-bladder (sometimes called swim-bladder) has lost its respiratory function and has become merely a hydrostatic organ, operating like the air-tanks of a submarine. The air-bladders of primitive bony fishes are homologous with the lungs of Amphibia and higher land vertebrates and it is noteworthy that air-breathing began in one group of true fishes long before land vertebrates arose, doubtless as an aid to respiration during the dry season when temporary ponds and pools dried up or became stagnant.

The Origin of Legs. — Another unfish-like contribution to the evolution of vertebrates introduced by the primitive bony fishes was the beginning of land legs. Although the paired fins of most modern Osteichthyes are of the ray-fin variety — in which the whole expanse of the fin consists almost entirely of slim horny rays upon which is stretched a fan-like membrane — most of the primitive fishes, and especially the lobe-finned fishes, possessed a rather large scale-covered fleshy lobe at the base of each paired fin, which was supported internally by a stout bony skeleton and well-developed muscles. The arrangement of bones is strikingly similar to that of the limb bones of the early Amphibia (Fig. 74), and it is not difficult to understand how a fish fin of this sort, with only a certain amount of elongation of the lobe, separation of terminal radials to form digits, and loss of the fin-blade, could become transformed into the leg of an amphibian.

Skull and Jaw Skeletons. — One of the most complex and difficult systems of fishes to understand and to describe is the skeletal system. Yet this system is the main dependence of the paleontologist, who has usually nothing but fossilized bones to work with. It is on the basis of such skeletal remains of extinct animals that our information regarding the evolutionary history of vertebrates must largely rest. For this reason it is important to try to get a fairly clear picture

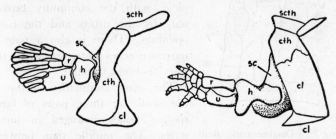

FIG. 74. The right pectoral limb (arm) and shoulder region of a lobe-finned fish (left) and a primitive amphibian (right), the latter turned back to a position comparable with the fish fin. cl, clavicle; cth, cleithrum; h, humerus; r, radius; sc, scapula; scth, supracleithrum; u, ulna. (From Romer.)

of the main advances made by primitive bony fishes with respect to the skeleton.

It will be recalled that in the surviving Chondrichthyes the skeleton is composed entirely of cartilage, but that primitive shark-like fishes had an internal skeleton at least partly ossified and sometimes a rather good exoskeleton composed of true scales and dermal bony plates. In the head region this superficial system of bones had not, in these early fishes, fused with the skull, but was near the surface.

In the bony fishes, however, the dermal plates of the head region sank beneath the skin and fused with the cartilage skull to form a double or reinforced brain-case. These bony plates are homologous with dermal scales or with groups of these fused together. They form an almost complete dome-like roof over the cartilaginous capsule and also largely cover its floor and side walls as well as the jaw cartilages and limb girdles. On this account these bony plates are called dermal investing bones, or membrane bones. While there was from the first considerable variation in the number and relative size of these investing bones, they settled down to a rather well-defined number and pattern that has persisted, in its main features, in all the higher vertebrates. Hence it is necessary at this time to get a picture of the complex vertebrate skull at this evolutionary level.

Confining our attention for the time being to the pattern of the investing bones, let us examine the diagram of the dorsal surface of the skull of a hypothetical primitive bony fish (Fig. 75). It will be noted that the covering is essentially complete, with the continuity broken only by the orbits and the nasal openings. There is also a pair of narrow notches posteriorly where the spiracles break through.

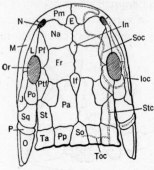

FIG. 75. Diagrammatic skull roof of primitive bony fish. E, ethmoid; Fr, frontal; If, interfrontal; In, internasal; Ioc, infraorbital canal; J, jugal; L, lacrimal; M, maxillary; N, external nostril; Na, nasal; O, opercular; Or, orbit; P, preopercular; Pa, parietal; Pf, prefrontal; Pm, premaxillary; Po, postorbital; Pp, postparietal; Ptf, postfrontal; So, dermal supraoccipital; Soc, supraorbital canal; Stc, postorbital and temporal canal; Sq, squamosal; Ta, tabular; Toc, transverse occipital canal.   Course of lateral-line canals shown only on right side. (From Goodrich.)

The main landmarks on top of the skull are three pairs of large roofing bones arranged in linear series. The middle pair between the orbits are the frontals, with the nasals anterior and the parietals posterior. Surrounding each orbit, beginning next to the frontal and proceeding counter-clockwise in the left orbit (and clockwise in the right) there is a ring of five bones: prefrontal, postfrontal, postorbital, jugal, and lacrimal. Lateral to each parietal lie two squarish bones, intertemporal in front and supratemporal behind. Forming the posterior border of the skull roof, just back of parietals and supratemporals, is a transverse row of five bones: the single median supraoccipital, paired postparietals, and paired tabulars. A median series includes, from top to bottom, ethmoid, internasal, and interfrontal.

It will be recalled that in the shark-like fishes (except Holocephali) the upper jaw was attached only loosely to the base of the skull. In the bony fishes, however, the upper jaw has become fused firmly with and is now an integral part of the skull. This is called the autostylic skull. Hence the membrane bones of the upper jaw form the front and lateral borders of the skull floor. In front are the premaxillary bones and on the sides the maxillary bones, both bearing the principal teeth of the upper jaws. Separated on each side by the spiracular notch from the intertemporals and supratemporals is a linear series of three cheek membrane bones: squamosal, preopercular, and opercular. These two latter bones in the bony fish are not strictly part of the skull proper, but are part of the gill cover. The squamosal, however, becomes a true part of the skull of land vertebrates.

The bones of the floor of the skull and roof of the mouth are of both cartilaginous and dermal origin. The principal membrane bones are: prevomers, vomers, and parasphenoid. For our purposes we need not consider this part of the skull further.

The lower jaw on each side consists of the two investing bones, the large tooth-bearing dentary in front and the almost equally large angulare, behind. These invest the original jaw cartilage.

This description does not include the cartilage, or replacing, bones of the skull nor the replacing bones of the limb girdles. It is felt, however, that for our purposes the above picture of the type of skull of the primitive bony fishes will serve to make clear how much these animals contributed to vertebrate evolution. In this place it should be pointed out that in the early fishes the head skeleton reached its highest degree of complexity and that in higher forms the trend of evolution is in the direction of simplification. In the early bony fishes there was a redundancy of skull structures, for there were two almost complete brain-cases, one of cartilaginous origin and the other of dermal origin. That such a double skull was more than was needed is shown by the fact that in higher forms, as we shall see, various parts of one or the other cranium were dropped out or modified for other functions.

ORIGIN AND EARLY HISTORY OF BONY FISHES

The earliest known fossil remains of bony fishes (Osteichthyes) come from rocks laid down in the middle of the Devonian. Just what forms were their immediate ancestors is not definitely known, but presumably they were derived from some shark-like fishes (Chondrichthyes), for these were for a time the only gnathostome fishes in existence, and, unless the bony fishes took their origin separately from some ostracoderm stock, they must have come from Chondrichthyes.

It will be recalled that even the early "sharks" were evolved in the fresh waters, presumably in the large rivers, and that they went out to sea only after a considerable period of life in fresh waters. The bony fishes also arose in fresh waters. Doubtless for a time there was keen competition between the "sharks" and the bony fishes in the large rivers. The "sharks," however, went down the rivers to the sea, while the majority of the bony fishes moved up the rivers to their sources, the swamps and ponds that fed the rivers. Living in the open waters, as they have always done, the "sharks" have always been exclusively gill breathers and never needed to develop any lung-like equipment for breathing air. All of the bony fishes, however, developed lungs, as will be more fully explained later.

Very soon after their origin, the bony fishes became the dominant vertebrates of the fresh waters, and ever since have far outnumbered the "sharks," which may be regarded as their relatively unsuccessful rivals. While it seems probable that, at first, all the bony fishes inhabited the swamps and ponds that drained into the rivers, several groups of them, especially of the ray-finned fishes, went back to the rivers, streams, and lakes, and many even went out to sea. For a long time the ray-finned fishes have dominated the sea as well as all kinds of fresh-water habitats.

When we get our first view of the bony fishes of the Middle Devonian, they had already split up into three great groups: a, Crossopterygii (lobe-finned fishes); b, Dipnoi (lung-fishes); c, Actinopterygii (ray-finned fishes). The subsequent careers of these three stocks were quite different. The Crossopterygii were by far the most abundant during the Devonian, but became almost extinct, as fishes, before the end of the Palaeozoic, only a few surviving into the Mesozoic. One branch of them, however, gave rise to the primitive Amphibia. The Dipnoi, while very abundant during the Palaeozoic, gradually declined and only a few of them have been able to survive up to the present by adapting themselves to temporary waters where ordinary fishes would not be able to live. The Actinopterygii have remained typical fishes and have culminated in the great group of teleost fishes of today. It is customary to assign the Osteichthyes to two subclasses: Dipnoi and Teleostomi, but recent work by Romer seems to show that the Dipnoi and Crossopterygii should be put together in one subclass, for which he suggests the name Choanichthyes, referring to the most striking common feature of the two groups, the internal nostrils. The other subclass would then consist only of Actinopterygii, the ray-finned fishes. In the following account we shall deal with the three main groups of

Osteichthyes separately without designating their taxonomic status.

DIPNOI (LUNG–FISHES)

This group had already diverged as a well-defined side branch of the bony fishes by the middle of the Devonian. They were almost certainly derived from primitive Crossopterygii. They are not now regarded as the fishes from which the Amphibia arose, although for a long time this was the prevailing view of comparative anatomists. As Romer puts it: "The lung-fishes are not, so to speak, the ancestors, but the uncles of the land dwellers." They and the amphibians had in the primitive lobe-fins a common "grandfather." The name "lung-fishes" is not a particularly fortunate designation for them, since we now know that all the early bony fishes were also lung

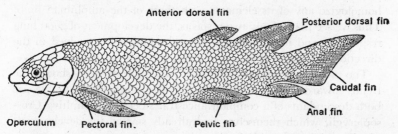

Fig. 76. *Dipterus*, a Devonian lung-fish. (From Goodrich, after Traquair.)

breathers. The Dipnoi are now regarded as a somewhat specialized, rather degenerate group that early became well adapted to life in temporary waters, but still remained purely fishes. While the great majority of them became extinct long ago, a few species have survived in isolated regions up to the present. The earliest lung-fishes, of which *Dipterus* (Fig. 76) is a typical example, were not greatly different from the lobe-fins, but they began at an early period to undergo several specializations that led them off at a tangent from the main line of vertebrate evolution and made it impossible for them to give rise to true terrestrial descendants.

The lung-fishes are peculiar and differ from the lobe-finned and ray-finned fishes in several important respects. They have better developed lungs, sometimes divided into lobes. The heart is nearly completely three-chambered, one of the paired auricles receiving freshly oxygenated blood through a special pulmonary arch from the lungs. Peculiar fan-shaped tooth plates, which are products of fusion of many separate teeth belonging to the bones of the roof of the mouth, are used for crushing shelled invertebrates. They early lost the maxillary and premaxillary bones of the upper jaw, which are the principal tooth-bearing bones of other fishes and of Amphibia. They, like the Crossopterygii, have internal nares, making possible breathing through the nose. And, most important of all from the standpoint of their possible ancestry to the Amphibia, they developed elongate, leaf-like paired fins, with a central skeletal axis, and attached to both sides of this numerous radials. This is an ancient type of paired fin (archipterygium), seen previously in some of the primitive sharks such as *Pleuracanthus* (Fig. 58). These fins are covered with scales, except for the soft, narrow edges. Such a type of fin architecture is so utterly different from that of an amphibian arm or leg that it is generally regarded as impossible to homologize any of its elements with those of the amphibian limb. Thus we see that in only two respects, the development of good lung respiration and internal nares, have the lung-fishes evolved in the direction of land-dwelling vertebrates.

The modern view as to the reason why the lung-fishes show some trends toward land vertebrates is that they and the Amphibia are both descendants of a common ancestral stock, the primitive Crossopterygii, which themselves had already started the development of adaptations favorable for land life.

SURVIVING LUNG-FISHES

There exist today in widely separated parts of the globe three genera of lung-fishes, which have been able to outstay their very numerous extinct relatives by finding a few limited niches of the environment that favor their special life needs. This is an illustration of a fairly common phenomenon. Throughout both the Animal and Plant Kingdoms there are many illustrations of the survival of the last relics of ancient groups once distributed almost universally, but now extinct except in a few widely separated especially favorable areas.

Of the three surviving genera of lung-fishes *Ceratodus* occurs in Australia; *Protopterus*, in Africa; and *Lepidosiren* in Paraguay. Of these, *Ceratodus* has been most extensively studied and will serve to illustrate a few of the principal anatomical features.

Some Aspects of the Morphology of Ceratodus. — The body has a generalized fish shape (Fig. 77, A). The scales are rather thin and covered with spines which are not regarded as denticles. The paired fins are rather leaf-like or paddle-like. The tail-fin is symmetrical and pointed and is regarded as belonging to the gephyro-cercal category, which implies that it is not an example of the primitive diphycercal type but has probably undergone secondary simplification from the heterocercal type. The skull is largely cartilaginous and there is but little replacing bone in the rest of the skeleton. The membrane bones on top of the skull are rather deeply sunk beneath the skin and are overlaid by scales. The notochord is continuous and not constricted by vertebrae. The latter are represented by paired basidorsal and basiventral cartilages, which form respectively, neural arches in the trunk and both neural and haemal arches in the tail. In the floor of the oesophagus there is a glottis opening into a trachea that passes around the right side of the oesophagus into the lung, a large sac lying above the gut. The sixth embryonic right afferent branchial arch acts as a pulmonary artery, as in the Amphibia. The auricle is partially divided by a septum, the left half receiving oxygenated blood from the lung, as in higher vertebrates. The brain differs from that of the dogfish particularly in two features: the cerebral hemispheres are rather large, though thin-roofed, and the cerebellum is poorly developed. The lateral line system is somewhat degenerate.

Protopterus. — The Nile lung-fish (Fig. 77, B) resembles *Cerato-dus* in most respects. These fishes are about a foot long, much smaller than *Ceratodus* which attains a length of five feet or more. The median fin system is a continuous fin-fold with dorsal and caudal fins united. The paired fins are long and streamer-like, with a skeleton composed of a central jointed axis and a few delicate lateral rays. The lung is paired instead of being single as in *Ceratodus.*

Lepidosiren. — The South American lung-fish (Fig. 77, C) may be regarded as an eel-type derivative of the *Protopterus* type, and the paired fins are even more reduced. In the brain of both *Protopterus* and *Lepidosiren* the olfactory region of the fore-brain is much reduced, which is perhaps just as well, for they spend much of their lives in a pretty bad-smelling environment.

HABITS OF PRESENT-DAY LUNG-FISHES

The lives of lung-fishes are more varied than those of fishes in general and are worth telling about, for they illustrate the way in which

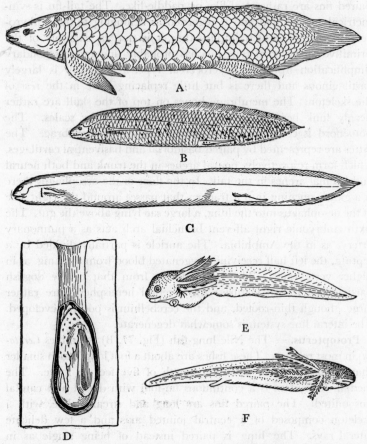

FIG. 77. Group of Lung-Fishes (Dipnoi). A. *Ceratodus forsteri*, Queensland.
B. *Protopterus annectans*, Gambia. C. *Lepidosiren paradoxa*, Paraguay. (The lozenge-
shaped markings in B do not represent scales, but areas of skin outlined by pigment cells. In a fresh specimen the scales are completely invisible, as in C.) D.
Diagram of *Protopterus* aestivating in the mud, showing the body coiled up and
the mucous sac with tube leading to mouth. E. Larva of *Protopterus* on the seventh
day, showing cutaneous gills, cement organ under head, and narrow paired
fins. F. Larva of *Lepidosiren* thirty days after hatching, showing some characters
as E. (Redrawn from Bridge, A, after Günther; B and C, after Lankester; D,
after Parker; E, after Budgett, and F, after Kerr.)

difficulties in the environment can be met by special adaptations.

Ceratodus forsteri (Fig. 77, A), a fish that reaches a length of over five feet, according to Bridge, "frequents the comparatively stagnant pools or water-holes all the year round. In these pools, filled with a rich growth of vegetation, and often the favorite haunt of the Platypus (*Ornithorhynchus*), the fish is fairly abundant. Inactive and sluggish in its habits, usually lying motionless on the bottom, the fish is easily captured by the natives with hand nets and baited hooks. *Ceratodus* lives on fresh-water crustaceans, worms, and mollusks, and to obtain them it crops the luxuriant vegetation much in the same way that a polychaet or a holothurian swallows sand for the sake of the included nutrient particles. Apparently the air-bladder is a functional lung at all times, acting in conjunction with the gills. At irregular intervals the fish rises to the surface and protrudes its snout in order to empty its lung and take in fresh air. While doing so the animal makes a peculiar grunting noise, 'spouting' as the local fishermen call it, which may be heard at night for some distance, and is probably caused by the forcible expulsion of air through the mouth. Useful as the lung is as a breathing organ under normal conditions, there can be little doubt that its value as such is much greater whenever gill breathing becomes difficult or impossible. This seems to be the case during the hot season, when the water becomes foul from the presence of decomposing animal or vegetable matter. Semon records a striking illustration of this in the case of a partially dried-up water hole, in which the water had become so foul that it was full of dead fishes of various kinds. Fatal as these conditions were for ordinary fishes, *Ceratodus* not only survived but seemed to be quite healthy and fresh. Such observations are of exceptional interest. Not only do they afford a clue to the conditions of life which, in the course of time, probably led to lung-breathing in *Ceratodus*, but they also suggest the possibility that a similar environment has been conducive to the evolution of air-breathing vertebrates from gill-breathing and fish-like progenitors. In spite of its pulmonary respiration, *Ceratodus* more closely resembles the typical fishes in its habits than any other Dipnoi. It lives all the year round in the water. There is no evidence that it ever becomes dried up in the mud, or passes into a summer sleep in a cocoon, and the well-developed condition of its gills suggest that these organs play a more important role in breathing than in either *Protopterus* or *Lepidosiren*."

The genus *Protopterus* (Fig. 77, B) has a wide range over the continent of Africa and consists of three species, *P. annectans*, *P. aethiopicus*, and *P. dolloi*. These fishes inhabit the marshes near rivers, living upon frogs, worms, insects, etc., that abound in marshy places. The long, slender fins are used probably as tactile organs though they may help in locomotion along the bottom. During the wet season they live and breathe much as does *Ceratodus*, but they are said to be absolutely dependent upon breathing air, and if prevented from coming to the surface for air will drown.

"In the dry seasons," says Bridge, "the marshes in which *Protopterus* lives become dried up, and to meet this adverse change in its surroundings, the fish hibernates, or passes into a summer sleep, until the next rainy season brings about conditions more favorable to active life. Preparatory to this summer sleep, and before the ground becomes too hard, the fish makes its way into the mud to a depth of about eighteen inches, and there coils itself up into a flask-like enlargement (Fig. 77, D) at the bottom of the burrow, which is lined by a capsule of hardened mucus secreted by the glands of the skin. The mouth of the flask is closed by a capsular wall or lid, which is perforated by a small aperture. The margins of this aperture are pushed inwards, so as to form a tubular funnel for insertion between the lips of the fish. While encapsuled in its cocoon the fish is surrounded by a soft slimy mucus, no doubt for the purpose of keeping the skin moist, and its lungs are the sole breathing organs, the air pouring from the open mouth of the burrow through the hole in the lid directly to the mouth of the animal. The nutrition of the dormant fish is effected by the absorption of the fat stored about the kidneys and gonads, somewhat after the fashion not unknown in the fat-bodies of insects and the hibernating glands of rodents."

Protopterus is highly prized as a food fish by African natives who find its cocooning habit most convenient. The fish are dug up in large numbers with dried mud left adhering. They are stored in this condition and used one by one as needed. The cocoons may be shipped great distances and the living fish appear active and healthy when the cocoons are placed in water, for the mud and mucous capsule soon soften up and the fish escapes and seems glad to be back in the aquatic element.

Lepidosiren (Fig. 77, C) is just a step more terrestrial in its habits than *Protopterus* and several degrees more degenerate than the latter. It lives in swamps, breathes air more largely, taking several breaths at a time when it comes to the surface. In the dry season it digs a burrow deeper than that of *Protopterus* in which it aestivates, the entrance to the burrow being plugged with a mud stopper ventilated by several round holes. After the water returns to the swamps the mud plug is pushed out of the entrance to the burrow, water enters, and the fish lays eggs in the burrow. The male remains in the burrow guarding the eggs till they hatch out into tadpole-like larvae (Fig. 77, F). While the fish is guarding the eggs the pelvic fins act as accessory gills, for they are provided with numerous vascular filaments that are waved about in the water.

CROSSOPTERYGII (LOBE-FINNED FISHES)

From the standpoint of their success as fishes, pure and simple, the ray-finned fishes are far the most important, but from the standpoint of contributions to the evolution of higher vertebrates the palm goes to the lobe-finned fishes, failures as fishes, but the ancestors of the first land vertebrates, the Amphibia. During the whole Devonian Period the lobe-fins were the most abundant of the bony fishes, but they declined during the Carboniferous Period and only a few of them persisted into the Mesozoic Era. They are the fishes that pushed farthest up the rivers and lived in the inland swamps and ponds that drained into the rivers. In these swamps and ponds fish life was somewhat precarious. Although animal and vegetable food was doubtless abundant, these waters were subject to seasonal changes, tending to dry up during the long rainless summers. Ordinary gill-breathing fishes could not survive through these vicissitudes, but the lobe-fins had a fairly good air-breathing equipment and the beginnings of land legs. In addition to the lungs that all primitive bony fishes possessed, the lobe-fins were able to breathe air without opening the mouth by taking it in directly through the nostrils, for the latter communicated through internal nares directly with the mouth cavity. This arrangement is not found in other bony fishes except the Dipnoi, which, so far as air-breathing is concerned, seem to have been even better equipped than were the lobe-fins.

The lobe-finned fishes had one great advantage over the Dipnoi in the possession of the makings of legs. It is this possession more than any other that enabled them to evolve into land vertebrates. One might question the advantage of legs to a fish. The most natural explanation would be that legs would enable the fishes living in

temporary ponds to walk about on land and exploit its food re-
sources, but there is no evidence that the land at that time afforded
even as good a food supply as the waters. Romer has an ingenious
theory as to why the lobe-fins needed to walk. Somewhat paradoxi-
cally, he states that the early lobe-fins got out of the water in order
to keep in the water. His idea is that, as one pond or pool in a stream
threatened to dry up the lobe-fins crawled out and clumsily ambled
overland to the nearest good pond or pool, and kept on moving as
the water dried up more and more. Thus the lobe-fins themselves
remained fishes and persisted in their fish-like ways as long as they
could, but could not go on that way forever, gradually dying out as
fishes. Some of their more progressive stocks, however, improved
their equipment for land life and evolved into the first Amphibia, a
feat that was most important in the evolution of vertebrates, in fact

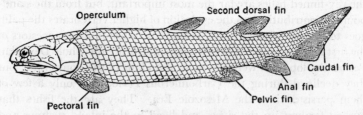

FIG. 78. *Osteolepis*, a typical Middle Devonian lobe-finned fish.
(From Goodrich.)

the greatest single evolutionary accomplishment of vertebrates. The
story of the rise and early success of the Amphibia would be out of
place here and we must leave its further elaboration for the chapter
on Amphibia.

One can get a good idea of the general appearance of the primitive lobe-fins by examining the picture of *Osteolepis* (Fig. 78), one of
the Middle Devonian lobe-fins. One may note the stout lobes of the
pectoral and pelvic fins; the head armored with dermal plates; the
complete body armor of closely fitting, heavy, cosmoid scales; the
terminal mouth with its sharp teeth; and the heterocercal tail fin,
reminding one of those of the sharks. Note also that the scales are
arranged in slightly diagonal vertical rows, one row being present
for each myotome.

For a long time *Polypterus* and *Calamoichthys* were regarded as surviving lobe-fins, but they are now classed as primitive ray-fins (see
below). There are no surviving Crossopterygii.

ACTINOPTERYGII (RAY–FINNED FISHES)

The ray-finned fishes owe their common name to the fact that the paired fins possess little of the fleshy basal lobes characteristic of previously described bony fishes, the main fin consisting of a membranous web supported by slender horny rays. The earliest ray-fins appeared in the Middle Devonian along with the other primitive Osteichthyes, but at first they were not nearly so numerous as the lobe-fins and lung-fishes. Some of the earliest of the ray-fins were the palaeoniscids, which did not at first differ greatly from the lobe-fins, from which they doubtless were derived. From these early, generalized ray-fins have sprung the majority of the common fishes of today, the teleosts. In addition, there have survived a few representatives of the various levels of the evolutionary history of primitive ray-finned fishes, sometimes designated collectively as the ganoid fishes, which belong to four orders: Polypterini, Chondrostei, Amioidei, and Lepidostoidei. The Teleostei constitute the most successful survivors of the ancestral ray-finned fishes.

ORDER POLYPTERINI

This order consists of two surviving genera of old-fashioned ray-fins, *Polypterus* and *Calamoichthys*, inhabitants of the Nile, Congo, and other African rivers emptying into the Atlantic Ocean. So similar to lobe-fin fishes are these that until rather recently they were classed as the only survivors of the once abundant Crossopterygii. In fact, most textbooks still treat them as such. They resemble the lobe-fins in having fleshy, scale-covered lobes on the pectoral fins, but their supporting skeleton is not at all like that of Crossopterygii, much less of Amphibia. The Polypterini are now regarded by experts as an extremely isolated type of ray-fins, with no close relatives among living types and even without any close known fossil relatives. Their nearest, but not very close relatives are probably the palaeoniscids, one of the earliest types of the Middle Devonian ray-fins. A description of the more striking features of the anatomy of *Polypterus* will serve to make the above statements more concrete.

General Anatomy of Polypterus. — Doubtless the chief reasons why Huxley regarded *Polypterus* as a crossopterygian were that this fish has at the base of each pectoral fin a fleshy lobe covered with scales, that the lung is used for respiration, and that the scaly body and head investments are at least superficially much like those of extinct lobe-fins. The lobose paired fins (Fig. 79, A), however, are only superficially like true lobe-fins. The internal skeleton is not at

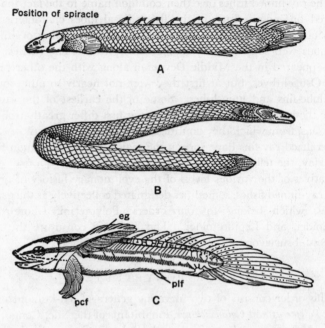

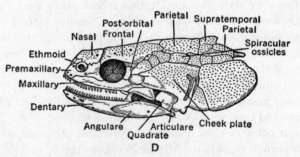

FIG. 79. POLYPTERINI. A. *Polypterus*. B. *Calamoichthys*. C. Larva of *Polypterus*, showing attitude when resting on bottom; eg, external gills; pcf, pectoral fins; plf, pelvic fins. D. Lateral view of left side of skull of *Polypterus*. (Redrawn, A, B, after Bridge; C, after Budgett; D, after Traquair.)

all comparable and does not resemble that of primitive amphibians. The swim-bladder-lung is characteristic of most primitive ray-fins, therefore not especially indicative of crossopterygian affinities. The body scales are really less like those of extinct lobe-fins than like those of other primitive ray-fins, such as *Lepidosteus* (the gar-pike). In other words, the scales are true ganoid scales. The median fin system is very odd, doubtless specialized rather than primitive. It seems to be composed of an almost continuous series of small dorsal fins, which may have been derived by breaking up of a continuous dorsal fin-fold. Each finlet is supported at its anterior border by a strong spine, which supports a series of four or five horny rays branching backward from it. Such a fin architecture is very peculiar and specialized. The tail fin is, superficially at least, diphycercal, but may not be primitively so. The skull structure is peculiar in a number of ways and is not very similar to that of lobe-fins. There are no internal nares, so that air must be gulped, as in other primitive ray-fins. The detailed structure of the brain is quite unlike that of either Dipnoi or Amphibia, but is a primitive ray-fin brain.

There is no question as to the general primitiveness of *Polypterus*. In addition to features already mentioned, we must add that the spiracle (first gill-slit) is functional in the adult, that the chondrocranium persists to some extent, that the intestine has a well-marked spiral valve. It is more modernized in having the notochord completely displaced by bony vertebrae, which are hour-glass shaped, and in having well-developed dentary and angulare bones in the lower jaws.

The larva of *Polypterus* (Fig. 79, C) is quite a striking object, beautiful in color and markings. Its most remarkable characteristic is a pair of pinnate external gills, quite similar to those of amphibian tadpole larvae and of the neotenic adult Amphibia such as *Necturus*, etc. It is interesting to note in this connection that the embryonic development is much more like that of Amphibia than of teleosts, but this is also true of the other primitive ray-fins.

Calamoichthys (Fig. 79, B), the other genus of Polypterini, closely resembles *Polypterus*, but is a greatly elongated eel-type degenerate. It has the dorsal finlets widely spaced, as though stretched apart when the body became elongated. Like other eel-type degenerates, it has entirely lost the pelvic fins, which are greatly reduced even in *Polypterus*.

ORDER CHONDROSTEI

This order, represented by a long pedigree leading back to nearly the dawn of ray-finned fishes, is now represented by five surviving genera: *Acipencer* and *Scaphyrhyncus* (sturgeons); and *Polyodon, Crossopholis*, and *Psephurus* (paddle-fishes or spoon-bills). These fishes present a curious admixture of primitive, specialized, and degenerate features. They are characterized by the long rostral snout, by mouth on the ventral side like that of sharks, and by shark-like, heterocercal caudal fin. They also have a complete cartilaginous skeleton which must be regarded as a degenerate condition, for that of their ancestors was well ossified.

The sturgeons (Fig. 80, A) are widespread and successful fishes, inhabiting lakes, rivers, inland seas, and are even found in the Mediterranean. They occur almost all over the northern hemisphere, being abundant in Europe, Asia, and North America.

The primitive features of the sturgeons are the persistent, unconstricted notochord, which is partially covered with a thick fibrous

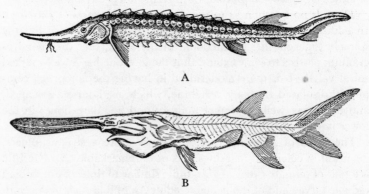

A

B

FIG. 80. CHONDROSTEI. A. Sturgeon, *Acipenser ruthenus*. (After Cuvier.) B. The spoon-bill or paddle-fish, *Polyodon folium*. (After Bridge.)

sheath; the vertebrae lack centra and are composed of dorsal cartilages (basidorsals and interdorsals) that form a tube about the nerve cord, and also a series of ventral cartilages (basiventrals and interventrals) forming in the tail a tube surrounding the dorsal aorta. The skeleton of the paired fins is more like that of the sharks than of modern ray-fins. There is a functional spiracle. The bony scales are very peculiarly arranged in five widely separated longitudinal rows. Each scale is shaped like a flat rose-bush thorn with the point turned backward.

The ventral mouth of the sturgeon is very specialized, being very narrow, and capable of being everted as a long spout that can be thrust into the mud in search of small food animals. The under side of the snout is provided with a number of sensory barbels that doubt-less are used to detect the presence of food. Sturgeons are relatively large fishes, one of them having been taken that weighed over 3000 pounds. The eggs, especially those of species inhabiting the inland seas of Russia, are the material out of which the food delicacy, caviar, is prepared.

Polyodon (Fig. 80, B), the Mississippi "shovel-billed cat fish," "spoon-bill," "shovel-bill" or "paddle-fish," is a very odd creature. It is rather sluggish in habit, feeding lazily about the river bottom by shoveling up mud with its spade-like snout and taking the loose mud with its food contents into the scoop-shovel mouth. The mud is then strained out through the gill-slits that are armed with a grating of gill-rakers so placed as to catch and retain food elements and let the finer mud go through. The paddle-shaped rostrum is richly sup-plied with sense organs that are believed to help in the detection of food in the mud. The general shape of the body is distinctly sela-chian. The skin is scaleless except for a small area in the tail, which is covered with typically rhombic scales covered with ganoin. The other two genera, *Psephurus* and *Crossopholis*, are, except for minor details, very much like *Polyodon*. The internal anatomy of all the paddle-fishes is similar to that of the sturgeons.

HOLOSTEAN ORDERS

This great group, one of the main subdivisions of ray-finned fishes, is now represented by but one genus of each of the two archaic or-ders, Amioidei and Lepidosteoidei, and by the modern order, Teleostei. In this chapter we shall deal with the relics of two nearly extinct orders of Holostei and shall give a separate chapter to the Teleostei.

ORDER AMIOIDEI

Of the twenty-one known genera of this order all are extinct ex-cept one species, *Amia calva* (Fig. 81, B), the familiar "bow-fin," or fresh-water dogfish, common in the Mississippi and St. Lawrence Rivers and lakes draining into them. *Amia* is the most generalized in form and appearance of all the surviving primitive Osteichthyes. So similar to certain common types of teleosts, such as bass, are they that fishermen have often been fooled by the resemblance until the fish was landed, only to find that instead of a fine bass they have caught only a despised and reputedly inedible bow-fin.

The salient features of *Amia* are: the continuous dorsal fin (from which the name "bow-fin" is derived); the heavy ganoin-covered slightly overlapping scales; the peculiar tail fin which is apparently homocercal, but is in reality a modified heterocercal; and, like most other primitive bony fishes, the swim-bladder is used for respiration, the fish coming to the surface and gulping air. The bow-fin breeds in May and June, building a nest in water weeds in which the female lays her batch of eggs. These are guarded by the male until they hatch. Even after hatching, the young tend to stay with the father. Several authors have described the way in which large males are accompanied by swarms of young over which they seem to exercise some parental care.

It is believed that the great order Teleostei took its origin from the order Amioidei, possibly from ancestors not unlike *Amia*.

ORDER LEPIDOSTEOIDEI

This order consists of but a single genus, *Lepidosteus* (gar-pikes), rather bizarre fishes of the fresh waters of North America. The oldest

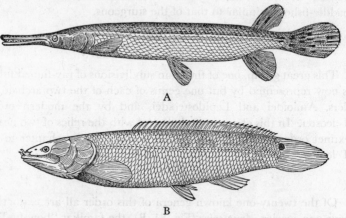

A

B

FIG. 81. HOLOSTEI.   A. Short-nosed gar-pike, *Lepidosteus platystomus*. (After Goode.) B. The bow-fin, *Amia calva*. (After Bridge.)

fossil relatives of the gar-pikes appeared early in the Age of Mammals, during Eocene times. Hence, as fishes go, the group is relatively modern, but they have retained many primitive features.

The gar-pike (Fig. 81, A) has an elongated cylindrical body with a long, narrow, bony snout armed with large sharp teeth. Because of the fact that they kill so many valuable food fishes some states pay a bounty for their destruction. The body is covered with a veritable armor composed of large rhomboidal tile-like scales, heavily coated with ganoin, and with numerous denticles fused to the surface. The caudal fin has the appearance of being homocercal, but is really a modified heterocercal fin. The swim-bladder is used as a lung and air is gulped through the mouth.

The great alligator gar of the lower Mississippi is said sometimes to reach a length of ten feet. Such a giant predator is truly a formidable enemy of other fishes. The gars may be regarded as an aberrant side line of an early holostean stock, that has been able to survive for millions of years with but little change. This may be due to their early attainment of an extremely efficient offensive and defensive equipment.

CHAPTER XI

TELEOST FISHES (ORDER TELEOSTEI)

INTRODUCTORY STATEMENT

The teleost fishes are essentially fishes of modern times, constituting over 90 per cent of all living species of fishes today. As a group, the teleosts appear to have separated off from a primitive holostean stock, possibly from the Amioidei, in Jurassic times, that is, before the middle of the Mesozoic Period. After a modest start they multiplied rapidly and underwent a very extensive adaptive radiation, especially during Cenozoic times. During the Cenozoic, including modern times, they have acquired the status of a dominant climax group, illustrating very well all sorts of evolutionary processes that will be discussed separately as we deal with various representatives of the teleost suborders.

In general, the teleosts represent the end product of peculiarly fishy types of specializations that have not led to any higher levels of vertebrate evolution. They show all sorts of specializations of nearly all the bodily systems, making it difficult to give a general description that will apply to the group as a whole.

It may be said, however, that they underwent a number of changes in common: a, the originally thick ganoin-covered scales lost all or most of the ganoin and much of the bone and became relatively small, thin, and rounded, tending to overlap one another like rows of shingles (in many species all scales are lost); b, the internal skeleton is, in most types, well ossified; c, the vertebrae are amphicoelous, hollowed out at both ends; d, there are commonly bones lying between the muscles (a feature that interferes with their edibility); e, the tail usually is homocorcal and forked into the conventional fishtail shape; f, the swim-bladder is no longer used for air breathing, but is purely a hydrostatic organ; g, skeletal changes are numerous and varied and of such a technical sort as to be beyond the scope of the present treatment, being of chief interest to specialists in the taxonomy of the group.

Of more general interest is the fact that teleosts, in spite of the fact that they are limited to an aquatic environment, have under-

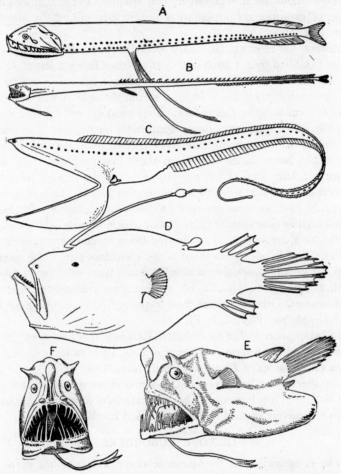

FIG. 82. Deep-sea fishes. A. *Photostomias guernei*, length 1.5 inches taken at 3500 feet. B. *Idiacanthus ferox*, 8 inches, 16,500 feet. C. *Gastrostomias bairdii*, 18 inches, 2300–8800 feet. D. *Cryptopsarus couesii*, 2.25 inches, 10,000 feet. E, F, *Linophryne lucifer*, 2 inches. (From Lull, after Goode and Bean.)

gone almost as extensive an adaptive radiation as have groups with a more varied environmental scope. Many of the changes, however, are difficult to interpret as primarily adaptive. Such changes, for example, as marked elongation of the body resulting in extreme eel-type forms, marked shortening of trunk and tail resulting in head-fish types, excessive development of fins, and other extravagant specializations, seem to be largely non-adaptive and to require some type of evolutionary explanation not strictly guided by natural selection.

Among the most extraordinary specializations among teleosts are those exhibited by the great variety of abysmal fishes, a few of which are shown in Figure 82. Some of these curious fishes live and thrive in this completely dark, cold, and seemingly uninhabitable region over two miles below the surface. They must depend for food upon organic débris that settles down from shallower regions. The smallest forms, including many invertebrates, feed upon the finer débris, somewhat larger forms feed upon these first food collectors, and there is a long food chain, the larger eating the smaller until the largest forms would seem to be immune to attack. This, however, is not the case, for there are some relatively small, highly predaceous fishes such as *Gastrostomias* (Fig. 82, C), which, though only about 18 inches long, are capable of swallowing fishes much larger than themselves. This is possible because of the enormous size of the mouth and the greatly distensible stomach. Some types of abysmal fishes, such as *Idiacanthus* (Fig. 82, B), are excessively elongated eel-type degenerates. Other voracious food traps are *Cryptopsarus* (Fig. 82, D) and *Linophyryne* (Fig. 82, E, F).

In adaptation to life in complete darkness many of these fishes possess specialized light-producing organs, such as those shown in rows on the sides of *Photostomias* and *Gastrostomias* (Fig. 82, A, C). Many species also have eyes of large size that are specialized for seeing in light of low intensity. The adaptations of abysmal fishes have been extensively studied and have aroused much controversy.

TELEOST SUBORDERS

The classification of the immense order Teleostei has been attempted by many ichthyologists and as yet there is no general agreement among the experts as to the number, content, or names of the suborders. To one not a specialist in this field the whole business is very confusing. About all that one can do is to take one's choice of the various classifications and our choice is that presented in 1930 by B. S. Goodrich, for whose encyclopedic knowledge of the whole field of vertebrate morphology we have the greatest respect.

Goodrich recognizes 16 suborders which, in the approximate order of their phylogenetic primitiveness or specialization are arranged as follows:

ORDER TELEOSTEI
    Division A
          Suborder 1. Leptolepiformes (extinct)
    Division B
      Group *a*. Ostariophysae
          Suborder 2. Cypriniformes
      Group *b*.
        Subgroup 1.
          Suborder 3. Clupeiformes
        Subgroup 2.
          Suborder 4.   Esociformes
          Suborder 5.   Scopeliformes
          Suborder 6.   Lyomeri
          Suborder 7.   Anguilliformes
          Suborder 8.   Amblyopsiformes
          Suborder 9.   Scombresociformes
          Suborder 10. Notacanthiformes
          Suborder 11. Symbranchiformes
          Suborder 12. Gasterosteiformes
          Suborder 13. Mugiliformes
          Suborder 14. Percopsiformes
          Suborder 15. Acanthopterygii
          Suborder 16. Gadiformes

Of these suborders the first, Leptolepiformes, is represented by a few extinct species more primitive than any surviving forms. Of the remaining suborders only those will be discussed that are especially significant as illustrations of the degree to which some have retained the primitive, unspecialized condition and others have departed more or less widely from the primitive condition, becoming specialized in a great variety of ways.

Suborder Cypriniformes. This group includes carps, catfishes, suckers, electric eels, etc. In many respects they are distinctly primitive. They are rather sluggish, mud-loving fishes. The carps are often cited as being the most generalized or most nearly ancestral of all surviving teleosts. Some of the catfishes (Fig. 83) reach a very large size, growing to nearly ten feet in length and weighing about 400 pounds.

Suborder Clupeiformes. This suborder is probably somewhat artificial, assembling as it does a number of lowly families not very closely related. It includes tarpons, herrings, trout, and salmon, and a number of less familiar groups. Some authorities regard the herrings as the most primitive of teleosts, but they seem on the whole a little less primitive than the carps. The tarpon (Fig. 84), sometimes

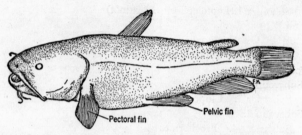

FIG. 83. *Ameiurus*, a common cat fish. (From Messer.)

called the "silver king," is one of the noblest of game fishes. It is a fine example of an almost ideally generalized teleost.

The salmon and trout tribes (Fig. 85) are of all fishes the gamiest and the most sought after by the devotee of the rod and fly. They are characterized by the presence of an adipose dorsal fin. "Of all

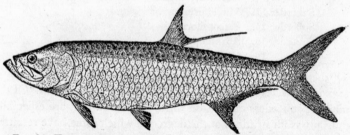

FIG. 84. Tarpon, *Megalops atlanticus*. (From Boulenger, after Goode.)

families of fishes," says Jordan, "the most interesting from every point of view is that of the Salmonidae, the salmon family. As now restricted, it is not one of the largest families, as it comprises less than a hundred species; but in beauty, activity, gameness, quality as food and even in size of individuals, different members of the group stand easily first among fishes." The salmon is a marine fish, but spawns far up among the small streams near the sources of large rivers. This habit has given rise to the "parent stream theory," according to which the young salmon go down-stream and out to sea, where they remain for five years until sexually mature, and then return to spawn in the same parent stream. This does not necessarily imply any marvelous homing instinct or geographic sense, for it has been found that when the salmon goes to sea it does not wander very far from the mouth of the particular river down which it has come. The instinct to spawn in the smaller streams must, nevertheless, be extremely impelling, for they frequently wear themselves out and die owing to

FIG. 85. Family SALMONIDAE. *Salvelinus fontinalis*, the brook, or speckled, trout. Natural size, about 8 inches long. (Courtesy, Shedd Aquarium, Chicago.)

the arduous up-stream journey of often more than a thousand miles, through rapids and even over waterfalls of considerable height.

Suborder Anguilliformes. These are the true eels, characterized by very elongated bodies. Paired fins are absent in all surviving types. Scales are rudimentary or absent. The median fins are continuous about the tail, the caudal fin being gephyrocercal. There are

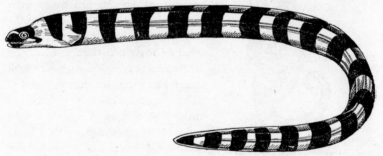

FIG. 86. Eel or moray, *Gymnothrax waialuoe*, from Hawaii.
(After Jordan and Evermann.)

no oviducts, the eggs being discharged through genital pores. The eels may be regarded as senescent, degenerate forms, rather than primitive. The elongated body with the excessive number of vertebrae may be interpreted as due to secondary polyisomerism. Some of the eels show extreme modifications of the generalized fish proportions in having excessively elongated, slender bodies, as is the case in the thread-eel (*Nematichthys*), which one can hardly believe to be

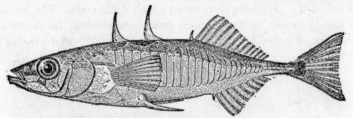

FIG. 87. *Gasterosteus aculeatus.* (From Boulenger, after Goode.)

a fish at all. The morays, a large family of marine eels, are savage, predaceous fishes with highly developed teeth and often with color patterns, strikingly elaborate and brilliant.   These patterns often simulate those of snakes, as in the banded species, *Gymnothorax* (Fig. 86), and it is said that their bite is often quite poisonous.

Suborder Gasterosteiformes. This is a group of rather highly specialized fishes including sticklebacks, pipe fishes, sea-horses, etc.

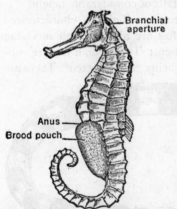

FIG. 88. *Hippocampus guttatus*, male sea-horse. (From Boulenger.)

This well-defined group of peculiar fishes exhibits a wide range of specialization and senescence. The sticklebacks themselves (Fig. 87), apart from their side-armor and prominent spines, are quite generalized in their proportions. Nothing less fish-like, however, could well be imagined than some of the extreme sea-horses, which look more like gargoyles than real fishes. The typical sea-horse (Fig. 88) might be compared with a knight of a set of chessmen, with a long, coiled tail instead of a base. The pipe-fishes may be regarded as the "eels" of the Gasterosteiformes, for they are like greatly attenuated sea-horses.

The breeding habits of all members of the suborder are peculiar. In the case of the sticklebacks the male builds a nest out of aquatic grasses and kindred materials, leaving a front and a rear entrance.

When the nest is complete he goes a-wooing and induces a female to enter his nest and lay her eggs there. As soon as she leaves by the back door he enters by the front and fertilizes the eggs. Usually several other females are employed in the same way until the nest is filled with a sticky mass of eggs. He then watches over the nest until the eggs are all hatched. Sea-horses carry to a higher degree of specialization this "paternal solicitude" for the welfare of offspring, for, instead of building a nest and guarding the eggs, the male uses a part of his body, a brood-pouch on the abdomen, as a nest. According to Jordan, the female lays her eggs on the sea-bottom, and the male, after inseminating them, transfers them to the brood-pouch (Fig. 88) and carries them about until they are hatched, thus making of himself an animated incubator. Some of the sea-horses are provided with an elaborate camouflage in the form of leaf-like

FIG. 89. *Phyllopteryx eques.* A type of sea-horse living in sargassa weed and resembling the latter. (After Boulenger.)

processes (Fig. 89) colored like seaweed, and are practically invisible in their native haunts.

Suborder Acanthopterygii. This tremendous assemblage of spiny-rayed fishes reminds one of the passerine birds in that they are the most modern of the suborders and show a more extensive adaptive radiation than do any of the other groups. The Acanthopterygii comprise no less than 36 families including such familiar forms as the bass, perch, flounder, goby, and a host of less familiar types.

The common perch is as good as any to illustrate the characteristics of the suborder since it is one of the most generalized members of the group. Many of the others, such as the little fresh-water sunfish, tend to become high, compressed, and short-bodied. Still other forms that live in the open seas have carried this type of body specialization to an extreme, as in *Zanclus* (Fig. 90).

Flounders, or flat-fishes (Pleuronectidae) are among the most aberrant of all fishes (Fig. 91). So unique are they in their peculiari-

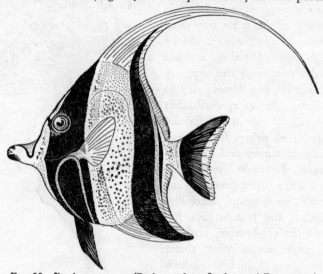

FIG. 90. *Zanclus canescens*. (Redrawn from Jordan and Evermann.)

ties that Jordan saw fit to place them in a separate suborder, which he called Heterosomata. The flounders are bottom-fishes that lie on the side instead of on the belly as do most other bottom-fishes. To adapt themselves to this position there is a remarkable twisting of the cranium that results in bringing both eyes to the upper side of the head and in making the mouth and other parts of the head decidedly asymmetrical. The upper side of the body becomes variously pigmented in harmony with almost any background. Experiments, involving the use of the most elaborately colored aquarium bottoms, have

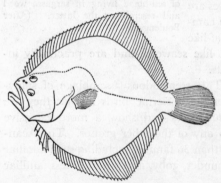

FIG. 91. *Psetta maxima*, a flounder, left side. (From Boulenger.)

proved their extraordinary capacity for background imitation. The
young flounder is at first bilaterally symmetrical and begins the

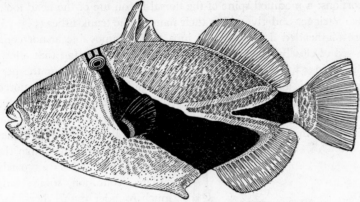

FIG. 92. Hawaiian trigger-fish, *Ballistapus rectangulus*. (Redrawn
after Jordan and Evermann.)

head-twisting process some time before it takes up the bottom-living
habit. Flounders are believed to have been derived from some one
of the high, laterally compressed types, which adopted the bottom-

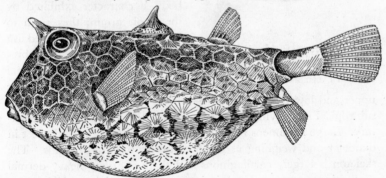

FIG. 93. Hawaiian trunk-fish, *Ranzania makua*, Jenkins. (Redrawn
after Jordan and Evermann.)

feeding habit and was forced to modify itself in a peculiar way to
meet the new conditions.

The fool-fishes, trunk-fishes, porcupine-fishes, puffers, and head-
fishes, all members of the family Plectognathi, are among the most
highly specialized of all teleosts. They comprise a collection of the
strangest creatures that the sea affords. Of these the trigger-fishes

(Fig. 92) are the most moderate in structure, not unlike some of the more generalized Acanthopterygii in their high, compressed proportions; a modified spine of the dorsal fin on top of the head looks like a trigger and gives them their name. The trunk-fishes (Fig. 93) are big-headed fishes enclosed in a heavy immovable armor composed of closely united plates, with a posterior opening that allows the curious little tail to waggle, and smaller openings for the pectoral, dorsal, and anal fins. Puffers, or globe-fishes, are unarmored forms, shaped, when deflated, much like trunk-fishes, but capable of blowing themselves up with water to several times their normal size, thus making themselves difficult to swallow. The porcupine-fishes are shaped much like the puffers in the deflated or partly deflated condition, some being much rounder than others; but they are covered with a heavy spiky armor that has suggested their name. The head-fishes (Fig. 94) represent the climax of relative increase of head over body, a character exhibited by the whole group; they seem to be little more than animated fish heads. The body is so abbreviated that the dorsal and anal fins appear to be attached to the upper and lower parts of the head.

Fig. 94. Hawaiian head-fish, *Ostrachion schlemmeri*. (Redrawn after Jordan and Evermann.)

They inhabit the tropical and subtropical seas, living a sluggish, floating life that is almost sedentary. Large specimens reach a giant size, being about eight feet in diameter and weighing as much as twelve hundred pounds. The skeleton is largely cartilaginous and there is a very heavy dermal cartilaginous armor. The skin is smooth and scaleless. All of these characters will readily be recognized as criteria of senescence.

CHAPTER XII

THE CLASS AMPHIBIA
THEIR ORIGIN AND EARLY CAREER

PAST AND PRESENT STATUS

The name of this class of vertebrates connotes an amphibious mode of living, partly in water and partly on land. By no means all amphibious vertebrates, however, are Amphibia, and not all Amphibia are amphibious. One recalls at once that many turtles, various kinds of snakes, lizards, alligators and crocodiles, seals, and many birds are almost equally at home in water and on land. Moreover, some modern Amphibia, such as tree toads, never resort to water even for breeding purposes.

The Class Amphibia is based not upon habitat but upon fundamental morphological and physiological characters. It includes newts and salamanders, frogs and toads, caecilians, and a large number of extinct forms, some of which were much larger than modern forms and exhibited many bizarre features.

A brief working definition of modern Amphibia is offered by Noble, who characterizes them as follows: "Cold-blooded vertebrates having a smooth or rough skin rich in glands which keep it moist; if scales are present, they are hidden in the skin." There are many other characters that distinguish modern Amphibia from other classes of vertebrates, but only a few of these apply to extinct groups.

The Amphibia should be viewed as a truly transitional group. They are neither fully aquatic nor fully terrestrial, but have struck a sort of compromise between two environments. The result is that they are not particularly well adapted to either.

The question of the origin of the Amphibia involves the whole problem of the beginnings of land life among the vertebrates and the radical evolutionary changes that have occurred as adaptations for an entirely new mode of life. While the aquatic habitat may be said to be a relatively uniform and constant one only slightly influenced by seasonal changes, terrestrial life, especially in temperate regions, involves a wide range of changing conditions.

It has already been noted that the fishes had shown marked tendencies to adopt various methods of invading the air-breathing realm, some for the sake of getting more oxygen and avoiding the respiration of too much CO_2 and other harmful gases in stagnant waters, others to tide over periods of drought. It must have been in association with conditions resembling these that the first true land vertebrates were evolved.

The Amphibia are undoubtedly the most primitive land vertebrates, but it is coming to be believed that the first Reptilia trod closely upon their heels. The Reptilia were much more truly land vertebrates than were the Amphibia, for the Amphibia are tied down to the aquatic medium during at least the developmental period in most groups, and during the entire life cycle in others. Fundamentally the Amphibia are aquatic because their developmental processes are aquatic. Only a few of the most highly specialized modern Amphibia lay their eggs out of water, and these have adopted various unique brooding habits, which are at best mere developmental make-shifts as compared with the methods employed by the reptiles with their land eggs and their amnion, allantois, and yolk sac.

The Amphibia have never attained the heights of success and of dominance in nature that has been attained by fishes, reptiles, birds, or mammals. Possibly this lack of complete success has been the result of their somewhat anomalous lives, involving the necessity of an amphibious environment. They are forced to occupy a narrow strip of territory between the waters and the dry land, a prey to the dominant denizens of the waters (fishes) on the one hand and to the various more vigorous enemies on the land (reptiles, birds, and mammals) on the other. If hard pressed in one environment the amphibian may seek the other; and this has saved him from complete extinction.

The Amphibia today are represented largely by a single highly specialized order, the Salientia (frogs and toads), that have undergone within comparatively recent times a wonderfully elaborate adaptive radiation into a great variety of habitat complexes. But for the frogs and toads the modern Amphibia would be largely unknown, for the salamanders, newts, and caecilians are furtive, inconspicuous forms that have sought safety in the hidden nooks and crannies of the world environment and persist through their extremely retiring habits.

At one time, however, the Amphibia occupied a comparatively honorable place in nature. They reached in some cases almost giant size and evidently were active and predaceous creatures. Their wane began with the rapid rise of the Reptilia, which, as a group, became much more completely adjusted to land life than did the Amphibia.

THE ORIGIN OF AMPHIBIA

When the statement is made that the Amphibia were derived from fishes one might have grounds for skepticism. If one were to compare a modern Amphibian, such as a frog, with an equally modern fish, such as a perch, the differences would seem so great as to overshadow their resemblances. It would be interesting to inquire just what one would have to do to a perch to change it into a frog. We would have to eliminate the gills and change the swim-bladder to a lung. The nostrils, which in the fish end blindly in nasal sacs, would have to be continued through to the roof of the mouth, making breathing through the nose possible. The median fins would have to go, along with the whole tail. The paired fan-like fins would have to be made into legs. The scales would have to go and the soft skin would have to be kept thin for cutaneous respiration; and an efficient system of glands would have to be added to keep the skin moist. The eyes, kept moist in the fish by water, would have to be provided with lids, tear glands, and ducts. The nasal passages would require to be kept moist by glandular secretions. The lateral-line organs would be useless in a land vertebrate and would be eliminated. The ear, which in the fish is largely an equilibrium organ with some ability to pick up vibrations in the water, would have to be changed so as to pick up sound waves from the air, and thus to become a true organ of hearing as well as an organ of equilibrium. The ear drum would have to be introduced with a bony connection, the stapes, between the ear drum and the inner ear. The eyes would have to be somewhat elevated from the surface and modified for vision in the air. Since the adult frog has no gills, that part of the circulatory system serving the gills would naturally have to be transformed in a fashion described later. The heart would have to be changed from a two- to a three-chambered condition to adapt it for pulmonary circulation. These and a number of other radical changes would have to be made to transform a modern fish into a modern amphibian.

The changes that actually took place, however, when the earliest Amphibia were derived from primitive fishes were really not radical at all, for some of the early bony fishes, while still fishes, had already acquired many of the fundamental adaptations for living part of the time on land. The earliest Amphibia, moreover, were far less adapted for land life than their modern specialized descendants, the frogs. In fact, many of the primitive Amphibia remained mainly, if not entirely, aquatic.

Far from involving a dramatic transformation from a purely aquatic fish ancestor into a largely terrestrial amphibian, the changes involved were relatively slight. Vertebrate paleontologists agree that the first amphibians were an offshoot from one family of Crossopterygii, the Osteolepidoti. These fossil fishes agree so closely with the earliest amphibians in fundamental skeletal features that there is no doubt that the first Amphibia were derived from fishes at least closely related to these osteolepidotids.

The earliest and most primitive of the fossil Amphibia are assigned to the suborder Embolomeri, which first appeared in the Lower Carboniferous and lasted into the Permian Period. The Embolomeri very soon underwent a rather extensive adaptive radiation. Some remained aquatic, some became terrestrial. All of them, however, were fundamentally uniform in their skeletal features. It seems obvious then that many of the changes from fish to amphibian occurred in the fishes themselves, as adaptations to seasonal drying up of waters, before the Amphibia were actually evolved.

The primitive Amphibia were decidedly fish-like in their skeletal anatomy. The change from lobose fins to arms and legs with separate fingers and toes was the most drastic of the innovations, but even this is less remarkable than it might at first appear. The change is made clear in Figure 74 where the pectoral girdle and fin skeleton of the pectoral fin of a lobe-finned fish was compared with the pectoral girdle and fore-limb skeleton of a primitive amphibian. In transforming the lobe-fin into a leg, the ray-supported blade of the fin is dropped and only the skeleton of the fleshy lobe goes over to form the skeleton of the leg. The bones of the fish fin are closely comparable with those of the amphibian leg in that the basal bone attached to the girdle is single and homologous with the humerus of the fore leg (Fig. 95). The next section of the fin consists of two bones (radius and ulna), while the rest of the bones correspond to the wrist, hand, and finger bones of the amphibian. The bones of the pectoral girdles of fish and amphibian are also clearly homologous except that the amphibian has added a new bone, the interclavicle. The homologies are equally close between the pelvic fin and the hind leg. It is clear then that the osteolepid fishes had all the makings for legs and that the origin of legs in their descendants,

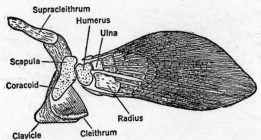

Fig. 95. Right pectoral fin of a lobe-fin fish, *Sauripterus*, Upper Devonian. (From Lull, after Gregory.)

the primitive amphibians, involved little more than quantitative modifications of elements already present.

Modern Amphibia, with the exception of the Gymnophiona, are naked-skinned, without scales, but this naked condition is probably a neotenic, or a retained larval condition. The early Amphibia were well provided with osteoscutes and these were especially well developed in the head region.

It has already been emphasized that all early bony fishes had functional lungs and some of them, the Crossopterygii and Dipnoi, had internal nostrils, enabling them to breathe without opening the mouth. The loss of gills in the adults of higher Amphibia involves a concomitant loss of gill circulation. The capillary part of the branchial circulation is simply dropped out and the afferent and efferent branchial arteries become directly continuous to form four or five pairs of aortic arches, the details of which are described in Chapter XIV.

Some of the Amphibia, notably frogs and toads, possess a new type of auditory apparatus not present in any fishes. This consists of an ear drum (tympanic membrane) at the surface of the head. This drum is attached to a bone (stapes, or columella auris) that transmits sound waves from the drum to the membranous labyrinth of the inner ear.   The inner end of the stapes works in and out piston-fashion in a cylindrical opening of the auditory capsule, called the fenestra ovalis.   This is the first true sound-conducting apparatus.   Many modern amphibians lack this apparatus and it seems to have been absent in the earliest Amphibia.

Among the somewhat less striking innovations introduced by Amphibia are the allantoic urinary bladder; parathyroid glands,

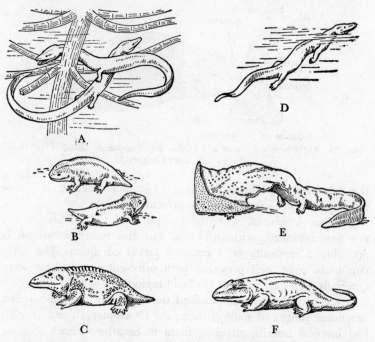

Fig. 96.   Group of Extinct Amphibia, A and B from the Carboniferous; C and F, Permo-Carboniferous.   A. *Pytonius*.   B. *Amphibamus*.   C. *Cacops*.   D. *Cricotus*.   E. *Diplocaulus*.   F. *Eryops*.   (Redrawn after Osborn, following restorations of Gregory and Deckert.)

derived from parts of the lost gill-slits; and paired occipital condyles, permitting head movement; uniting of cortical and medullary tissue to form the adrenal glands.

From what has been said it is evident that the lobe-finned fishes did not need to add so very much to their equipment for land life in order to become transformed into the first Amphibia.   They had already while still fishes acquired many of the characters necessary for at least temporary land existence.

We have already discussed the conditions that led the lobe-finned fishes to acquire an equipment for land life and have already noted that the earliest amphibians were far from completely terrestrial forms. They were probably still pretty thoroughly aquatic in their habits. We may picture them as living alongside their ancestors, the osteolepid fishes, and differing from the latter mainly in having feet instead of fins.

The Devonian Period was a time of seasonal droughts in the inland regions. During these periods the streams ceased to flow and the remaining pools grew foul and stagnant. For fishes with lungs this would not be fatal, but suppose a pool were to dry up altogether, the condition would become critical. The crossopterygians without legs would perish, but their descendants with legs could crawl downstream or across the land to another pool. "Land limbs," says Romer, "were developed to reach water, not to leave it." From such a start as this many of the more definitely terrestrial Amphibia were developed. One after another appeared the various accessory adaptations for land life that were commented upon in an earlier connection. Large numbers of specialized types of Amphibia appeared during the Carboniferous and Permian Periods, showing many sorts of changes in body form: slender, eel-like types; short-tailed, somewhat frog-like types; salamander-like types; and types approaching the condition of primitive reptiles (Fig. 96). During the Upper Carboniferous and Permian periods the Amphibia reached the climax of their career, but after that period they declined, doubtless unable to compete with their much better equipped descendants and rivals on the land, the reptiles.

EXTINCT ORDERS OF AMPHIBIA

The Palaeozoic Amphibia have been assigned to three Orders, which may be characterized as follows:

Order 1. Labyrinthodontia. — These have also been called stegocephalians and are described as crocodile-like or salamander-like. The skull was heavily armored above with bony plates. The teeth were large and had the enamel layer infolded so that a transverse section of a tooth has a labyrinthine appearance: hence the name of the order. That many remained fully aquatic is shown by the presence of well-defined lateral-line canals on the surface of the skull bones. Others, notably *Cacops*, a frog-like form (Fig. 96, C), were probably terrestrial. Three suborders (Embolomeri, Rachitomi, and Stereospondyli) are distinguished mainly by marked differences in their vertebrae. In the Embolomeri the centra of the vertebrae were double. Each vertebra was composed of two bony discs, the intercentrum and the pleurocentrum, with the neural arch attached to one or both. The occipital condyle was single or triple. In the Rachitomi each vertebra consists of a half ring above the notochord with one or two pairs of pleurocentra and a neural arch. The occipital condyle was double or triple. A well-known

example of Rachitomi is *Eryops* (Fig. 96, F). The Stereospondyli possessed a type of vertebra composed almost entirely of the intercentrum, the other elements being absent or vestigial. The occipital condyle was always double. It seems certain that the first groups of reptiles arose from the labyrinthodont amphibians.

Order 2. Phyllospondyli. — These were small salamander-like Amphibia. It is highly probable that these were the ancestors of all modern Amphibia except the caecilians, and that they did not give rise to any reptiles. The vertebrae were peculiar in that they were tubular and both notochord and nerve cord lay in a common cavity. The skull and limb girdles are modified along lines seen in frogs and salamanders. The skeleton of *Branchiosaurus* (Fig. 97), a typical phyllospondylous amphibian, doubtless is that of a larva or of a neotenic species. The skull of another species of *Branchiosaurus* is shown in Figure 98. One can note the fish-like branchial arches, the two occipital condyles, characteristic of modern amphibians, the broad, heavily roofed skull with a highly diagrammatic arrangement of the investing bones, readily comparable with those of the crossopterygian fishes. This skull should be compared with that of the primitive bony fish shown in Figure 75.

Order 3. Lepospondyli. — This is a sort of residual group in which are placed many small Amphibia of the Carboniferous and

Fig. 97. Skeleton of a phyllospondil amphibian, *Branchiosaurus amblystomus*. (From Eastman-Zittel.)

Permian periods that are neither Labyrinthodontia nor Phyllospondyli. In most of them the vertebra is cylindrical and consists of a
single piece, with the neural arch fused to the centrum. It is from
one of the suborders of this order that the modern caecilians were
probably derived, although there are no known fossil caecilians.

Summary of Palaeozoic Amphibia. — The Amphibia have had
their day. They arose from osteolepid lobe-finned fishes in adapta-

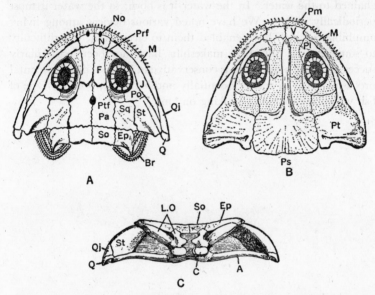

FIG. 98. A, dorsal and B, ventral views of the cranium of *Branchiosaurus sala-
mandroides*. (After Fritsch.) C. Posterior view of cranium of *Trematosaurus*. (After
Fraas.) Br, branchial arches; C, condyle; Ep, epiotic; F, frontal; J, jugal;
L.O, lateral occipital (exoccipital); M, maxillary; N, nasal; No, nostril; Pa,
parietal; Pl, palatine; Pm, premaxillary; Po, postorbital; Prf, prefrontal; Ps,
parasphenoid; Pt, pterygoid; Ptf, postfrontal; Q, quadrate; Qj, quadratojugal;
So, supraoccipital; Sq, squamosal; St, supratemporal; V, vomer. (From Gadow.)

tion to life in regions that were subject to seasonal droughts. Because they were for a long time the only terrestrial vertebrates they
had an early prosperity and became specialized in many directions,
splitting up into three orders which took three different courses of
evolution: one leading to the reptiles; a second to the modern
frogs, toads, and salamanders; a third surviving only as the worm-
like caecilians. Romer has picturesquely described the failure of
the amphibians as follows:

"The amphibians are a defeated group. They were the first vertebrates to emerge from the waters on to the lands; but they were not destined to complete the conquest, and, at first abundant, they have shrunken into insignificance among four-footed vertebrates. Only by the reptiles, their descendants, was the land truly won. The reason for amphibian failure and reptilian success is not far to seek; it lies in the mode of development. The amphibian is still chained to the water. In the water it is born; to the water it must periodically return. We have noted various devices among living amphibians which have enabled them to circumvent this difficulty to some extent; but these makeshifts have not been particularly successful. The amphibian is conservative in its basic developmental processes. It is in reality essentially nothing but a peculiar type of fish which is capable of walking on land."

CHAPTER XIII

LIVING AMPHIBIA

CLASSIFICATION

As was pointed out in the previous chapter, three orders of Palaeozoic Amphibia, though extinct as such, appear to have left some surviving descendants. The Order Labyrinthodontia became extinct as Amphibia, but gave rise to primitive reptiles; the Phyllospondyli, to modern Caudata and Salientia; and the Lepospondyli, probably to the Gymnophiona. The classification of Amphibia used here is that employed by G. Kingsley Noble in his recent volume on *The Biology of the Amphibia.* Also much of the information here given is drawn from that important work.

The three surviving Orders of Amphibia, with their suborders, are as follows:

> Order I. Gymnophiona (Apoda)
> Order II. Caudata (Urodela)
>   Suborder 1.   Cryptobranchoidea
>   Suborder 2.   Ambystomoidea
>   Suborder 3.   Salamandroidea
>   Suborder 4.   Proteida
>   Suborder 5.   Meantes
> Order III.   Salientia (Anura)
>   Suborder 1.   Amphicoela
>   Suborder 2.   Opisthocoela
>   Suborder 3.   Anomocoela
>   Suborder 4.   Procoela
>   Suborder 5.   Diplasiocoela

ORDER I. GYMNOPHIONA (APODA)

The members of this order are commonly called caecilians or blindworms (Fig. 99). They are very much elongated creatures, probably eel-type degenerates of some unknown extinct form. They have no legs and almost no tail, for the vent is almost terminal. In general appearance they resemble large earthworms, for the skin is depressed into numerous transverse grooves or wrinkles that remind one of the segments of the earthworms. At the bottom of these skin grooves there are found in some genera minute scales, embedded in the skin. These are the only Amphibia of today in which the ancestral amphibian scales have been retained.

As might be assumed from their body form, nearly all the caecilians are subterranean in habit, burrowing in the ground and feeding

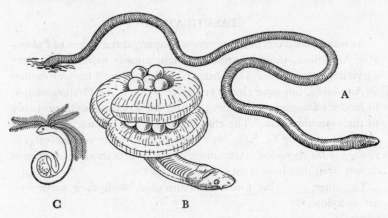

FIG. 99. Group of Gymnophiona. A. *Caecilia*, emerging from burrow. B. *Ichthyophis glutinosus* (nat. size), female guarding her eggs, coiled up in hole in the ground. C. A nearly ripe embryo, with cutaneous gills, tail-fin, and still a considerable amount of yolk. (Redrawn after P. and F. Sarasin.)

upon small ground-dwelling animals. They are widely distributed in the tropics. They all are classed in a single family consisting of 19 genera and 55 species.

In spite of the fact that they are highly specialized for a burrowing life and are decidedly degenerate in many respects, they are regarded as, in general, the most primitive of modern Amphibia. Their most degenerate features are the absence of limbs and limb girdles; short, vestigial tail; and minute, lidless eyes buried deep in the head, sometimes hidden under the bones of the skull. The males possess a rather large, protrusible copulatory organ, provided with hooks, roughly resembling that of snakes. Whether this is a primitive or a specialized character one can not say, but such an organ is very unusual for modern Amphibia. Between the nostril and the eyes there is a protrusible tentacle, which is doubtless an important sense organ used for exploring in the dark burrow.

Because of the fact that the caecilians are confined to tropical or semitropical regions, and because they live a subterranean life, they are seldom seen except by zoologists.

Natural History of Ichthyophis glutinosa. — This species is chosen as an example of Gymnophiona because it has been adequately studied and described by the Sarasins. The species extends from the foot-hills of the Himalayas to Ceylon, the Malay Archipelago, and Siam. It reaches a length of about a foot. In color it is dark brown or bluish black with a yellow band along the side. The eggs are oval, about 4 X 6 mm. There is about each egg a heavy coat of albumen with chalazae, much as in the birds, these chalazae uniting the eggs in strings. The egg mass is laid not in water, but in a shallow hole near the water. The female coils herself about the glutinous egg mass (Fig. 99, B) to protect it from ground-burrowing animals. The gilled larval period is passed through in the egg before hatching. The three pairs of larval gills (Fig. 99, C) are of the external type and are very long and finely branched. These gills seem to be used for the absorption of nutriment rather than for respiration, for they shrivel up and are lost before the embryo hatches. The female takes the eggs into shallow water shortly before hatching time. One pair of gill-slits remains open and is used for respiration during aquatic larval life. The larva swims about in the water for a time like an eel, but comes frequently to the surface to breath air. The larval period is a long one, but finally the gill-slits close, the skin changes its character, the tail-fin disappears, and the adult emerges upon the land and lives a burrowing life. So exclusively terrestrial does it become that it drowns if after metamorphosis it is kept under water for any length of time. Several other genera of caecilians are viviparous, the embryos becoming several inches in length before birth.

ORDER II. CAUDATA (URODELA)

This order consists of tailed amphibians, commonly called salamanders and newts. They form a natural group and their ancestry has been traced back to the extinct amphibian order, Phyllospondyli. The larvae are quite like the adults, and there is no very pronounced metamorphosis when the larva changes into the juvenile adult form, a fact that distinguishes them readily from frogs and toads.

Neoteny. — In order to understand the modern classification of the Caudata it is necessary first further to discuss the phenomena of neoteny, which is particularly striking in this order. As has already been pointed out for the Larvacea, neoteny is a condition in which larval characters are more or less completely retained throughout life, and hence sexually mature animals possess larval characters. On this account neotenic types are commonly called "permanent larvae." The persistence of larval, or even embryonic, characters into adult life is probably a much commoner phenomenon than is generally realized. De Beer regards it as a very common evolutionary process, which is the converse of one in which adult (or at least more advanced) characters are pushed back to earlier developmental stages.

Among the Caudata there are many more or less completely neotenic genera and species. Formerly all the fully neotenic genera

Fig. 100. *Cryptobranchus allegheniensis*. (After Lydekker.)

were regarded as the most primitive of living Amphibia and were assigned to two subfamilies. At the present time neoteny is not considered as a criterion of primitiveness. Rather, it is believed to be the result of secondary, relatively recent, changes that have occurred independently in several different taxonomic groups. Hence we find neotenic or partially neotenic forms assigned to as many as four suborders of Caudata. The classification into suborders and families is now based upon deep-seated morphological differences, chiefly those involved in the components of vertebrae and skull, rather than upon such characters as the greater or less retention of larval characters. In discussing these suborders only a minimum of technical diagnostic criteria will be given. We shall be more interested in their natural history.

Suborder 1. Cryptobranchoidea. — In these salamanders fertilization of the eggs is external, which may not be primitive but degenerate. There are two families: Hynobiidae and Cryptobranchidae, the former Asiatic in distribution, the latter both Asiatic and North American. The Family Hynobiidae consists of five genera of

Asiatic land salamanders of which the best known is *Hynobius,* which seems to be close to the central stock from which the others have been derived. Little need be said about the hynobiid salamanders except that in several respects they are the most primitive of caudate amphibians.

The most familiar example of this suborder is *Cryptobranchus allegheniensis* (Fig. 100), the "hellbender" of the eastern United States. These are giant, fully aquatic salamanders which are semilarval in the adult stage. Gills are absent in the adult, but the first gill-cleft is left open and acts as an outlet for water taken into the mouth for

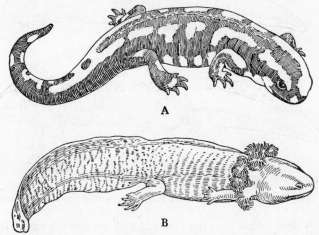

Fig. 101. A. *Salamandra maculosa,* a European ambystomid salamander. B. Axolotl larva of *Ambystoma tigrinum.* (A, after Lydekker; B, after Gadow.)

purposes of mouth respiration. The eyes are small and lidless, and well-developed lateral-line organs are present, both regarded as retained larval characters. In most other respects the adult status is reached.

The eggs are laid in gelatinous sacs pulled out into two long strings and are fertilized when the males deposit sperm masses near the egg-laying females. As many as 300 to 400 eggs are deposited by a single female. Hellbenders are large animals, reaching a length of two or more feet, and are broad-headed and powerfully built. They are predaceous fish eaters and hence are unpopular with fishermen frequenting mountain streams.

Megalobatracus japonicus, the only other species, is a native of Japan and China. Except that it is a larger form, reaching five feet or more in length, it does not differ very much from *Cryptobranchus*. It is, however, somewhat less neotenic than the latter.

Suborder 2. Ambystomoidea. — These salamanders are pretty obviously derived from ancestral hynobiid salamanders. They are, however, quite distinct in a number of ways. In them fertilization is internal, as in most higher salamanders. The male deposits packets of sperms (spermatophores) on the stream bottom and the female nips off these little masses of sperm with the lips of the cloaca. These

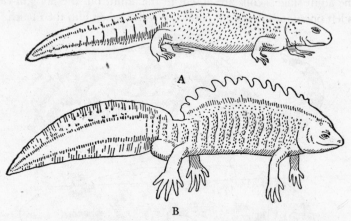

FIG. 102. *Triton cristatus*. A. Female. B. Male in nuptial dress. (After Gadow.)

sperms then migrate up the oviducts and fertilize the eggs. In the adults of most species (Fig. 101, A) very few traces of larval characters persist, but in *Ambystoma tigrinum*, the tiger salamander, a species very widely distributed throughout most of North America, neotenic types occur in mountain regions, especially in Mexico. When this type was first discovered it was named *Siredon axolotl* (Fig. 101, B) and was regarded as a new genus of primitive salamanders. When, however, some of the larvae were collected and transported to Paris the true situation was revealed. Some of the axolotls lost their external gills and metamorphosed into adult tiger salamanders. It seems probable that the cold waters of the mountain lakes and the scarcity of iodine compounds in the water were partly responsible for the failure of these axolotls to metamorphose under the mountain conditions. On the other hand, axolotls have been kept in Chicago laboratories and elsewhere for long periods without showing any signs of spontaneous metamorphosis. Metamorphosis, however, is readily induced in these by injecting thyroid extract. Probably these various axolotls belong to different subspecies or geographic races. Here we seem to have a species in process of becoming neotenic. Doubtless in the completely neotenic types the condition arose in much the same fashion.

Suborder 3. Salamandroidea. — This is an extremely diversified suborder consisting of three families: Salamandridae, Amphiumidae, and Plethodontidae.

The Salamandridae are typical newts, some of them decidedly primitive. Most of them are European or Asiatic, there being only one American genus, *Triturus*. They are typically aquatic in habit.

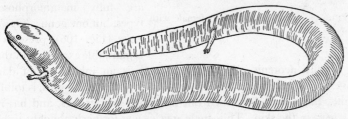

FIG. 103. *Amphiuma means*, an eel-like degenerate salamandroid amphibian. (After Lydekker.)

Fertilization is internal. They are fully metamorphosed. To this group belongs the famous European salamander, *Triton*, probably more correctly named *Molge cristatus* (Fig. 102, A and B), in which there is a marked sexual dimorphism. This species is famous on account of the important experimental embryological work in which it has been used.

The Amphiumidae are the "Congo Eels" belonging to the genus *Amphiuma* of the southeastern United States. They are semilarval forms and probably were derived from salamandrid ancestors, since they agree with the latter in fundamental characters. *Amphiuma* (Fig. 103) may be regarded as an eel-type degenerate, with very long, cylindrical body and tiny, almost vestigial fore and hind legs, which can not be of much value in locomotion. They live in swamps and muddy waters, often invading the rice lands of the Mississippi lowlands. The lidless eyes and a small pair of open gill-slits are regarded as persistent larval characters.

The Plethodontidae are small brook-dwelling or terrestrial Caudata. Most American Caudata belong to this family. Many of them are rather strikingly colored. One finds them commonly in damp woods concealed under loose stones or other shelters. They are all lungless, using only the skin for respiration. Two well-known genera are *Desmognathus* (Fig. 104) and *Spelerpes* (Fig. 105). The former is shown protecting her eggs in an underground burrow; the latter is noteworthy for its remarkably specialized tongue with which it captures insects.

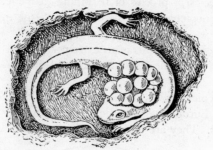

Fig. 104. *Desmognathus fuscus;* female with eggs in hole underground. (From Gadow, after Wilder.)

Most of the plethodontids are fully metamorphosed types, but one genus, *Typhlomolge* (Fig. 106), presents a remarkable exception in that it is fully neotenic. This curious form is an inhabitant of dark caves in central Texas. It has well-developed external gills, is totally blind, has a well-developed tail fin, long, slender legs, and has no pigment in the skin. This single species was formerly thought to belong to the Suborder Proteida, but it has now been shown to have the distinctive characters of the plethodontids. It is so fully neotenic that it does not metamorphose even after prolonged thyroid feeding.

Suborder 4. Proteida. — This group comprises the American mud puppy, *Necturus*, and the European blind cave salamander, *Proteus*. These are typical per-

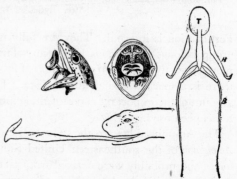

Fig. 105. *Spelerpes fuscus*, showing the position and shape of the partly protruded tongue and the tongue skeleton on the right. T, tongue; B, branchial arch; H, hyoid. (From Gadow, after Berg and Wiedersheim.)

manent larvae, so much so that they do not possess enough adult skeletal features to indicate their taxonomic relationships. There are two species of *Necturus*, *N. punctatus* and *N. maculosus* (Fig. 107, A), both of them North American. They are larval in having well-developed external gills, in being completely aquatic, in having lidless eyes, skull largely cartilaginous, larval musculature, larval circulatory system, etc. It would be interesting to know what the ancestral adult form of these creatures was like. Attempts have been made to force *Necturus* to undergo metamorphosis, but with-

FIG. 106. *Typhlomolge rathbuni*, a neotenic plethodontid from Texas. (After Lydekker.)

out success. It has an active thyroid gland, but the difficulty may be associated with some other gland or may be due to a lack of tissue responsiveness to the thyroid hormone.

Proteus, the European "Olm" (Fig. 107, B), is an eel-type with small legs that are larval in character in their possession of only three

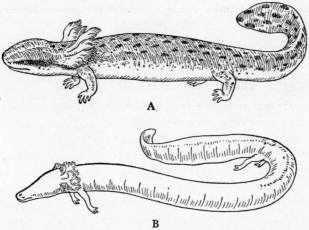

FIG. 107. A. *Necturus maculosus*. B. *Proteus anguineus*. (After Lydekker.)

fingers and two toes. The animal is blind, with minute eye rudiments sunk deep in the head and pigmentless skin. If, however, the larvae are reared in red light, fairly well-developed eyes appear and the skin becomes very heavily pigmented, indicating that the genetic basis for these characters has not been lost in the species. In ordinary mixed light the eyes do not develop.

Suborder 5. Meantes. — These are the "sirens," eel-type permanent larval forms, with but few adult characters. They are like the very young larvae of other groups in having only anterior appendages, the hind legs having been lost. The jaws are sheathed with horn, like those of frog larvae. They have well-developed external gills and the eyes are lidless. The group is probably degenerate in the respect that fertilization is external. There is but one family, Sirenidae, composed of two genera, *Siren* (Fig. 108) and *Pseudobranchus*. *Pseudobranchus* is a burrowing form, tending to hide in the sand, while *Siren* merely hides in the dense aquatic vegetation of its native ponds. Because of the extreme neotenic condition of the

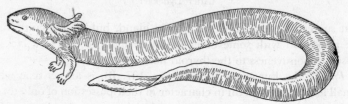

FIG. 108. *Siren lacertina.* A representative of the suborder Meantes. (After Lydekker.)

adults the exact phylogenetic relationships of the Meantes are uncertain.

ORDER III. SALIENTIA (ANURA)

These are tailless Amphibia with short, broad bodies and long hind legs, with a jumping mode of locomotion on land that has suggested one of the names of the order. Frogs and toads are by far the most familiar of the Amphibia, but they are not very representative of the class in general, being a specialized side line of amphibian evolution. In spite of this fact, the frog is one of the most widely used types for classroom study. For purposes of comparative anatomy a relatively primitive salamander would be far superior to the frog, but salamanders are not abundant enough to furnish the amount of material needed, and most of them are rather too small for ready dissection.

As was remarked in introducing the Amphibia, the class has never held a position of dominance in nature and among vertebrates they surpass in dominance only the cyclostomes. What little prominence the Amphibia may now claim is due almost entirely to the Salientia. The frogs and toads are today almost a climax group, at the height of their adaptive radiation. They are at present found in a great variety of habitats: aquatic, terrestrial, subterranean, arborial, and to a slight extent aerial. In a sense, they occupy a position in their class equivalent to that occupied by the teleost fishes among the Pisces. It would not be quite correct to call the frogs and toads modern Amphibia, for fossil frogs have been found as far back as the Jurassic. Hence they have been in existence for at least 150,000,000 years. It seems probable, however, that they have gained their present prominence only within relatively recent times. It seems fairly certain that the Salientia arose from some early Mesozoic group of Caudata, but the fossil record is not very illuminating on this point, for the earliest known Caudata were already frog-like.

The Salientia differ from the Caudata markedly in that there is a great difference between the adult and the larva. The larvae are usually tapoles, with a long, finned tail and with both external and internal gills; while the adults are tailless, have no gills, and respire with both lungs and skin. The metamorphosis from the larval to the adult condition involves, therefore, a very striking transformation. Neoteny in its typical form is never exhibited by frogs, though there are some frogs that have a prolonged larval life during which the tailed tadpoles occasionally become sexually mature. Even these forms, however, sooner or later metamorphose into typical adult frogs.

The terms "frog" and "toad" are not used very discriminatingly. Ordinarily one thinks of frogs as more or less aquatic and of toads as terrestrial forms, but this usage is not consistent. Thus the same species may be called "tree-frog" or "tree-toad." Strictly speaking, the true toads belong to the family Bufonidae, but even the leading herpetologists refer to the members of several other families as "toads."

The Salientia form a natural and well-defined group, easily distinguished from all other Amphibia. They are classified into five suborders and numerous families and subfamilies, largely on the basis of differences in the form of vertebrae and other skeletal features. We shall deal rather briefly with the five suborders.

Suborder 1. Amphicoela. — These are the most primitive of all frogs, one genus being found in New Zealand, the other in North America. The vertebrae are amphicoelous (concave at both ends). These rare frogs are the only ones that have retained two tail-wagging muscles, though the tail itself is lost. The genus *Ascaphus* is also the only genus of Salientia in which fertilization is internal, the male possessing a primitive copulatory extension of the cloaca, on which a few spines occur. The presence of copulatory organs in these primitive frogs, as well as in the Gymnophiona, suggests that this structure may have been general for earlier Amphibia, has been lost by most of the modern Amphibia, but has been retained by caecilians, some frogs and the reptiles, descendants of primitive amphibians.

Suborder 2. Opisthocoela. — These are relatively primitive forms with opisthocoelous vertebrae (concave only posteriorly). To this suborder belong the mid-wife toad, *Alytes obstetricans*, and the famous Surinam toad, *Pipa pipa*. We shall confine our account to these two species, as illustrations of peculiar methods of caring for eggs and rearing of young.

Alytes (Fig. 109, C) is much like the common bull-frog in appearance. It occurs in France and Italy. It is of especial interest on account of the odd method of egg laying and the fact that the male takes care of the eggs. The male is described as assiduously massaging the cloaca of the female with its "hands." After this treatment the female, apparently with great effort, expels her eggs all in a bunch. The male then fertilizes the eggs and carries them off with him, attached to his hind legs. He then buries the eggs in a hole in the ground, moistening them now and then and occasionally taking them into the water with him attached to his legs. When the eggs are nearly ready to hatch he betakes himself to the water for the period of hatching. This appears to be an instance of unusual paternal solicitude, but one must be cautious about such interpretations.

Pipa pipa (the Surinam toad) is a classic object to the zoologist on account of its unique breeding habits (Fig. 109, A). The creature is an odd, ugly, aquatic toad, with exceedingly large hind feet and a very short, broad head. The following description of its spawning is described by Bartlett: "About the 28th of April the males became very active and were constantly heard uttering their most remarkable metallic call-notes. On examination we then observed two of the males clasping tightly around the lower part of the bodies of the females, the hind parts of the males extending beyond those of the females. On the following morning the keeper arrived in time to witness the mode in which the eggs were deposited. The oviduct of the female protruded from the body more than an inch in length, and the bladder-like protrusion being retroverted, passed under the belly of the male on to her own back. The male appeared to press tightly upon the protruded bag and to squeeze it from side to side, apparently pressing the eggs forward one by one on to the back of the female. By this movement the eggs were spread with nearly

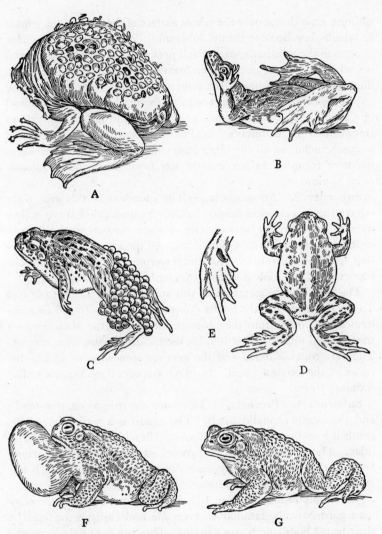

Fig. 109. Frogs and Toads (Salientia) I. A. Surinam toad, *Pipa pipa*. B. Fire-bellied toad, *Bombinator igneus*. C. Midwife toad, *Alytes obstetricans*. D. Spade-foot toad, *Pelobates cultripes*. E. Foot of *Pelobates* showing tarsal spur. F. Common toad, *Bufo lentiginosus s. americanus*, with vocal sac inflated. G. Same stalking its prey. (A and C, redrawn after Lydekker; B, D, and E, redrawn after Gadow; F and G, redrawn after Dickerson.)

uniform smoothness over the whole surface of the back of the female to which they become firmly adherent." The eggs then sink into pockets in the soft, puffy skin. Each pocket develops a sort of hinged lid, which the young pushes open from time to time, as shown in the illustration. This is one of the oddest breeding habits exhibited by any vertebrate. The members of this suborder are sometimes placed in a separate division from all other Anura and are called Aglossa (tongueless) in distinction to Phaneroglossa (with well-defined tongue), including all the other frogs and toads. This distinction is not now regarded as particularly significant from the taxonomic point of view.

Suborder 3. Anomocoela. — The members of this group are referred to as pelobatid toads. In their anatomical characters they seem to be somewhat intermediate between the two preceding suborders and the true toads, Bufonidae. All the vertebrae are procoelous (concave in front). The sacral vertebrae are fused with the coccyx, or if free, only a single articulating condyle is present.

The best known members of this suborder are the "Spade-foot Toads" belonging to the genus *Pelobates* (Fig. 109, D). Their common name comes from the presence on each of the hind feet of a sharp-edged tubercle (Fig. 109, E), used as an instrument in digging. They are rough-skinned and the eyes are somewhat snake-like because of the vertical pupil. In other respects they are not unlike ordinary frogs.

Suborder 4. Procoela. — These are the true toads, tree toads, and the brachycephalid toads. The group is a well-defined one, consisting of three families: Bufonidae, Brachiciphalidae, and Hylidae. Their vertebrae are all procoelous, with the coccyx articulated to the last vertebra by means of two condyles. There is one extinct family, Palaeobatrachidae.

The family Bufonidae (Fig. 109, F, G) is represented by the common garden toads, familiar to everyone and easily recognized by their broad body and warty exterior. They are definitely terrestrial except during the breeding season when they resort to ponds to lay their eggs.

The American genus, *Bufo*, is the most familiar. The fingers are webless and the toes have a greatly reduced web. They lack teeth in the upper jaws, and ribs are wanting. They are largely nocturnal in habits, feeding on worms, insects, and snails. One sees them commonly under electric lights waiting for dazed insects to drop to the

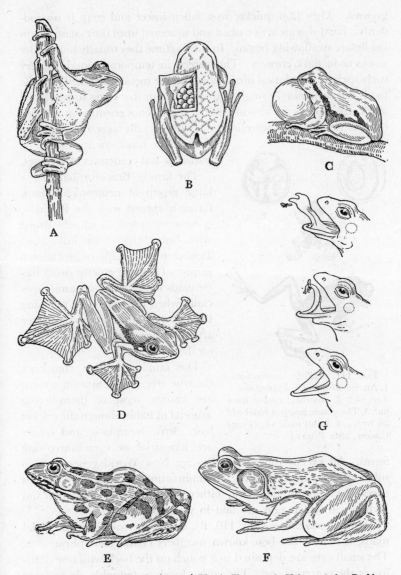

Fig. 110. Frogs and Toads (Anura) II. A. Tree-toad, *Hyla versicola*. B. *Nototrema marsupium* with brood-pouch laid back to show inclosed eggs. C. *Hyla arborea*, with vocal sac expanded. D. Javan flying frog, *Rhacophorus pardalis*. E. Leopard frog, *Rana pipiens*. F. Bull-frog, *Rana catesbiana*. G. *Rana esculenta*, showing the movement of the tongue in capturing a fly. (A, E, and F, redrawn after Dickerson; B and G, after Gadow; C and D, redrawn after Lydekker.)

ground. They hop quickly to a fallen insect and snap it up suddenly. Earthworms are crushed and squeezed until they cease writhing before swallowing begins. In the daytime they usually hide under stones or in dark corners. They breed in temporary ponds in very early spring. The larval life is short and the metamorphosed juvenile toads are surprisingly small, requiring about five years to reach full adult size. Toads are almost without predaceous enemies on account of their noxious skin secretions. About the only agency in keeping down their numbers appears to be parasites and epidemics of diseases.

FIG. 111. *Hylodes martinicensis.* 1. An egg with embryo about seven days old. 2. Another, twelve days old. 3. The young frog just hatched; all by ³/₄. 4. Adult male x1. (From Gadow, after Peters.)

The family Brachicephalidae, a large group of neotropical toads, formerly classed with the Ranidae, is now regarded as closely allied with, but distinct from Bufonidae. *Dendrobates* is perhaps the best known genus. They are chiefly small forest toads found along streams, especially when the males are releasing their load of tadpoles into the water after carrying the eggs and young on the back.

The family Hylidae comprises the true tree frogs. Sixteen genera are known, most of them being arborial in habit, though the cricket frog, *Acris,* is aquatic and others are terrestrial or even burrowing forms. All except the genus *Hyla* are New World genera. Two subfamilies are distinguished: Hemiphractinae, in which the females carry the eggs on the back, either exposed or in a pouch; and Hylinae, in which eggs are laid in water or near it.

Nototrema marsupium (Fig. 110, B), one of the so-called marsupial toads, is one of the best known members of the Hemiphractinae. The small eggs are deposited in a pouch on the back with one opening at the posterior end. The young hatch as tadpoles. In another species of the same genus, *H. ovifera,* the eggs are large and the young short cut the larval stages and are hatched as fully formed young frogs, as is also the case in another member of the group, *Hylodes martinicensis* (Fig. 111).

The genus *Hyla* is one of the best known of the Hylidae. *H. versi-color* (Fig. 110, A) and *H. arborea* (Fig. 110, C) are typical tree frogs. They have suction pads on the toes that aid them in clinging to smooth surfaces. A notable feature of some of the tree frogs is the loud voice, made possible by the greatly expanded vocal sac in the throat region (Fig. 110, C). They are also remarkably protectively colored, often with patterns that resemble bark or leaves. In some of the Hylidae the eggs are car-ried on the back of the female, as in *Hyla goeldii* (Fig. 112).

The tiny cricket frog, *Acris gryllus*, of eastern and central United States, is one of our smallest Hylidae. It is described as a merry little frog, chirping constantly even in captivity. It is one of the most aquatic of the "tree frogs," frequenting the

FIG. 112. *Hyla goeldii* x1. Female with eggs in incipient dorsal brood-pouch. (From Gadow.)

borders of pools, jumping into the water if disturbed and quickly burying itself in the mud at the bottom. It lays its eggs in the water. It should be said that by no means all frogs that live in trees belong to the family Hylidae or even to the suborder Procoela.

Suborder 5. Diplasiocoela. — This is a very large and diversi-fied group, including the true frogs, many Old World tree frogs, the "flying frogs," and the narrow-mouthed toads. They are defined as having procoelous sacral vertebrae, a double condyle for the attach-ment of the coccyx, the eighth vertebra amphicoelous, and the seven anterior vertebrae procoelous. The group includes the more gen-eralized frogs of the family Ranidae (Fig. 110, E, F, G), the tree frogs of the family Pelopedatidae, and the narrow-mouthed toads of the family Brevicipitidae.

Little need be said here about the Ranidae, as their character-istics are usually described in general textbooks and they are familiar to everyone. The Pelopedatidae are exemplified by the so-called "flying frogs," which are tree frogs with unusually large webbed feet that are used as planes in gliding from branch to branch or tree to tree. Wallace seems to have somewhat exaggerated the flying capacity of the Javan flying frog, *Rhacophorus pardalis* (Fig. 110, D). Their air leaps can hardly exceed twenty to thirty feet.

The Brevicipitidae are narrow-mouthed toads of wide distribu-tion and highly varied habits. They are sometimes called "toothless toads" on account of the loss of teeth in the most specialized members. They exhibit a great variety of habits, some being tree frogs, others burrowers, and one species is described as an amphibian "ant eater." One narrow-mouth toad of the United States, *Engystoma carolinense*, is described as having a narrow mouth, protruding snout, lack of teeth, hidden ear drum, and with feet and shoulder girdle modified for digging. These are characters associated with the ant-eating habit in other vertebrate classes such as reptiles and mammals.

We shall close this general account of living Amphibia with a description of the development of a typical frog of the genus *Rana*.

THE DEVELOPMENT OF THE FROG

The early embryology of the Amphibia is perhaps the most generalized found among the vertebrate classes, and that of our commonest frogs is as primitive as can be found. Why the development of the Amphibia is more primitive than that of most fishes is not an easy question to answer. It appears probable, however, that the earliest bony fishes, such as the Crossopterygii, had a type of egg and a process of development even more like that of the Amphibia than have the modern fishes, and that the amphibian descendants of these ancestral fishes have retained more nearly than their fish descendants the primitive features of development. A study of comparative embryology of chordates usually begins with the development of amphioxus and then proceeds directly to that of the frog. Then follows the development of the chick, as an example of conditions in the Sauropsida, and finally that of a placental mammal.

The life history of the frog may conveniently be divided into four periods:

1. The period of germ-cell formation, which terminates with spawning.
2. The period of embryonic development, which begins with fertilization and ends with hatching.
3. The larval period, which extends from hatching to the completion of the process of metamorphosis.
4. The period of adolescence, extending from the end of metamorphosis to sexual maturity.

1. The period of germ-cell formation includes both oögenesis and spermatogenesis, which involve the processes of maturation. These stages are quite typical and require no special comment. The eggs are laid in a string, attached to one another by means of a continuous gelatinous envelope, which is at first dense and viscous, but soon absorbs sufficient water to cause it to swell to several times its original thickness. This jelly, which is laid down in two layers, has the double function of conserving heat for incubation purposes and of preventing the attacks of bacteria.

The fertilized egg (Fig. 113) is rather highly organized before cleavage begins, for the various axes of the future embryo (antero-posterior axis, dorso-ventral axis, and the axis of bilaterality) are already clearly defined. These relations can be made out readily from the pigment pattern of the peripheral parts of the egg. The upper hemisphere of the egg is covered with black pigment, which is like an obliquely placed cap. A gray crescent, thick at one side and fading out on the other, separates the pigmented area from the pale yellow area at the vegetal pole. Only one plane from pole to pole of the egg exists

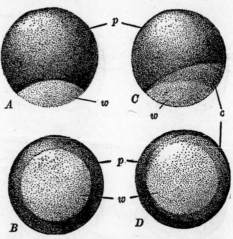

FIG. 113. Frog's egg before and after fertilization, showing symmetry relations. A. Unfertilized egg, from side. B. Unfertilized egg, from vegetal pole. C. Fertilized egg just before cleavage, from side. D. Same from vegetal pole. c, gray crescent; p, pigmented animal pole; w, unpigmented vegetal pole. (From Kellicott.)

that divides it into bilaterally equal halves. Thus bilateral symmetry is determined before cleavage begins. The yolk is abundant, and only a small region at the apical pole is free from yolk granules. Maturation of the egg occurs partly before laying, one polar body being given off during the descent of the egg in the oviduct. The second maturation division occurs after insemination.

2. The Embryonic Period (Fig. 114). — Fertilization occurs while the eggs are being laid, the spear-shaped spermatozoon penetrating the jelly layers, and its nucleus forcing a path through the yolk to the egg nucleus. Cleavage is total, or holoblastic, in spite of the relatively large amount of yolk. The first and second cleavage

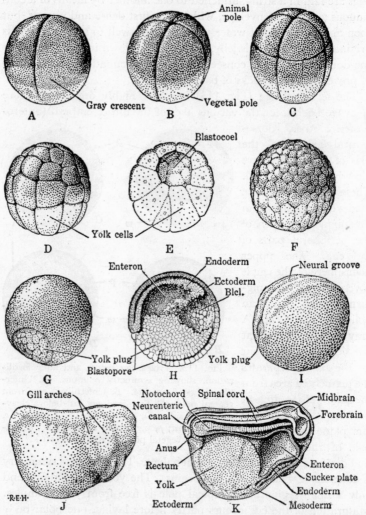

Fig. 114. Early embryonic development of the frog. A, B, C. Eggs at two-, four-, and eight-cell stages. D. Early blastula. E. Section of D. F. Late blastula. G. Early gastrula: showing ectoderm spreading over endoderm which is all covered but the yolk plug. H. Section of G, showing germ layers, etc. I. Late gastrula, showing formation of neural groove and folds. J. Older embryo with closed neural groove. K. Section of J. (From Woodruff.)

furrows are meridional, the third unequally latitudinal, cutting off four micromeres from the animal and four macromeres from the vegetal pole of the egg. The micromeres cleave much more rapidly than the yolk-laden macromeres, resulting in the formation of a rather thick-walled but fairly typical hollow blastula, with numerous small pigmented cells above and comparatively few large unpigmented cells below. The hollow of the blastula, or segmentation cavity, is much reduced in volume because of the thickness of the cells at the vegetal pole. Gastrulation, while not so simple as in amphioxus, is clearly homologous with the latter. The departure from the diagrammatic condition is due to the accumulation of yolk, which prevents the typical embolic invagination of the very thick layer of vegetal-pole cells. The difficulty is evaded by having the invagination take place at the edge of the thickened area, where a flat infolding of surface cells takes place just below the edge of the pigmented area, leaving a crescentic blastopore on the surface. This constitutes the embolic phase of gastrulation. The main part of the gastrulation process is accomplished by the overgrowth of the endoderm cells by the ectodermal cap, a phase known as epibolic gastrulation. The archenteron, at first flat and without a lumen, soon expands and largely displaces the segmentation cavity. The gastrula is morphologically a two-layered embryo, with a layer of ectoderm on the outside and a layer of endoderm within, though in the frog each of these layers is more than a single cell layer in thickness. Mesoderm formation is accomplished by the ingrowth of a sheet of cells around the closed blastopore. This zone-like layer soon splits into two layers, an outer somatic and an inner splanchnic layer, with the paired ventral unsegmented coelomic cavities between. Mesoblastic somites, which are, from the first, solid blocks, arise from the edges of the closed blastopore, and between the rows of somites a median dorsal strip of tissue is left over to form the notochord.

The development of the central nervous system is decidedly precocious, for even in a late gastrula stage the medullary plate is clearly defined. At a time when the blastopore is nearly closed the dorsal parts of the embryo show the broad primitive groove, flanked on both sides by two pairs of medullary folds, inner and outer. The outer folds fade away, but the inner ones arch over the groove and meet first in the region of the future mid-brain, the closure proceeding thence backward and forward. Thus the groove is converted into the

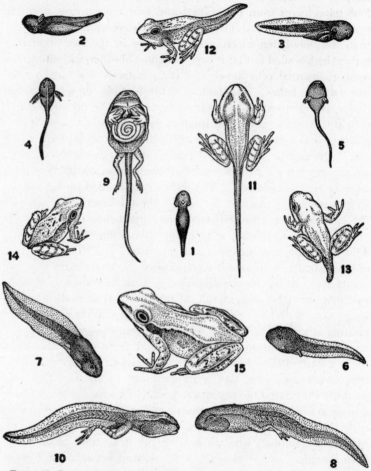

FIG. 115. Larval development of the frog and Metamorphosis. **1.** Tadpole just hatched, dorsal aspect. **2, 3.** Older tadpoles, side view. **4, 5.** Later stages, dorsal views showing external gills and development of operculum. **6.** Older tadpole, left side, showing single opening of operculum. **7.** Older stage, right side, showing hind leg and anus. **8** and **10.** Lateral view of two later stages showing development of hind legs. **9.** Dissection of tadpole to show internal gills, spiral intestine, and anterior legs developed within operculum. **11.** Advanced tadpole just before metamorphosis. **12, 13, 14.** Stages in metamorphosis, showing gradual resorption of tail. **15.** Juvenile frog after metamorphosis. (Redrawn after Leuckart-Nitsche wall chart.)

neural tube. The anterior part of the tube soon becomes differentiated into the primitive brain, with the three primary brain lobes representing the primordia of the fore-, mid-, and hind-brain. During these changes the embryo has been elongating and before hatching has reached a length nearly three times its breadth.

3. **Larval Period** (Fig. 115). — At the time of hatching the larva is a somewhat fish-like creature possessing a fairly long laterally flattened tail with a continuous median fin unsupported by rays. The mouth is ventral in position and is soon surrounded by a horny margin, or scraper, which is used as a larval organ in scraping off nutritive scum from lily pads, etc. Two pairs of branching external (larval) gills are the first functional respiratory organs. After the loss of the external gills, internal gills, homologous with those of adult fishes, are formed and take over the respiratory function for a considerable period. Soon the external gills disappear, and a fold of skin grows backward from in front of their original location, forming an operculum under which lie the internal gills. The operculum has but one outlet, a small unpaired spiracle on the left side. Some writers have interpreted this operculum as the equivalent of the atrium of amphioxus, but the homology has not been established. The hind limbs are the first to appear, closely followed by the fore limbs, which for some time are concealed beneath the operculum. Only in the later stages of larval life are the lungs developed, and as long as the larva uses the gills the lungs remain very small.

4. **Metamorphosis** (Fig. 115). — The period of metamorphosis is really a part of the larval period and can not be sharply marked off from the latter, since the change is a gradual one. Toward the close of the larval period the tail begins to be resorbed and its materials are stored up in the liver. The long, spirally coiled intestine shortens. The mouth loses its horny rim and grows much wider as the hinged jaws develop. The gills disappear and the lungs grow rapidly in size and the larva comes frequently to the surface to breathe air. When these changes are complete the animal is no longer a larva, but a juvenile frog. Some species of frog go through to metamorphosis in a few weeks, others require months, and some require two or three years.

5. **The Period of Adolescence** has not been very fully studied. It is a long, slow process involving changes in the relative proportions of the parts, elaborations of the histological structure, and

ossification of the cartilaginous skeleton. The most significant changes are those that are last to take place, namely, those that have to do with the onset of sexual maturity. Shortly before the beginning of the first breeding season, the cells of the ovaries and testes begin the processes known as oögenesis and spermatogenesis, that constitute the chief features of the first period considered in this brief life history. Hence we have completed the cycle for one generation.

CHAPTER XIV

ANATOMY OF A SALAMANDER

(*An Example of a Generalized Tetrapod*)

ANATOMY OF TRITON

Introduction. — The following brief account of the anatomy of a salamander is intended primarily to indicate the evolutionary advances made by Amphibia over Pisces. Most students of vertebrate zoology are already familiar with the anatomy of the frog and therefore a full account of amphibian anatomy is unnecessary. The frog is not a very typical amphibian, being highly specialized in many ways, while a salamander is relatively primitive and generalized. The following account is based largely on the European genus *Triton* (*Molge*), but will in most particulars apply to *Ambystoma*. The conditions in the salamander are transitional between those in a fish and those in a reptile. This is particularly true of the vascular system, for we find in one animal two systems combined — that of a fish and that of a land vertebrate.

It is, of course, a rather big jump from the anatomical conditions described for the dogfish to those of a salamander. It must be understood, however, that many transitional stages present in the primitive bony fishes, especially lobe-finned fishes, have been dealt with incidentally, although it has not been considered advisable to describe the anatomy of a bony fish in detail. The following account will, for purposes of more ready comparison, follow the same order of topics as was used in the account of the dogfish.

External Features. — The body is an elongated cylinder, retaining the general form of a fish (Fig. 102, A). Instead of paired fins there are typical tetrapod arms and legs. The tail is provided with a median fin above and below, but this is unsupported by fin-rays. The skin is soft and covered with slime, secreted by skin glands. No scales are present. The deeper skin is provided with pigment cells (chromatophores) that are arranged in different patterns in different species. Lateral-line organs are found in the larva and appear

229

in pattern similar to those of fishes, although they lie in open grooves, a condition intermediate between that of cyclostomes and that of fishes. When the animal metamorphoses and leaves the water the lateral-line organs degenerate somewhat, but reappear when the adults go back to the water for breeding. The mouth is wide and just above it there are paired external nostrils. As in the shark, alimentary tract, excretory ducts and the gonadal ducts all open into a cloaca. The eyes, much smaller than in the frog, have upper and lower lids. There is no ear drum (tympanum), a character so conspicuous in the frog. It is probable that this is a degenerate, or larval, condition rather than primitive.

Skeletal System. — The skull is a complex one composed of an almost complete chondrocranium like that of the dogfish, reinforced on the outside by many membrane bones. Some of the cartilaginous cranium has become ossified: on each side near the anterior are paired orbitosphenoids; posteriorly, there are the prootics and the exoccipitals that form the two condyles by means of which the skull articulates with the first vertebra. The membrane bones on top of the skull are the paired nasals, prefrontals, frontals, and parietals. The membrane bones of the ventral side are paired prevomers and pterygoids with the single median parasphenoid. The upper jaw bones consist of membrane bones, the fused premaxillaries, and the paired maxillaries, both bearing teeth. The lower jaw skeleton consists of the articulare (an ossified portion of Meckel's cartilage), which is encased by two membrane bones, dentary and splenial. The articulare articulates with a process of the skull, the tip of which is the still cartilaginous quadrate attached to the long squamosal, which is a membrane bone largely covering the quadrate.

The elements of the second pair of branchial arches form the hyoid apparatus, which lies in the floor of the mouth and is of importance in air breathing.

The teeth are homologous with those of the dogfish but are firmly attached to the membrane bones that bear them.

Vertebrae. — The vertebral column consists of a series of elongated cylindrical bones with cartilaginous pads between them. The notochord persists as a much constricted rod running through the centra. In the trunk region there are neural arches and in the tail region both neural and haemal arches. Dorsal ribs articulate with processes of the vertebrae. In the sacral region one vertebra has broad processes to which the ilia of the pelvic girdle are articulated.

Skeleton of the Fore Limbs. — The pectoral girdle is largely cartilaginous, without dermal investing bones. It consists of the scapula above, and below a fully cartilaginous precoracoid and a partly ossified coracoid. Partly overlapping the paired coracoids is a cartilaginous sternum. The fore limbs proper consist of upper arm, fore arm, wrist, and hand. The skeleton is derived from the radials of the fleshy lobe of the ancestral crossopterygian fin. In the upper arm is the humerus, in the fore arm radius and ulna, in the wrist seven small carpal bones, and in the hand the metacarpals and phalanges, the latter consisting of several joints. There are only four digits, the thumb being absent.

Skeleton of the Hind Limb. — The pelvic girdle consists of a bony dorsal ilium, articulated with the first sacral vertebra; and two ventral elements, a posterior bony ischium and an anterior cartilaginous pubis. The leg is divided into thigh, shank, ankle, and foot. The thigh bone is the femur, those of the shank fibula and tibia, those of the wrist tarsals, and those of the foot metatarsals and phalanges. There are five toes. There is a rather complete serial homology between arm and leg skeletal elements.

Alimentary System. — The mouth region differs from that of the shark in a number of features that are related to land life. Salivary glands keep the mouth cavity moist and aid in swallowing dry food. Internal nares, permitting breathing of air through nostrils, are present. A glottis in the floor of the pharynx opens into the trachea. The chief changes in the alimentary tract involve an elongation of the intestine, which has several loops. A sort of derivative of the hind gut is the urinary bladder, which is a ventral outgrowth of the rectum. This is an allantoic bladder, a structure which becomes in the reptiles an embryonic lung.

Respiratory System. — Gills are lost in the adult and lungs and skin act as respiratory organs. The windpipe, or trachea, divides into two bronchi, leading to the two lungs. The most profound result of the change from gill to lung breathing involves the circulatory system.

Circulatory System. — In the dogfish the architecture of the circulatory system was laid out in accord with the branchial apparatus, there being five paired afferent branchial and the same number of efferent branchial arteries. In *Triton* the afferents and efferents, since there are no gills in the adult, unite to form arterial arches which run around the pharynx. These arches are packed rather closely, as though the branchial region had been telescoped, and they have acquired new functions. The ancestral first and second arches, though present in the embryo, have disappeared in the adult; the third embryonic (first adult) arch becomes the carotid arch, supplying the head; the fourth embryonic (second adult) arch becomes the systemic arch, supplying most of the trunk; the fifth embryonic arch is absent in the adult of *Triton;* and the sixth embryonic (third adult) arch becomes the pulmonary arch, carrying blood to the lungs. The paired systemic arches unite above the gut to form the dorsal aorta, which gives off, as in the shark, several main arterial trunks: subclavians, cutaneous, coeliaco-mesenterics, renals, iliacs, and the single caudal. The changes from the fish condition are not great with respect to these arteries.

The *venous system* is not so greatly modified as is the arterial. The main differences, apart from the loss or modification of the afferent branchial arches, are: *a*, that the blood from the hind end of the body does not return through the renal portal veins to the kidney, but some of it enters the pelvic veins which unite in the mid-ventral line to form the single anterior abdominal vein, and this in turn enters the hepatic portal vein; *b*, there are paired pulmonary veins that bring blood from the lungs back to the left auricle of the heart.

The heart is three-chambered, consisting of two auricles and a single ventricle. The partition between the two auricles is incomplete, being perforated by small windows, permitting some mixing of blood between the two auricles. The conus arteriosus is supplied with valves, as in the dogfish. The conus opens into a short tube (the truncus arteriosus) leading to the aortic arches. The truncus is more or less subdivided by longitudinal septa into two passages, one leading to the lungs and the other to the systemic and carotid arches. This helps to keep venous and arterial blood separate, but the separation is far from complete.

Muscular System. — With the transformation of the swimming paddles of the fish to the arms and legs for support of the body, there has been a marked differentiation of muscles associated with the limbs. These muscles operate a system of levers (bones) and serve to bend the limb at its various joints. The limb muscles, without going into detail, are classed as flexors, extensors, and rotators. The muscles associated with the limbs extend out over the body in the limb regions and obscure the segmental arrangement of the body musculature. In other regions the myotomes are as clearly defined as in the fish. The myotomes of *Triton* differ from those of the fish in that they form simple rings or bands and are not W-shaped in side view.

Nervous System. — The main advance in brain structure is seen in the fore-brain region where the cerebral hemispheres are fairly large elongated lobes, with nerve cells in the roof, but these are not regarded as true cortical cells. The floor and sides of the cerebrum constitute the corpus striatum. The olfactory lobes are much reduced as compared with the dogfish. Most of the other nervous elements are similar to those of fishes.

Sense Organs. — The lateral-line organs, as was said, are degenerate in the adult. As compared with the frog, the ears of the newt are degenerate, actually no better than those of the dogfish. There is no ear drum nor middle ear. The eyes have not changed in any very fundamental way except that eyelids are added and the lens is adapted for short-range vision.

Urogenital System. — The functional kidney is still a mesonephros, as in fishes, and the relations of Müllerian and Wolffian ducts to kidneys and gonads remains essentially the same as in fishes. The more posterior tubules of the kidney, however, are purely excretory and remain separate from the Wolffian duct until just before the latter enters the cloaca. The more anterior kidney tubules of the male act almost solely as sperm ducts. These kidney tubules drain into the Wolffian ducts which empty into the cloaca.

Endocrine System. — The thyroid gland is divided into paired glands. Parathyroid glands on each side of the thyroid glands are the vestiges of the ventral regions of the lost gill-slits. The adrenal glands are in a condition intermediate between those of the fish and those of reptiles, for in the kidney region the glands are composed of both cortical and medullary tissue; while those in front of the kidney are like those of the dogfish in being composed entirely of medullary tissue. The pituitary body consists of four parts: the pars nervosa, derived from the floor of the brain, the pars anterior, the pars intermedia, and the pars tuberalis, derived from the hypophysis.

SUMMARY OF AMPHIBIAN MORPHOLOGY

Amphibia in general show the following advances over the fishes:

1. Long, jointed limbs ending in digits.
2. Arterial arches are reduced in number and, in the absence of gills, short-circuit the region where gills once existed.

3. An allantoic bladder is introduced.
4. The pelvic girdle is divided into three parts: ilium, ischium, and pubis.
5. Parathyroid glands are introduced.
6. Part of the adrenal gland is composed of both medullary and cortical tissue.
7. Salivary glands are introduced.
8. In some Amphibia a tympanic membrane is introduced and a part of the hyomandibular arch persists as the stapes bone that connects the ear drum with the inner ear.
9. As compared with the dogfish there is great advance in the skeleton through the ossification of bones in the chondrocranium and the introduction of many investing bones in the skull and elsewhere. These changes, however, had already taken place in the lobe-finned fishes that gave rise to amphibians. Hence this is not strictly an amphibian advance.
10. Eyelids and tear glands are introduced.

Characters peculiar to living Amphibia:

1. Naked skin, without scales, except in Gymnophiona.
2. An aquatic larval stage is usually present.
3. The heart has incompletely divided auricles and only one ventricle.

Characters of Triton which may be regarded as degenerate, or at least neotenic:

1. Reduction of some bones of the skull and limb girdles that are present in higher Amphibia.
2. Lack of ear drum and accessories.
3. Presence of lateral-line organs, even though reduced, in the adult.

CHAPTER XV

CLASS REPTILIA (INTRODUCTION)

THE DRAMATIC CAREER OF THE REPTILES

When one surveys the whole career of the reptiles from their obscure beginnings in the Palaeozoic, through their exceedingly dominant status in the Mesozoic and into their relatively obscure position in the Cenozoic, he can not but be impressed with the fact that of all the vertebrate classes the Reptilia have played the most spectacular role in the history of the animal world, except possibly that played by man.

The reptiles seem to have split off gradually during late Carboniferous times from the labyrinthodont Amphibia. For a time they so closely resembled Amphibia that, on the basis of skeletal remains alone, it is difficult to be sure whether some of them are actually reptiles that have just ceased being Amphibia, or Amphibia on the verge of becoming reptiles. During the Permian, however, this ancestral reptilian stock underwent a fairly extensive radiation into four or five well-defined groups among which were the mammallike reptiles that gave rise later to the mammals.

From some of these Palaeozoic stocks arose the beginnings of the remarkable reptiles that for a hundred million years dominated the earth, the waters, and the air during the Age of Reptiles, the Mesozoic. No more dramatic story of the evolution of life is revealed by the fossil record than that of these reptiles, and especially spectacular is the history of the rise and fall of the Ruling Reptiles, of which the dinosaurs and pterosaurs are the most striking examples. Extraordinary as was the rise to dominance of the greater reptilian orders during the Mesozoic, their relatively rapid extinction near the close of this long period was even more remarkable. Just when they seemed to be at the height of their careers and to have everything their own way they began a rapid decline and nearly all of the great specialized types faded out of the picture.

The causes of their extinction are obscure and one can only guess as to why they ceased to exist. One theory of their extinction is that, with the continental elevation that ushered in the Cenozoic Age, vegetation became too sparse to afford an adequate food supply for the giant herbivorous types, and hence these died off from starvation. Since the herbivores were doubtless the main food source of the carnivores, the latter were doomed to die for lack of food. The struggle for life between these two was probably accelerated toward the end by the desperate hunger of the carnivores. Another factor in the extinction of the great reptiles may have been the rise of the active, warm-blooded mammals that were becoming numerous during

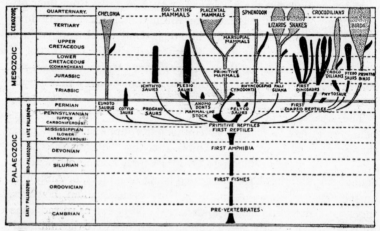

FIG. 116. Chart, showing origin and adaptive radiation of the reptiles. Dotted areas represent existing groups, black areas, extinct groups. This chart also shows the origin of the birds and mammals from reptilian stock. In the cases of several modern groups (Chelonia, egg-laying mammals, placental mammals, *Sphenodon* and crocodiles) the dotted areas should reach the top. (After Osborn, *Origin and Evolution of Life*.)

the latter days of the dinosaurs. It is suspected that the mammals raided the nests of the reptiles at night and ate their eggs and young. Osborn, on the other hand, has offered a theory to explain the passing of the great Mesozoic reptiles, which states that they died off for no better reason than that they had run their course, had reached the limits of their various types of specialization, had become stereotyped, senescent, and could evolve no further. They had proceeded to the end of an evolutionary cul-de-sac from which there was no egress. This is, however, a descriptive rather than an explanatory view.

Whatever it was that caused the extinction of the great Mesozoic reptiles, the fact remains that when the Cenozoic Age was ushered in the great reptilian dynasty had ceased and only a relatively few reptilian orders had succeeded in weathering the vicissitudes of the new climates. The story of the rise and fall of the great reptilian dynasties is told in some detail in Chapter XVI.

Only the crocodiles, turtles, lizards, snakes, and the primitive and now rare *Sphenodon* lived to be contemporaries of the dominant birds and mammals. These reptilian remnants have had a hard time, for they were preyed upon by the offshoots of their own reptilian stock, birds and mammals, and today they are waging a losing battle. The reptiles appear to be doomed. That supermammal, man, has taken a dislike to reptiles in general, especially to snakes, and as a consequence reptiles are scarce in most areas of human habitation. There will doubtless be wild places where reptiles can thrive for a century or so, but sooner or later we suspect that reptiles will survive chiefly in turtle and snake farms, in zoological gardens, and in a few regions uninhabitable for man.

A good general idea of the whole history of the reptiles and their descendants may be acquired by study of the accompanying chart (Fig. 116).

WHAT IS A REPTILE?

People in general have only a vague idea as to what constitutes a reptile. They picture reptiles as something like snakes, but do not go much further. Often salamanders are regarded as reptiles, for they look like lizards. One way of presenting the distinctive characteristics of reptiles is to imagine the changes necessary to transform a typical amphibian such as a salamander or newt into a typical reptile such as a lizard. To be more specific, let us see what we would have to do to the newt, *Triton*, to transform it into the lizard, *Lacerta*.

The greatest contrast between a newt and a lizard, or between Amphibia and Reptilia in general, has to do with the fact that the newt is fundamentally aquatic, especially during the breeding season, while the lizard is completely terrestrial. This change of habit involves a number of fundamental adaptive changes, chief of which are those associated with eggs, mode of fertilization, mode of respiration, water-proof skin, and loss of aquatic adaptations.

THE LAND EGG AND DEVELOPMENT ON DRY LAND

The most striking change from the newt to the lizard condition involves the introduction of the land egg. In the newt, as in most amphibians, the eggs are laid in the water. The male newt deposits small packets of sperm on the bottom and the female nips these off with the lips of the cloaca thus introducing sperms into the oviduct. Eggs are thus fertilized internally, as in reptiles, but without sexual copulation. The eggs of the newt are laid in small groups on the bottom where they hatch out as gilled larvae and subsequently metamorphose into terrestrial adults. The eggs of the lizard, on the other hand, are laid on dry land. Each egg is covered with a protective porous shell, and has a thick layer of albumen around the yolk, which is the egg cell proper. A lizard egg is large and has enough yolk to furnish nutriment to carry the embryo through to an advanced stage, the young, on hatching, being able to take care of itself. During development within the egg the lizard embryo makes for itself out of living membranes derived from tissues adja-

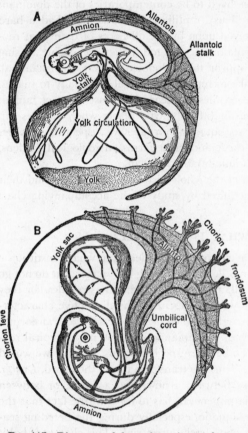

Fig. 117. Diagrams of the embryonic membranes, amnion, allantois, yolk-sac, of amniotes. A. Sauropsida (reptiles and birds). B. Mammal with primitive allantoic placenta. (After Wilder.)

cent to the embryonic body a sort of private aquarium, the **amnion.** Another membrane, derived as an outgrowth of the hind gut, grows out and spreads over nearly the whole inner surface of the shell. This is the **allantois,** derived from the ancestral allantoic bladder. It is highly vascular and functions as an embryonic lung, taking in oxygen that penetrates the porous shell and giving off carbon dioxide. The amnion and allantois are not only universal among reptiles, but have been retained by the birds and mammals. Reptiles, birds, and mammals are commonly called Amniota, while Amphibia are called Anamnia (without an amnion). The yolk-sac, with the vitelline circulation, constitutes a third embryonic membrane. Figure 117 shows the land egg with its various membranes.

THE COPULATORY ORGANS

As in the newt, fertilization of the lizard egg is internal, but in the lizard the sperm is introduced into the oviduct by means of paired evertible copulatory organs. Since the Gymnophiona and at least one type of primitive frog also have simple copulatory organs, this may be a retained ancestral amphibian character and not a new one introduced by reptiles themselves. It is significant, however, that internal fertilization, though common in Amphibia, is not necessary for them, while it is necessary in reptiles, since the egg must be fertilized high up in the oviduct before albumen and shell are added during the descent of the egg toward the cloaca.

RESPIRATORY EQUIPMENT

In the newt the skin is soft, moist, and scaleless. This condition is associated with cutaneous respiration. Though most Amphibia have lungs, much of the respiration in the adult is carried on through the skin. Any respiratory surface exposed to dry air must be kept moist, and in the newt this is done by means of an abundant supply of skin glands. In the aquatic larva of amphibians there are both external and internal gills.

In the lizard, however, skin respiration has been abandoned and lung respiration improved. The skin is covered by horny epidermal scales (corneoscutes) quite different from fish scales, which are dermal osteoscutes. As a result, the body surface of the lizard is dry and water-proof. The skin also has lost most of its glands, only a few local glands remaining that are probably scent glands functioning in mating. At no time during embryonic development are gills formed, for the allantois is adequate to handle embryonic respiration.

As a part of the scaly integument may be mentioned the horny claws (modified corneoscutes) that appear at the ends of the fingers and toes, the equivalent of which as claws, hoofs, and nails are characteristic features of birds and mammals. The scaly integument of the reptile doubtless serves the important function of preventing the loss of water from the body and permits them to live in arid regions in which there is but little water supply.

Lung breathing is rendered more efficient in the lizard through the aid of movable ribs that are so moved by muscles as to enlarge the body cavity, thus expanding the lungs and filling them with air. When the rib muscles relax, the air is expelled. This is an improvement upon the method of breathing in the newt, which consists of merely swallowing air by means of throat muscles. It may also be said that in the lizard the first five pairs of thoracic ribs are attached ventrally to a sternum.

OTHER CHANGES INCIDENT TO TERRESTRIAL LIFE

In the newt there is an elaborate system of lateral-line organs, sense organs adapted to aquatic life. These are all eliminated in the lizard, except that the inner ear apparatus is regarded as a derivative of the lateral line. In connection with the auditory apparatus it may be mentioned that, whereas in some Amphibia the ear drum (tympanic membrane) is exposed on the surface, it is depressed in a shallow pit in the lizard, thus removing this important structure from danger of puncture or other injury from contact with sharp spines or other objects that are commonly encountered in thickets. The internal auditory apparatus in the newt has also become more specialized through the development of a special auditory chamber in the membranous labyrinth, the sacculus, predecessor of the cochlea in mammals.

Heart and Circulatory System. — Advances in the direction of an improved pulmonary circulation are found in the lizard. The ventricle is partly subdivided by a septum into right and left chambers. This aids in keeping freshly oxygenated blood that returns from the lungs into the left half of the ventricle from mixing with used blood returning to the right half from the systemic veins. The separation of "pure" and "impure" blood is further aided by the fact that what was the truncus arteriosus of the newt is in the lizard split down to the heart itself into three separate branches, so that three main arteries pass out separately from the heart. The more ventral of these coming from the right ventricular chamber soon divides into two pulmonary arteries, and the other two leaving the left ventricle are the right and left systemic arches, the left arch coming from the right side of the left ventricle and the right from the left side. The two systemic arches, as in the newt, meet above to form the single dorsal aorta. Thus the pulmonary circulation is almost distinct from the systemic. The left systemic arch, however, still receives mixed blood, leaving room for further improvement. The veins and arteries of the lizard are not very different from those of the newt. The cutaneous vein associated with skin respiration in the newt is, however, absent in the lizard, which has no cutaneous but only lung respiration. The renal portal system of the newt is much reduced in the lizard in connection with the change from mesonephric to metanephric kidneys.

Urogenital System. — As just said, the kidneys of the lizard, as of all amniote vertebrates, are posterior kidneys, *metanephroi*, in contrast with the mesonephroi, or mid-kidneys, of the newt and other lower vertebrates. The metanephroi of the lizard empty into the urinary bladder by paired ureters, new ducts that function solely as urinary ducts. The ancestral mesonephros and the ducts associated with it still persist in the lizard as functional organs, but their function has changed in that they are purely reproductive. Their excretory function is entirely lost.

In the adult female lizard the mesonephros disappears altogether along with the Wolffian duct, but the Müllerian ducts remain and serve as the paired oviducts leading to the cloaca. In these oviducts are special glands that secrete albumen and shells for the eggs. In adult male lizards the Müllerian duct is absent or vestigial, but the Wolffian duct persists and acts solely as a vas deferens, carrying sperms to the copulatory organs. The mesonephros itself remains in the males in a modified form, consisting of an important structure, the epididymis, a long glandular tube through which sperms from the testis have to pass to get to the vas deferens. The secretions of the epididymis serve to nourish and to activate the sperms.

Nervous System and Sense Organs. — Associated with much greater activity and complexity of behavior of the lizard, as compared with the newt, we find that the brain is improved. This is particularly true for the cerebral hemispheres, which are considerably larger in the lizard. Particularly noteworthy is the introduction of the first signs of superficial gray matter in the roof of the hemispheres. This constitutes a minute cortex, a prophecy of the neopallium. Two additional pairs of nerves (the 11th and 12th pair), called respectively, the spinal accessory and the hypoglossal, are added to the brain region, and these nerves emerge from the skull. This may be regarded as another forward step in cephalization.

Sense Organs. — A third eyelid, or nictitating membrane, is introduced by the lizard. This is a transparent membrane which moves over the eyeball from the inner to the outer side and serves to protect the eye without shutting out vision. The pineal eye, or third eye, is well developed. Changes in the auditory organ have already been dealt with. The loss of lateral-line organs has also been mentioned.

Skeleton. — The skull of the lizard is more completely ossified than that of the newt. Instead of being solidly roofed over, there is an aperture behind the eye orbit called the temporal fossa, which is associated with the attachment of jaw muscles to the skull. In some reptiles there is no such aperture, in others there are two. The lower jaw articulates with the quadrate bone through the pterygoids and the quadrate articulates with the osseous end of the articulare, which is a part of the ancestral Meckel's cartilage. The lower jaw still includes several pairs of membrane bones: dentaries, angulares, super-angulares, splenials, and coronoids.

The skull articulates with the first vertebra by a single median condyle. The first two vertebrae are specialized in the lizard (and higher vertebrates) into atlas and axis. The axis is hollow in front to receive the condyle. Its centrum is separated from it and attached to the axis (second vertebra) forming a peg, upon which the atlas and skull can rotate, giving free head movement.

The fore-limb skeleton of the lizard, though longer and stronger than in the newt, is otherwise much like that of the latter, but there are five digits on each limb. Many minor skeletal changes have occurred, but these are somewhat too technical for description in this place.

SUMMARY STATEMENT OF THE CHARACTERISTICS OF REPTILIA

In describing the changes necessary to transform a newt into a lizard we have dealt with most of the distinctive characters of reptiles. Let us briefly summarize this situation by listing the characteristics of the class Reptilia:

1. The land egg
   a. Large yolk and yolk-sac.
   b. Shell.
   c. Albumen.
   d. Amnion.
   e. Allantois.
2. Copulatory organs.
3. Epidermal scales, corneoscutes.
4. Claws, modified corneoscutes.
5. Few skin glands.
6. No lateral-line organs.
7. Slightly depressed ear drum.
8. Sacculus well defined.
9. Ventricle of heart partly divided.
10. No truncus arteriosus.
11. Separate pulmonary arteries.
12. Paired systemic arches.
13. Metanephros with ureters.
14. Loss of mesonephros in female, retained as epididymis in male.
15. Müllerian duct retained as oviduct in female, Wolffian duct retained as vas deferens in male.
16. Spinal accessory and hypoglossal nerves (11th and 12th cranial nerves) emerge from the skull.
17. Beginning of cerebral cortex.
18. Breathing effected by rib movements.
19. Auditory apparatus always with a tympanic membrane and with the stapes (columella auris) acting as transmitter.
20. Atlas and axis specialized.
21. Temporal fossa (except cotylosaurs and chelonians).
22. No gills at any time.

CHAPTER XVI

THE FOSSIL PEDIGREE OF THE REPTILES

ORIGIN AND EARLY EVOLUTION OF REPTILES

As has already been said, the first reptiles undoubtedly arose from a primitive amphibian stock belonging to the order Labyrinthodontia. So gradual were the changes involved that some of the transitional forms of fossil vertebrates are difficult to classify as either amphibians or reptiles. Such connecting-link types afford the best possible evidences of the evolution of a higher from a lower group. It is a simple matter to distinguish living reptiles from amphibians by their soft parts, by the land egg and egg membranes, and by numerous skeletal features. Unfortunately, we have no knowledge of the eggs or embryos of primitive reptiles and can only assume that they were like those of modern reptiles. Only a few indications of soft parts are preserved, including muscle scars, shape of brain, and some other features. Hence we have to rely almost entirely on hard parts for distinguishing these early reptiles from amphibians. Modern reptiles can be easily distinguished from Amphibia by several skeletal features, such as the single condyle, five toes on the front feet (four or less in Amphibia), two or more ribs fused with the sacrum (one in Amphibia). Some of the primitive reptiles, however, lack even some of these features. The fact is that some of these so-called primitive reptiles are so similar in skeletal features to some of the labyrinthodont Amphibia that they are still sometimes classed as amphibians. The best opinion, however, favors the view that they are primitive reptiles only a little removed from an ancestral amphibian stock. Some writers evade the difficulty by calling them amphibio-reptiles. We shall designate them Stem Reptiles.

STEM REPTILES (COTYLOSAURIA)

These reptiles, grouped together into the order Cotylosauria, were contemporaneous with numerous primitive amphibians during late Pennsylvanian and early Permian times, but before the end of the

Permian the amphibians had been out-competed and nearly exterminated by the reptiles, and the latter had become dominant. We are interested here mainly in the earliest reptiles.

The best known and most primitive of these is *Seymouria* (Fig. 118, C), a rather small form about two feet in length. Adequate fossil

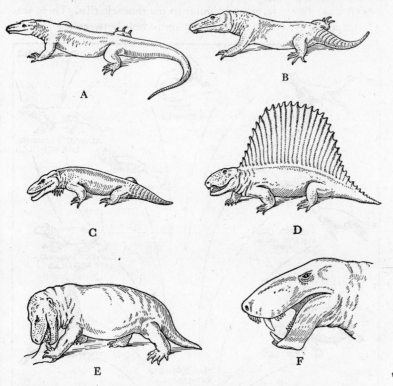

FIG. 118. Group of Palaeozoic Reptilia. A. *Varanops.* B. *Labidosaurus.* C. *Seymouria.* D. *Dimetrodon.* E. *Cynognathus* (a mammal-like reptile). F. Head of *Scymnognathus* (a South-African "dog-toothed" reptile). (Redrawn from Osborn, after Williston and after Gregory.)

remains of this little reptile show that it differed from some Amphibia in only a few particulars. It had but one condyle, five digits on the hand (manus), but had, like Amphibia, only one pair of sacral ribs, whereas nearly all reptiles have at least two. The number of joints in the fingers is also more like that of Amphibia than of reptiles. *Seymouria* may then be regarded as incompletely reptilian.

Like other cotylosaurs, *Seymouria* had short stubby legs that sprawled out laterally in locomotion and thus did not raise the body from the ground. The skull is primitive in being anapsidan (without temporal vacuities), an amphibian condition. They were probably carnivores as judged by the long, sharp teeth. There was no true neck, the head being united broadly to the trunk. The prethoracic, or cervical ribs are large and similar to the thoracic ribs. There was a large pineal eye which emerged through a hole between the parietal

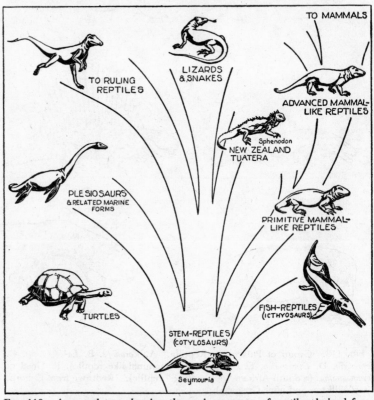

FIG. 119. Ancestral tree showing the various groups of reptiles derived from the stem reptiles. (From Romer, courtesy University of Chicago Press.)

bones. In many other features, interesting chiefly to specialists, *Seymouria* has proved itself to be the most primitive reptile yet discovered. From some such form as *Seymouria* have come all higher vertebrates. The various lines of descent from the primitive reptiles are indicated in figure 119.

During the Permian Period the Stem Reptiles underwent a considerable radiation, some types becoming peculiarly specialized. Among the more specialized members of the group may be mentioned the Diadectomorpha. *Diadectes* was a large form about 5 feet in length, with trunk and limbs like those of *Seymouria*, but with skull and teeth more typically reptilian. Noteworthy is the fact that the back teeth were short and blunt and evidently used for crushing. The captorhinomorphs were another suborder of the cotylosaurs that also showed considerable tooth specialization and a more advanced type of skull. Such forms as these are surely reptiles, though decidedly primitive.

Among surviving reptiles the turtles (Order Chelonia), in spite of their highly specialized armor complex, are more like the cotylosaurs than are any other recent forms. They are anapsid forms, with no temporal vacuities, and have the same sprawling position of limbs as had the most primitive reptiles. A Permian reptile, *Eunotosaurus*, with many chelonian characters and a contemporary of the cotylosaurs, was probably ancestral to the true turtles. This matter will be more fully discussed in the section on Chelonia.

MAMMAL-LIKE REPTILES

Perhaps the most remarkable achievement of the Palaeozoic reptilian stocks was the rise and early evolution of a large and varied group of forms showing many sorts of trends toward mammalian conditions. These reptiles belong to the subclass Synapsida, with a single temporal vacuity. They belong to two orders: Pelycosauria (Fig. 118, A, D), in which only slight progress toward mammalian conditions had been made, and Therapsida (Fig. 118, E, F), which are the true mammal-like reptiles, from some of which mammals seem undoubtedly to have arisen. In view of this fact it seems well to postpone any further discussion of this group until we come to deal with the origin of mammals. In this place we need merely call attention once more to the principle that radically new evolutionary departures, involving the origin of a higher from a lower group, come off not from later, specialized members of the lower group, but from near the base of the lower group. Some of the mammal-like reptiles are nearly as old as the earliest known reptiles.

THE GOLDEN AGE OF REPTILES (MESOZOIC REPTILES)

While the reptiles made a good start during the Palaeozoic and underwent considerable diversification, they did not really come into their own until the Mesozoic Age, the Golden Age of Reptiles. During this long era, lasting about 100,000,000 years, there evolved

FIG. 120. Group of Mesozoic Reptilia. A. Long-necked plesiosaur, *Elasmosaurus*. B. Short-necked plesiosaur, *Trinacromerion*. C. Ichthyosaur, *Baptanodon*. D. Pterodactyl. E. "Ostrich" dinosaur, *Struthiomimus*. F. Carnivorous dinosaur, *Tyrannosaurus*. G. Giant herbivorous dinosaur, *Brachiosaurus*. H. Hooded "duck-bill" dinosaur, *Corythosaurus*. (Redrawn after Osborn.)

many remarkable and spectacular forms and a number of less striking groups. In this place we shall discuss only a few of the more conspicuous types: ichthyosaurs, plesiosaurs, pterosaurs, and dinosaurs.

ICHTHYOSAURS

These rather moderate-sized reptiles represent the extreme of secondary adaptation to aquatic life among reptiles. As the name of the order indicates, they are "fish reptiles." The shape of the body, the fin-like limbs, and the dorsal and caudal fins (Fig. 120, C) are superficially extremely fish-like. It is suspected that they were efficient fish hunters and that they played a similar role in their time to that of dolphins and porpoises today. Resemblances to fishes, however, are only skin-deep, so to speak, for internally they are all reptile (Fig. 121). No doubt the chief locomotor organ was the large caudal fin, which seems not to have been supported by bony rays.

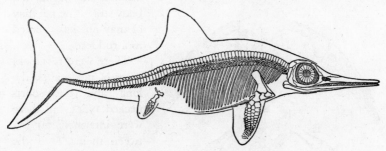

Fig. 121. A Jurassic ichthyosaur. (From Romer, after Strome.)

The paddle-like paired fins are extremely modified and doubtless act as balancing and steering devices. The long beak, armed with very numerous sharp teeth, the greatly enlarged eyes with sclerotic plates like those in birds, and the external nares far back and on top of the head, are all distinctive of the group.

The paired limbs, and indeed the whole body, are so essentially aquatic that one wonders how they could come ashore to dig nests and lay eggs. This was a mystery for some time, but when fossil females were found with fossil young in the body cavity, it became clear that these "fish reptiles" did not lay their eggs at all but kept them in the oviducts till the embryos reached an advanced stage of development, and then gave birth to them alive. They were, therefore, viviparous. The ichthyosaurs first appear in the Triassic, reached their climax in the Jurassic, were rarer in the Cretaceous, and became extinct before the end of the Upper Cretaceous. There is no satisfactory explanation of their extinction.

PLESIOSAURS

The second of the aquatic types of specialized reptilian orders were the Plesiosauria, sometimes called "swan dragons." In contrast with the ichthyosaurs, which swam like fishes by lateral undulations of the body and a tail paddle, these forms swam after the fashion of sea turtles, using the paired limbs as oars, and keeping the broad, flat body stiff. The tail may or may not have served as a rudder.

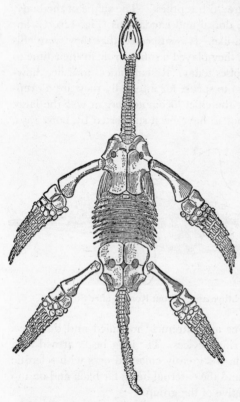

There were two main types of plesiosaurs, the long and the short-necked types, but there were intermediates between them. It is the long-necked types that have been called "swan dragons" (Fig. 120, A). In some of them the neck was nearly as long as the rest of the body, having as many as 76 vertebrae. These creatures sometimes attained a length of 50 feet. The head with its tiny brain was ridiculously small for such a large animal and could evidently be made by the long neck to strike out like that of a snake. Some one has described these curious reptiles as like a "snake strung through the body of a turtle." The paddles, while somewhat less specialized than those of the ichthyosaurs, were large and strong. These "swan dragons" are believed to have been surface swimmers that cruised about, darting the head down into

FIG. 122. Skeleton of a relatively short-necked Jurassic plesiosaur, *Thaumatosaurus*, to show anatomy of legs and limb girdles. (From Romer, after Williston.)

the water after fish or possibly up into the air after flying reptiles or even primitive birds.

The short-necked forms (Figs. 120, B, and 122) had even more powerful paddles than the long-necked types and may have chased their fish prey under water, depending upon sheer speed to overtake them.

RULING REPTILES (SUBCLASS ARCHOSAURIA)

This great subclass includes the orders Thecodontia, Crocodilia, Pterosauria, Saurischia, and Ornithischia. They are all diapsids,

Fig. 123. Restoration of *Ornithosuchus*, a primitive ruling reptile of the order Thecodontia. From some such type all the higher orders of ruling reptiles, as well as birds, are believed to have been derived. (From Heilmann, *The Origin of Birds*, by permission of D. Appleton-Century Co.)

with two temporal vacuities. Perhaps the most conspicuous feature of the archosaurs was their tendency to adopt the bipedal mode of locomotion. Other land reptiles merely improved upon the primitive four-footed mode of walking, but the archosaurs got up on their hind legs and ran. Some of them, having originally acquired the bipedal gait, reverted to the quadrupedal posture, while others developed powers of flight. The more or less erect bipedal posture carried with it many adaptive changes in the structure of the hip, leg and arm bones, which will be especially dealt with in connection with the dinosaurs.

The thecodonts (Fig. 123) were the most primitive of the archosaurs and are regarded as the ancestral stock from which the higher

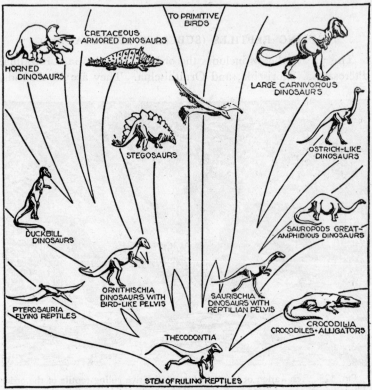

FIG. 124. Ancestral tree of the ruling reptiles and their descendants, the birds. (From Romer, courtesy University of Chicago Press.)

archosaurs were derived. These early archosaurs were rather small forms not unlike modern lizards, but were bipedal and diapsid. They seem to have been swift-running little carnivores, with long, sharp, socketed teeth. Their whole organization is in harmony with the view that they were the common ancestors of pterosaurs, dinosaurs, crocodiles, and birds. Figure 124 shows the various descendant lines derived from the primitive thecodonts.

FLYING REPTILES (PTEROSAURIA)

While not bipedal forms after they had attained the power of soaring in the air, the pterosaurs, or "flying dragons" as they are sometimes called, are believed to have attained their wings as a secondary result of bipedality. Running on only the hind legs is thought to have freed the arms for other functions, and the arms became specialized as wings.

These wings (Fig. 125) differ strikingly from all other types of vertebrate wings in that they were mainly "little-finger" wings. The fifth digit, or little finger, became extremely long and strong and served to stretch out a skin plane of great length but rather narrow. The thumb and the other three fingers were small and armed with claws. Possibly they were used for climbing up cliffs from which to secure a good take-off for soaring flight. The fact that all the fossil remains of pterosaurs are found in marine rocks makes it seem unlikely that they were inhabitants of inland regions. It seems improbable that the ptero-

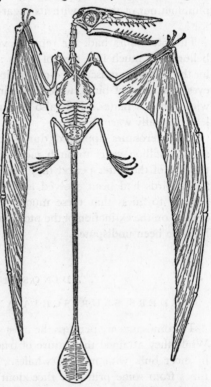

Fig. 125. Skeleton and wing membranes of *Rhamphorhynchus*, a long-tailed Jurassic pterosaur. (From Williston.)

saurs were able to use the wing very effectively for propulsion in the air, for there is no indication of any powerful wing musculature. It is more reasonable to think of them as launching themselves from cliffs or trees near the water and soaring over the water searching for fish, then diving in like a tern. The pterosaurs, for the most part, were of moderate proportions with a size range approximating that of birds, though a few were larger than any flying birds.

Rhamphorhynchus (Fig. 125), a long-tailed Jurassic type, is fairly typical, but others specialized in a number of other directions. *Pteranodon* (Fig. 120, D) is one of the most specialized forms, being a giant type with a wing spread of about 27 feet. Its enormous head, with great toothless beak and long bony crest on the back, looks like a wicked weapon. Imagine this creature dropping like a plummet out of the sky with its spear-like beak aimed at a luckless fish!

The pterosaurs had, for reptiles, very large brains. The cerebellum was much like that of birds and doubtless was the center for the elaborate muscular co-ordinations associated with flight. The eyes, like those of birds, were exceedingly large and were provided with sclerotic plates. It is also not improbable that they were at least partially warm-blooded.

The pterosaurs appeared during the Jurassic, had a reign of several million years through most of the Cretaceous, but toward the end of the latter period they became extinct. By this time the flying birds had been evolved and had become numerous. It is natural to guess that these much better fliers had a marked influence on the extinction of the pterosaurs, whose reign in the air had hitherto been undisputed.

DINOSAURS

(ORDERS SAURISCHIA AND ORNITHISCHIA)

The dinosaurs are perhaps the most spectacular of extinct animals. While they attained the stature of true giants they hardly compare in sheer bulk with modern whales. They arose in early Triassic times from some primitive thecodont stock, steadily progressed in size and specialization throughout practically the whole Mesozoic, and became extinct at the close of the Cretaceous. During this long period they were lords of the terrestrial world. The dinosaurs were not all giants. Some of them were hardly larger than large lizards. They were also not all members of a single order, but belong to two great assemblages, the orders Saurischia (reptile-like dinosaurs) and Ornithischia (bird-like dinosaurs), which differ sharply from each other in a number of ways. The key character that distinguishes the two orders concerns the pelvis. The Saurischia had a pelvis much like that of the ancestral thecodonts, described as

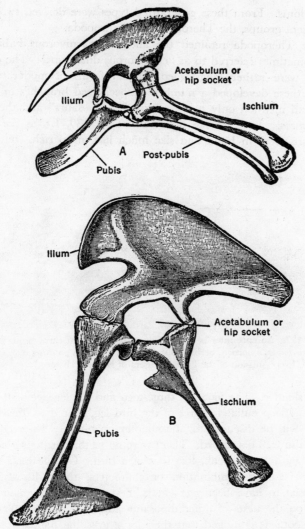

FIG. 126. A. Tetraradiate pelvic girdle of bird-like dinosaur. B. Triradiate pelvic girdle of reptile-like dinosaur. (From Lull.)

triradiate (Fig. 126, B) with three prongs. The Ornithischia had a tetraradiate pelvis (Fig. 126, A) much like that of birds. We shall trace the evolution of the two dinosaur orders separately.

Reptile-like Dinosaurs (Order Saurischia). — The early saurischians were small bipedal carnivores quite similar to the ancestral thecodonts. From these generalized types were derived two main divergent groups, the Theropoda and Sauropoda.

The Theropoda retained the ancestral carnivorous habit and are sometimes referred to as "carnivorous dinosaurs." The earlier forms were rather long-legged bipedal forms of moderate size. From these developed a number of specialized branches of which we shall mention only two, the "ostrich dinosaurs" and the great carnivores. The "ostrich dinosaurs" (Fig. 120, E), as the name suggests, were in build and size much like an ostrich, but were

Fig. 127. An encounter between *Tyrannosaurus*, a giant carnivorous dinosaur and *Triceratops*, a horned, herbivorous dinosaur. (From a painting by Charles R. Knight, by permission of the Field Museum of Natural History.)

more slender. The foot was three-toed and the leg decidedly bird-like. (The peculiar features of the bird leg, shared by these dinosaurs, will be discussed in the chapter on birds.) The fore limbs were also well developed. There were no teeth, but their place was taken by a horny beak, like that of a bird. On the basis of this rather peculiar combination of characters, these dinosaurs are supposed to have been egg eaters, nest robbers, that made swift raids on the nests of other dinosaurs and sped swiftly away with their loot. It is judged that their large grasping hands were used to carry the eggs and their sharp beaks for tearing off the tough egg shells. The specialized carnivorous dinosaurs appeared first in the Upper Triassic. They became progressively larger and more powerful and culminated during the Cretaceous in giant forms such as *Tyrannosaurus* and *Dinodon*. *Tyrannosaurus* (Figs. 120, F and 127), the "tyrant dinosaur," was the most formidable animate engine of destruction that ever lived. It roamed the plains of western North

America. Even though massive and heavily built, it reached a length of 47 feet and was nearly 20 feet high in walking position. The hind legs were tree-like in size and adapted for running. The feet were like those of a mammoth bird, with three powerful toes, each armed with a massive curved claw. The head was about four feet long and rather broad. The large jaws were armed with numerous flattened saw-edged, dagger-like teeth varying in length from 3 to 6 inches. This great beast is pictured as holding down its prey with its feet and tearing it to shreds with its teeth. The front legs were almost vestigial, being too short to reach the mouth and too feeble to be of much help in grasping or holding the prey. The digits of the hand were reduced to three as in birds. One wonders what kind of predaceous opportunity would justify such a tremendous attacking equipment as that just described. It seems that the only contemporaneous forms that would give such an armament a workout were the horned dinosaurs, triceratopsians, soon to be described (Fig. 127).

FIG. 128. *Brontosaurus*. (From Lull.)

Another and quite different branch of the Saurischia were the Sauropoda, which started out as small bipedal forms but subsequently, as they became large and massive, came down on all fours again and thus secondarily became quadrupeds. In almost all of them, however, the hind legs remained disproportionately long, giving them a curious high-hipped and low-shouldered appearance. Some of the later forms attained a size unparalleled by any four-footed animals past or present. Among the better known genera are *Brontosaurus* (Fig. 128) and *Brachiosaurus* (Fig. 120, G). *Brontosaurus* reached a length of about 70 feet and had comparatively small fore legs, while *Brachiosaurus* though a little shorter was even more massive, and the size of the fore legs had secondarily increased so as to more than equal that of the hind legs. With the head raised *Brachiosaurus* could have looked over the roof of a three-story building. The sauropods, judging by their teeth had become herbivorous. Such massive creatures could not conceivably have been swift of foot and therefore could not have been predaceous. The head of a giant sauropod was very small for so large an animal. The brain was hardly larger than that of a cat. There is much discussion about the habitat of the giant sauropods. The weight of the largest of them was not far short of 50 tons and it seems improbable that such heavy creatures could have supported themselves on land. The backbone, in particular, was extremely massive but the vertebrae

Fig. 129. Restoration of *Iguanodon*. (From Lull, after Heilmann.)

were much hollowed out on the sides and these hollows may have been filled with air-sacs, as in birds. This would lessen the weight but might have detracted from the strength of the bridge between the fore and hind limbs. These and other considerations have led some writers to believe that these great reptiles were swamp dwellers, living largely in rather deep water, for they could stand or walk on the bottom and still reach the surface, to breathe. It occurs to us that such a habitat might also have been of great advantage as a protection from the attacks of carnivorous enemies, for the latter were probably not good swimmers. These unwieldy giants were apparently adapted to a rather narrow range of habitats. While relatively numerous during Triassic times, they became progressively rare and finally extinct during the Cretaceous Period. The suggested reason for this extinction is that the continental masses had already begun to be elevated and the marshlands to disappear. With the on-coming drying up of swamps and inland streams, and increasingly cold climate, these great cold-blooded amphibious reptiles had to go.

Bird-like Dinosaurs (Order Ornithischia). — Four suborders of Ornithischia are recognized: Ornithopoda, Stegosauria, Anklyosauria, and Ceratopsia. The ornithopods were doubtless descended from some primitive thecodont stock, but there are no good transitional forms. They were the most primitive of the bird-like dinosaurs and had the typical tetraradiate pelvis. While they were

FIG. 130. Restoration of the armored dinosaur, *Stegosaurus*. (From Lull, after Schuchert.)

bipedal, they did not develop such long legs as did the early saurischians and the fore legs were not so much reduced, being two-thirds as large as the hind legs. The best known of the ornithopods are *Camptosaurus* and *Iguanodon*. *Iguanodon* (Fig. 129) was fairly large and heavy, about 15 feet in length, and is represented in the figure as a good runner. It is peculiar in having the thumb formed like a sharp dagger that may well have been a good defensive weapon. Since all the ornithischians appear to have been herbivorous the thumb dagger could hardly have been used for attack.

Among the most abundant of the Ornithischia were the duck-billed dinosaurs (Fig. 120, H) which reached their height during Cretaceous times. The bill was broad and flat and there was sometimes a prominent crest on top of the head. They are believed to have been amphibious.

The extraordinary stegosaurians (Fig. 130) were characterized by a very unique armature of heavy plates and spines. The two rows of enormous dorsal plates could probably have been flattened out horizontally across the back and rump in such a way as to form an almost complete roof. On the powerful tail were two or more pairs of foot-long spines that doubtless made the tail a powerful weapon of defense. The animals were about as large as elephants, but the head was extremely reduced. Brain casts indicate that the brain was hardly larger than the terminal joint of one's finger. At the base of the tail, however, there was a tremendous enlargement of the spinal cord which was doubtless the real "brain" of the animal. One pictures this creature as a rear-end fighter. When attacked it would pull in its head and turn its rear end to the enemy, with roof plates extended and spiky tail lashing vigorously about. *Stegosaurus* has sometimes been cited as the last word in racial senescence. Certainly it is difficult to imagine a less effective animal.

The Ankylosaurs, a very different type of armed dinosaurs, seem to have taken the place of the stegosaurs during the Cretaceous. They have been called "reptilian tanks" on account of the completeness of their armament (see middle of top row of figure 124). Next to turtles they were the most completely fortified of reptiles.

The Ceratopsia, or horned dinosaurs (Figs. 127 and 131), already mentioned as probably justifying the attacking equipment of the great carnivorous dinosaurs, are known only from the Upper Cretaceous. They constituted one of the end products of dinosaurian evolution. The most striking feature of these reptiles was the enormous head and its great bony collar-frill. This heavy frill extended sideways and backward, forming a shield over the shoulders and protecting the animal almost completely from frontal attack. In addition, the head was armed with enormous horns over the eyes and sometimes a smaller nose horn. The front part of the jaws constituted a short hooked beak which displaced the front teeth. The molar teeth were broad and flat, indicating a herbivorous diet.

The horned dinosaurs were animals of moderate size, not truly giants. The largest were only a trifle larger than a rhinoceros, which they somewhat resembled. They were very numerous during late Cretaceous times, but faded rapidly from the picture toward the end of that period. Whether they were exterminated by the great carnivorous dinosaurs or were unable to adjust themselves to the changing geologic conditions no one can say. Along with all the other great dinosaurian stocks that survived to near the end of the Mesozoic, they vanished as living creatures, but have left abundant fossils, not only of adults and young but of eggs and unhatched embryos.

Many other kinds of reptiles lived during the Mesozoic, but they were less interesting than those mentioned. It is of course obvious that the ancestors of all surviving Cenozoic orders must have existed

FIG. 131. Restoration of the horned dinosaur, *Triceratops*. (From Lull, after Schuchert.)

during the Mesozoic. There are good fossil pedigrees of turtles, crocodiles, rhynchocephalians, lizards, and snakes, but these all played relatively modest roles as compared to those played by the Ruling Reptiles. Perhaps their relative inconspicuousness or their lack of marked specialization gave them an advantage in surviving through the vicissitudes that ushered in the Cenozoic Age.

CHAPTER XVII

MODERN REPTILIAN ORDERS

INTRODUCTORY STATEMENT

In this chapter we shall deal with the four orders of reptiles that comprise the surviving remnant of the vast assemblage of reptiles that dominated the animal world during the Mesozoic Age. These four orders are: Chelonia, Rhynchocephalia, Crocodilia, and Squamata. They will be considered in some detail in the order named. In dealing with these living reptilian groups a good deal of attention will be paid to taxonomic aspects, especially in those groups that exhibit a wide variety of diverse types. In the accounts of these sub-orders and families matters of natural history will predominate over anatomical peculiarities and some groups will be so described as to illustrate the phenomenon of adaptive radiation.

The only order which will be given any extensive anatomical treatment is the Chelonia. The reason for going into some detail with respect to the anatomy of Chelonia is that the turtle is, perhaps, much the commonest reptilian type used in courses in comparative anatomy. The turtle is chosen not because it is the most representative reptilian type, but because it is the most available and most convenient form in most parts of the United States. Lizards or alligators would be better in many ways, but the former are usually too small and difficult to procure and the latter are too expensive.

In dealing with the anatomy of the turtle a good deal of attention will be given to the skeleton, especially to the peculiar armature so characteristic of the order. The internal anatomy is, in general, similar to that of the lizard, which has already been sufficiently described in Chapter XV. Before beginning the account of the anatomy of the turtle, however, it should be emphasized that the Chelonia are in many respects the most primitive of surviving reptiles and exhibit some of the characters of the Palaeozoic stem reptiles. These resemblances will be pointed out in the appropriate places.

262

ORDER CHELONIA

THE ANATOMY OF A TURTLE

External Characters

The turtle is a reptile in a box. This box, whether it forms a complete or only a partial housing for the body, head, limbs, and tail, has a dome-shaped roof, called the carapace and a flat floor called a plastron. Paired lateral pillars join the floor to the roof. The house is open broadly in front and behind in order to allow the head, legs, and tail to emerge, but these appendages can all be withdrawn within the shelter of the eaves, and in some cases the front and rear sections of the floor (plastron) are hinged in such a way that they

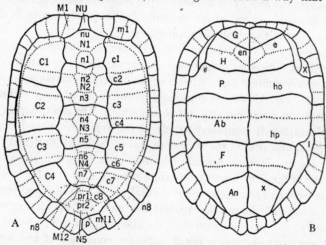

Fig. 132. A. Carapace. B. Plastron of tortoise, *Graptemys*. Capital letters refer to chitinous scales or scutes, small letters to bony plates whether cartilaginous or dermal. Ab, abdominal scute; An, anal scute; C1–4, costal scutes; c1–8, costal plates; e, epiplastral plate; en, endoplastral plate; F, femoral scute; G, gular scute; H, humeral scute; ho, hyoplastral plate; hp, hypoplastral plate; I, inguinal scute; M, marginal scutes; m, marginal plates; N1–5, neural scutes; n1–8, neural plates; NU, nuchal scute; pr1–2, procaudal plates; X, axillary scute; x, xiphiplastral plate. (From Newman.)

can bend upward and completely close the house after the appendages have been drawn in. The head is of moderate size and somewhat flat; the neck is characteristically long and flexible and capable of being folded up when the head is withdrawn; the mouth is large and toothless, but is provided with a sharp-edged, horny beak.

The external nares (nostrils) are close together near the end of the snout, sometimes protruding into a regular proboscis. The eyes are situated laterally and have three eyelids: a short opaque upper lid, a longer lower lid which makes the turtle shut its eye upwards instead of downwards as a man does, and a third eyelid, or transparent nictitating membrane, which may be drawn across the eye from the inner corner. The tympanic membrane is quite similar to that of the frog, is at the surface, and just back of the gape of the jaws. The feet are pentadactyl and each digit is usually armed with a claw. As a rule the feet are webbed as in aquatic amphibia and birds. The skin of the head is usually smooth and scaleless, as is also the neck in most species; but the rest of the body is usually covered with scales, except the base of the legs. The tail is as a rule poorly developed, but in the more primitive types, as for example the snapping turtles, it may retain its primitive reptilian proportions.

The carapace and plastron (Fig. 132) are, in most of our modern chelonians, somewhat stereotyped structures: they have settled down upon a very definite arrangement of the principal components. The carapace (Fig. 132, A) is composed of two kinds of bony elements (dermal and cartilaginous) and corneoscutes. The main part of the bony carapace is composed largely of the much broadened tips of the spinal processes of the vertebrae and of the much flattened ribs; there are usually eight neural plates and eight pairs of costal plates. In front of the first neural is a dermal plate, the nuchal; back of the eighth neurals are usually three dermal plates, the first and second procaudals and the pygal. Around the margin of the carapace are usually eleven pairs of dermal plates, the marginals. Overlying the bony carapace there is a horny carapace composed of five neural corneoscutes, four pairs of costals, a small anteriorly placed nuchal, and twelve pairs of marginals. This elaborate composition prevails in nearly all of our modern turtles as well as in many species long extinct.

The plastron (Fig. 132, B), like the carapace, is also composed of two kinds of bony plates covered with horny scutes. The bony elements consist of four pairs of plates: the epi-, hyo-, hypo-, and xiphi-plastrals. The epiplastrals are the modified clavicles, the hypoplastrals and xiphiplastrals are broadened abdominal ribs (gastralia), the hyoplastrals appear to be dermal elements without homologues. A small median dermal element between the epiplastrals and hyoplastrals is called the endoplastral. There are usually six pairs of corneoscutes that break the joints of the bony plastron. The pillars between the carapace and plastron are derived from the hyoplastrals and hypoplastrals.

The conventionalized pattern of bones and scutes in the armature has evidently been arrived at after a long period of evolution. Many evidences indicate that the ancestral condition was much more plastic and variable and that there were originally many more plates and scutes than at present. By dropping out some of the longitudinal and transverse rows of elements the whole system has been greatly simplified. Most species of turtles today show a certain percentage of individuals with supernumerary scutes and plates, that are regarded as vestiges of ancestral rows of elements, now typically lost.

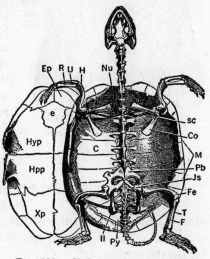

Internal Skeleton

The vertebrae in the trunk region are rigidly united to the narrowed bases of the paddle-like ribs (Fig. 133). They are not very numerous: 8 cervical, 10 thoracic, 2 sacral, and a variable number of caudal vertebrae, which are procoelous in form.

FIG. 133. Skeleton of tortoise, *Cistudo lutaria*, seen from the ventral side with plastron removed and placed to one side. C, costal plate; Co, coracoid; e, endoplastron; Ep, epiplastron (clavicle); F, fibula; Fe, femur; H, humerus; Hyp, hyoplastron; Hpp, hypoplastron; Il, ilium; Js, ischium; M, marginal plates; Nu, nuchal plates; Pb, pubis; Py, pygal plates; R, radius; sc, scapula; T, tibia; U, ulna; Xp, xiphiplastron. (From Parker and Haswell, after Zittel.)

The pectoral girdle consists of a triradiate group of flattened bones: the scapula, the procoracoid, and the coracoid, the last being the largest. Together they unite to form the socket which receives the head of the humerus. The pelvic arch is more compact and is composed of the pubis, ischium, and ilium, uniting to form the acetabulum for the head of the femur.

The skull is highly specialized in some ways, but primitive in others. Perhaps the most primitive feature is the solidly roofed

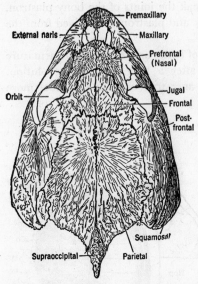

FIG. 134. Dorsal view of the skull of a turtle. (From Messer.)

brain-case, the anapsid condition. A number of typically reptilian bones have been lost, including tabulars, temporals, postfrontals, lacrimals, and sometimes nasals. The pterygoids send inwards wings of bone, that, with the aid of the palatines, form a continuous roof to the mouth resembling the hard palate of mammals; the supraoccipital is prolonged backwards into a large narrow process upon which are inserted the heavy neck muscles. All of these bones, even the quadrate, are firmly united into a solid cranium. Further details of the skull are shown in the figure (Fig. 134). The jaws are devoid of teeth, and maxillary, premaxillary, and dentary bones are covered with hard chitinous sheaths, that form the upper and lower members of the cutting beak.

CLASSIFICATION AND NATURAL HISTORY OF CHELONIA

The members of this order are so uniquely modified that there is no difficulty in recognizing them and in distinguishing them from all other living creatures. Their short, broad body, covered by the characteristic carapace and plastron, the anapsid skull, and the horny, toothless jaws, constitute their outstanding characteristics.

They occupy a very wide range of habitat zones without displaying any very radical departures from the typical chelonian form and proportions. They range from the pure marine types, which come on land only for the purpose of laying their eggs in the sand; through a whole series of amphibious forms, living in ponds and spending a considerable part of the time on land; culminating in the giant purely terrestrial forms that are found on several groups of oceanic islands. Their adaptive radiation does not include arboreal, cursorial, or volant types, for the reason that the shape and weight of the armature does not readily lend itself to these modes of life.

Ancestry of the Turtles. — The origin of the turtles is still something of a mystery. No light is thrown upon their prechelonian ancestry through a study of fossil turtles, for even the earliest Triassic turtles were already fully chelonian, though a little more primitive in some features than modern forms. It long ago became obvious that the turtle family tree ran back to Permian times and that they must have been derived from some stock close to the base of the reptilian trunk. The only light on this problem is furnished by a small reptile, *Eunotosaurus*, of which only an incomplete skeleton is preserved, from the Middle Permian of South Africa. The roof of the skull is missing, so we can not tell whether or not it was an anapsid. Teeth were still present and the limbs were primitive. The main resemblance to the turtle is in the ribs, which are eight in number, broad and flat like those of the turtle. The trunk was also very short and broad, in general form much like that of a turtle. There were apparently no dermal plates in the carapace. In this respect it differs sharply from turtles, but it seems probable that the dermal plates were a later acquisition.

Modern chelonians are divided into three suborders: Pleurodira (side-neck turtles), Cryptodira (in which the neck is drawn straight back into the shell), and Trionychoidea (the soft-shelled turtles).

Suborder Pleurodira

The side-necked turtles are regarded as relatively primitive. The present forms are little changed from Mesozoic types. They are confined to the three southern continents and illustrate a general principle that the more primitive members of terrestrial groups are usually found in southern regions of the world.

The Pleurodira play the same role in the southern hemisphere that is played by the Testudinidae of the Cryptodira in the northern regions. They are less diversified, however, than the northern tortoises in that they are all aquatic. They differ from our tortoises mainly in that the neck, instead of being withdrawn within the carapace between the shoulders as in the Cryptodira, is bent laterally and tucked under the edge of the shell on one side. The pelvic girdle, unlike that of our tortoises, is fused to the carapace and the plastron.

The genus *Chelodina* will serve as an example of these southern tortoises. The carapace is much like that of *Chrysemys*, but the plastron has a novel feature in the form of a small median scute, the interplastral, which is believed to be a vestige of an ancestral row of scutes that has been lost by most turtles. They are good swimmers and feed exclusively upon aquatic animals such as frogs and water insects. The long neck undulates from side to side like that of a snake. When basking they tuck the head away under the shell in the manner described. There seems to be no striking difference between these tortoises and our own with respect to breeding and nest-making habits. The snake-necked turtle, *Hydromedusa maximiliani* (Fig. 136, A) is another familiar example of this suborder.

Suborder Cryptodira

The Cryptodira are almost entirely turtles of the northern hemisphere and are more progressive, more specialized, more numerous, and more successful than are the Pleurodira. They have lost the mesoplastral plate and the pelvic girdle is never attached to the carapace. The head is withdrawn between the shoulders, the neck being bent in S-shaped fashion. Some seven families are distinguished.

Family 1. Dermochelidae. — This family is represented by but one genus, *Dermochelys*, the leather-back turtle (Fig. 135, A). Until recently this type was regarded as so different from all other turtles that it was placed in a separate suborder, Athecae, which implies that it lacks the carapace and plastron. This condition is, however, now regarded as secondary and as merely an example of a general tendency for purely aquatic turtles to reduce or lose the armature. Instead of the usual closely knit carapace and plastron it has twelve longitudinal rows of dermal plates (5 dorsal, 5 ventral, and 2 lateral). The homologues of these can be recognized in the scute rows of some of the other types. The limbs are large, flipper-like paddles of a highly specialized aquatic type. The tail is rudimentary. *Dermochelys* has a wide distribution, ranging over all of the intertropical seas, but is nowhere abundant. It is carnivorous, feeding chiefly on mollusks, fishes, and crustaceans. One of the most peculiar facts about this species is that only large specimens and "babies" have ever been found. Where they pass the many years of their youth and early maturity is a mystery. Possibly there is in some obscure corner of the world an undiscovered *Dermochelys* rookery.

Family 2. Chelydridae (Snapping Turtles). — The common snapper (*Chelydra serpentina*) and the alligator snapper (*Macrochelys temmincki*), both North American species, are the only living representatives of this primitive family. The common snapper (Fig. 135, C) is our most generalized modern turtle. Its head, body, and tail are rather evenly balanced, and the limbs are proportionally heavy

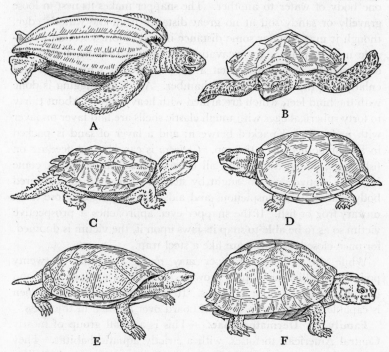

Fig. 135. Group of Chelonia, I. A. Leather-back turtle, *Dermochelys* (*Sphargis*) *coriacea*. B. Hawksbill turtle, *Chelone imbricata*. C. *Chelydra serpentina* (snapping turtle). D. Pennsylvania mud turtle, *Cinosternum pennsylvanicum*. E. European pond-tortoise, *Emys orbicularis*. F. Carolina box tortoise, *Cistudo* (*Terrapene*) *carolina*. (Redrawn after Lydekker.)

and typically reptilian. There is also less complete boxing in of the movable parts than in most other species. In the tail of *Chelydra* are found not only the rows of plates and scutes that are homologous with those in the armature, but at least five rows that have disappeared from or are merely vestigial in the latter. Hence the ancestral condition of the armature is probably more nearly duplicated in the basal portion of the tail of *Chelydra* than anywhere else.

The snapper is a slow and clumsy creature, exceedingly sullen and ill-tempered in captivity, When irritated it snaps blindly with widely open mouth, and seizes indiscriminately any object within reach. It is decidedly aquatic in habit and is not fond of basking in the open. More often it is found in shallow, warm pools partly buried in the mud. At times it goes on cross-country journeys from one body of water to another. The snapper makes its nest in loose gravelly or sandy soil at no great distance from the water's edge, though it may wander some distance inland before selecting a suit-able nesting place. In excavating the nest a shallow, funnel-like depression is first made; then a crude tunnel is scraped out and enlarged at the bottom into a chamber. All of the digging is done with the hind feet, which are armed with heavy claws. About thirty to forty spherical eggs with tough elastic shells are laid layer on layer with pads of sand packed between; and a layer of sand is packed in and smoothed over the top. *Chelydra* is carnivorous, feeding on fish, frogs, young ducks, and all other aquatic animals that come its way. Active prey is caught by stealth. The dull, mud-colored body renders it inconspicuous and aids it in slipping up close to an unwary frog or fish. If the snapper ever approaches a prospective victim so as to be able to snap its jaws upon it, the victim is doomed, for once closed, the jaws are like a steel trap.

While the ordinary snapper may reach a weight of twenty pounds, the alligator snapper grows to twice that weight or more and is proportionately more ferocious. It is said that a large specimen is capable of biting off a piece of board over an inch in thickness.

Family 3.   Dermatemydae. — This is a small group of mostly Central American tortoises, with a strictly aquatic habitat. They are primitive in having a row of scutes between the marginals and plastrals, called inframarginals. This row is represented by the merest vestiges in other families of Chelonia.

Family 4.   Cinosternidae (Skunk or Musk Turtles). — This is another group that is primarily aquatic, but not so exclusively so as the first two families described. They are small turtles (Fig. 135, D) that show in their structures evidence of having reverted to an aquatic abode after a prolonged ancestry upon the land. Their box-like shell is not the type of armature that is characteristic of the really aquatic turtles. The commonest representative of the group is *Aromochelys odorata*, a name redolent of the peculiar sickening odor of a yellow fluid that it gives off from the inguinal glands when disturbed. The "stink pot," as it is commonly called, lives at the bottom of ponds, crawling over the mud, but seldom swimming freely in the water. In warm weather it is often seen floating at the surface supported upon a mass of floating pond-scum. They rarely bask openly above the water. On land they are slow and clumsy of gait, but in spite of this they wander about at night through the grass and shore herbage, hunting for worms and slugs. We have also found them in the daytime rooting about in the moss for insects or grubs, using their snouts for the purpose and snuffing like little pigs. Sometimes they stay out of water so long that they become light in weight from desiccation. When caught they make a great show of fierceness, hissing and opening the jaws widely, looking almost as formidable as a small snapper; but this is either a mere "bluff" or due to fright, for when given the opportunity to bite they do not take advantage of it. Their appetite is insatiable and indiscriminate; anything that could by any stretch of courtesy be described as edible meets with their approval. *Aromochelys* is a curious mixture of a primitive and specialized turtle. It is very aquatic at certain times and decidedly terrestrial at others. It pretends to be fierce, but is gentle; it is omnivorous. It makes the crudest nest of any of the species that the writer has studied. On one occasion a female was observed to dig a shallow hole about two inches wide and about as deep. Two china-like eggs were laid in the nest and covered up loosely with débris. Sometimes the nest is constructed with somewhat greater care, but it is less elaborate than in other species studied.

Family 5. Platysternidae. — This family is represented by one species native to Borneo, Siam, and southern China. *Platysternum* is an extremely flat type, with unusually large head and hooked beak.

Family 6. Testudinidae (the common pond tortoises). — This is much the largest family of chelonians and is represented in North America by *Graptemys geographica* (the map tortoise), *Chrysemys picta* (the painted tortoise), *Nannemys gutatta* (the spotted tortoise), *Terrapene carolina* (the box tortoise) and, as an aberrant derivative of North American chelonians, the giant land tortoises of the Galapagos and other oceanic islands. In habits they range from aquatic to purely terrestrial forms. Some are purely carnivorous, other purely herbivorous.

Perhaps the commonest example of our pond tortoises is *Chrysemys picta* (eastern variety) or *C. marginata* (western variety). These rather small tortoises are found in ponds or sluggish streams. They are most frequently seen when basking in the sun along the shore or upon floating logs. They are excellent swimmers and somewhat difficult to catch. They feed upon dead fish and other carrion in the water, tearing up the flesh with their long, sharp claws and sharp-edged

FIG. 136. Group of Chelonia, II. A. Snake-necked tortoise, *Hydromedusa maximiliani*. B. Soft-shelled tortoise, *Aspidonectes spinifer*. C. Giant land tortoise or elephant tortoise, *Testudo elephantina*. D. The "matamata," *Chelys fimbriata*. (All redrawn, A and C after Lydekker, B and D, after Gadow.)

beaks. The nest is made with a narrow neck and a flask-shaped chamber at the bottom. It is situated in moist sand along the shores of still waters. Four to eight oval eggs are laid; these are placed in the flask-like enlargement and are covered up neatly with sand, which is pounded down with the knuckles of the hind feet. *Chrysemys* is a bright, intelligent little tortoise, showing little sullenness when captured, and no disposition to snap or to take alarm. They soon learn to come to one who habitually feeds them and will eat from the hand.

Terrapene carolina (Fig. 135, F) is the common land terrapin of the southern and eastern states. Structurally they differ little from some of the pond tortoises, but they have exclusively terrestrial habits. If put in the water they soon drown. They are, like the pond tortoises and unlike the giant land tortoises, largely carnivorous. In captivity they become very tame and are often used as pets. There are records of individuals having lived in captivity for fifty years or more. They bask in the heat of the sun most of the day, but at dusk they become active, hunting for slugs and worms, which form their chief diet. At night they retire to their burrows. Their nesting habits are much like those of the pond tortoises.

The true land tortoises range from forms of moderate size, like *Testudo graeca*, the common European species, to the giant land tortoises of the oceanic islands (Fig. 136, C). These creatures do not differ materially from others except in size, a character which may have been the result of the easy conditions of life on oceanic islands or it may be merely one of the effects of senescence. They are herbivorous and devour quantities of young plant shoots and other succulent vegetation. In the Galapagos Islands there is a different species of land tortoise for almost every island. It is believed that the first individual or pair of these animals reached the Galapagos land mass when it was a single small continent, that subsidence of that part of the earth's crust left only the high places above water, and that these are the present islands. Isolation of the tortoises on the different islands is supposed to have been the principal agency in establishing different species on the various islands. The largest specimens of land tortoises weigh over five hundred pounds and are over four feet in length of shell. They are said to exhibit remarkable longevity, some having a record of about one hundred and fifty years.

Family 7. Chelonidae (Sea Turtles). — This group is best known for the so-called tortoise-shell, a product derived from the horny scutes with which the carapace is covered. They are large turtles with paddle-like limbs, small head, short neck, and rudimentary tail. They come ashore only to lay their eggs in the beach sand of the tropical sea-shores. At that time they are captured in large numbers and brought to the metropolitan markets, where their flesh meets with a ready sale as a material for soup. When they are out of the water they are very clumsy and are easily caught. All that the hunter has to do to capture his prey is to turn them over on the back, where they are safe until such time as it is convenient to load them into boats. Usually they are kept in water-filled enclosures till needed and shipped alive to the market.

Chelone mydas, the "green turtle," is the largest and best known species of edible sea turtle, though the "hawksbill," *Chelone imbricata* (Fig. 135, B) is a close rival in popularity. *Thallasochelys caretta*, "the loggerhead turtle," though it is of no commercial value on account of its rank flesh, is of considerable interest on account of the fact that it exhibits a remarkable diversity of scute and plate number and arrangement. This is probably an evidence of primitiveness, and may approach the ancestral condition.

Suborder *Trionychoidea* (*Soft-shelled Tortoises*)

The distinguishing character of these tortoises is their lack of the scaly or chitinous armature. They also lack parts of the bony armature possessed by other groups. All over the body there is a reduction of the scaly elements; on the feet the scales are reduced to soft folds of skin. The "soft shells" are, however, not to be pitied for their defenseless state, for they make up for their loss of armor by their greatly increased intelligence and rapidity of locomotion. *Aspidonectes spinifer* (Fig. 136, B) is the common "soft shell" of the Mississippi basin and is familiar to most residents of that region. Of all our tortoises they are the most exclusively aquatic, coming inshore only for nesting purposes, and seldom basking except upon floating logs and upon low river banks very close to the water's edge. They always turn around after crawling out of the water, so as to have the head turned toward the water, ready to scramble into the river again at the slightest suggestion of danger. They have need to be wary, for they are excellent food for both man and beast. We have frequently seen young specimens lying in shallow water with only the proboscis-like snout and the dorsally placed eyes protruding above the surface. The body is usually covered over with a film of mud which has been thrown up by rocking the body from side to side and allowing the sediment to settle. When thus camouflaged they are reasonably safe from their enemies. But so swift and alert are the adults that it is unlikely that they would be caught by any of the creatures that inhabit their native waters. Even man with all his equipment for catching animals has the greatest difficulty in capturing these tortoises. When one happens to be caught, however, it "keeps its wits about it," as our assistant once said, and is ever on the alert to escape. The captor must be equally wary, for the long neck and strong jaws have an unerring aim quite in contrast with the blind, furious lunge of the "snapper." The food of the "soft shell" consists chiefly of crayfish and insect larvae, which they swallow whole without rending them to pieces. The nest of this species is a rather deep, neatly made, flask-shaped cavity dug in clean, moist sand. The female comes ashore with the greatest caution, usually very early in the morning, and while making the nest stretches the head on high on the lookout for danger. There are from 15 to 25 spherical tough-shelled eggs, placed in several layers, with sand pads between. The completed nest is covered over so neatly that no trace of it is to be seen from the surface. All of the activities of this species of tortoise appear to indicate a considerably higher order of intelligence than that shown by any other chelonian.

ORDER RHYNCHOCEPHALIA

While members of this order were relatively common during Mesozoic times only one lonely species survives today, if indeed it still does survive. This species is called *Sphenodon* (*Hatteria*) and was last seen on a few small islands off the coast of New Zealand. A generation ago it was fairly common, as is attested by the fact that the writer in his student days was permitted to dissect a specimen. Unless something is done to protect it, this interesting species is doomed to become extinct.

Sphenodon (Fig. 137, A), called by the natives "tuatara," is viewed with great respect by comparative anatomists. Gadow refers to it as "the last living witness of by-gone ages, this primitive, almost ideally generalized type of reptile, this 'living fossil.'" That the term "living fossil" is justified is shown by the fact that it is almost identical in structure with the ancient Jurassic genus, *Homaeosaurus*. Its extreme southern location is in harmony with the general rule that archaic living groups are most likely to be found farthest south. New Zealand, an extremely southern land, has long been known to be a "museum" of archaic animals and plants.

Sphenodon is a rather large lizard-like reptile. It resembles lizards in external appearance, but differs from them in several important

ways. Whereas lizards have but one temporal fossa high up on the
skull, *Sphenodon* and its relatives have two, an upper and a lower
(Fig. 137, B). In this respect *Sphenodon* resembles the archosaurs

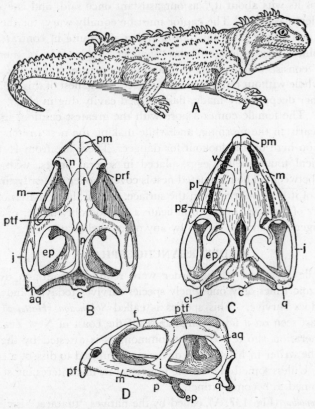

FIG. 137. *Sphenodon punctatum.* A. Lateral view. B. Dorsal view of skull. C.
Ventral view of skull. D. Lateral view of skull. c, condyle; cl, columella; ep,
ectopterygoid; f, frontal; j, jugal; m, maxillary; pm, premaxillary; n, nasal; p,
parietal; pl, palatine; prf, prefrontal; ptf, postfrontal and post-orbital; pg, pterygoid; q, quatrate or quadratojugal; v, vomer. (After Gadow.)

and birds. Unlike lizards, *Sphenodon* has a small overhanging beak
at the tip of the upper jaw. The palate is more primitive than that
of lizards. The vertebrae are amphicoelous (hollow at both ends)
instead of being procoelous as in lizards. There is no copulatory
organ, a very non-reptilian character, which probably is due to
secondary loss and is not really a primitive condition.

In general, it is believed that the Rhynchocephalia are an aberrant group which first appeared in the Triassic, had a modest career through the Mesozoic and is now represented by one very conservative living species.

Sphenodon is nocturnal in habits, living in burrows in the daytime. It shares its capacious burrow with various kinds of petrels that live with it on amicable terms. It will tolerate no other guests, not even other members of its own species, and viciously attacks any intruder no matter how formidable. The general appearance of this odd reptile and its skull peculiarities are illustrated in Figure 137, A.

ORDER CROCODILIA

These rather large and somewhat fearsome reptiles are the last survivors of the great dynasty of the Archosauria (Ruling Reptiles).

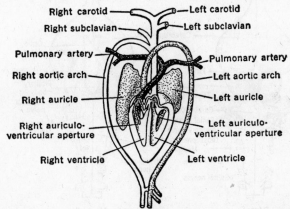

FIG. 138. Heart and principal blood vessels of crocodile. (After Parker and Haswell.)

They are a very ancient group of diapsid reptiles and are represented by a continuous fossil series leading off from a primitive thecodont stock. The crocodiles are regarded as an unprogressive, conservative archosaurian group, for the living forms differ but little from the extinct Jurassic forms. Crocodiles apparently did not go very far in the characteristic archosaurian trait of bipedality, yet the hind legs are much larger than the fore legs, and, while in ordinary locomotion the crocodile is quadrupedal, when in a hurry it is said to raise the head and trunk high off the ground, tucking the knees under and running like a dinosaur.

Structural characters. — The exoskeleton is composed of squarish corneous thickenings, with narrow channels of flexible skin separating the islands of hard horn. On the back and down the tail the scales are supported by bony cores, and the principal scale rows are keeled, giving a ridged effect to the middle of the back and tail. The hide is used extensively in commerce.

The tongue is flat and thick and incapable of protrusion. The lungs are large and better developed than in most other reptiles.

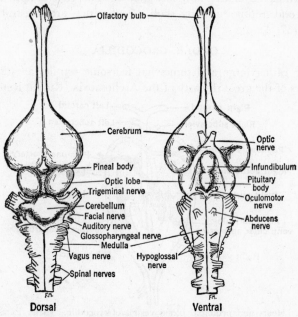

Dorsal   Ventral

Fig. 139. Brain of the alligator. (From Messer.)

The teeth are large and formidable and very irregularly arranged. Though the mouth is provided with very powerful muscles for closing the jaws, those for opening them are very weak, so that a man can easily close with his hands and keep closed the jaws of a large specimen. The heart (Fig. 138) and vascular system are more advanced in the crocodiles than in any other living reptiles, for the ventricle is almost competely divided by a septum into a right and a left chamber, leaving only a small foramen between. Thus there is practically a complete separation of venous and arterial blood, as in the warm-blooded vertebrates.

The brain (Fig. 139) is decidedly advanced in structure for a reptilian brain, the large cerebral hemispheres being especially noteworthy. The tympanic membrane is sunk in a pit, a tendency that is carried much further in the birds and mammals. It will thus be seen that the crocodiles have followed part way several of the evolutionary paths that have been carried out fully by the birds.

The geographic distribution of the crocodiles is wide, but confined chiefly to the tropical regions. They are found over a large part of Africa, in India, southern China, Malaysia, South and Central America, and along the Gulf of Mexico in North America. Formerly they occurred in Europe and northern Asia.

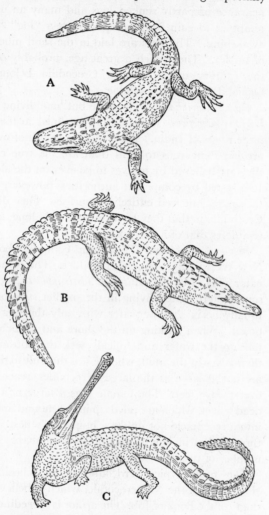

FIG. 140. Group of Crocodilia. A. *Alligator mississippiensis.* B. *Crocodilus americanus.* C. *Gavialis gangeticus.* (Redrawn, A and B, after Ditmars, C, after Lydekker.)

Habits. — The crocodiles, alligators, and gavials are all fierce predaceous creatures, most of them being enemies of both man and beast. The older they become the

more wily and dangerous they are and the more apt to become
man-hunters. Their rusty, bark-like backs give them the appearance of partly sunken logs and many an unwary creature attempting to gain support upon such a "log" has suffered a rude
awakening. The eggs are laid in the sand much after the fashion
of turtles. They reach a great age, probably often breaking over
the century mark. Living Crocodilia belong to two families:
Gavialidae and Crocodilidae.

Family Gavialidae. There is but one living species of gavials,
Gavialis gangeticus (Fig. 140, C), confined to the Ganges and other
large rivers of India. They reach a length of over twenty feet, but
are less dangerous to man than are the true crocodiles, although
they are believed by natives to be ever on the alert to capture man.
It is stated by competent authorities, however, that they never attack man, but feed entirely upon fish. They differ from the other
Crocodilia in that they have an extremely long, narrow snout, which
resembles that of a gar-pike.

Family Crocodilidae. This group comprises both Old World and
New World alligators and crocodiles. The common American alligator (Fig. 140, A), *Alligator mississippiensis*, occurs largely in the
southeastern states, living in the smaller streams and ponds. They
usually lie in shallow water with only the eyes and the nostrils exposed. When basking on the shore and disturbed by enemies they
take to the water and quickly seek the bottom, where they bury
themselves in the mud, whence it is difficult to dislodge them. They
are not as large as the largest crocodiles, reaching a length hardly
over twelve feet. The female digs a large nest in the humus and
dead leaves, which are piled up into a mound and then hollowed out
into a receptacle not unlike a huge bird's nest. The eggs are about
three inches in length and of an oval shape and are laid to the
number of twenty to thirty to a nest.

The most typical crocodile is the classic *Crocodilus niloticus*
(Fig. 140, B), the Nile crocodile, which is believed to be the "levia-
than" of the Book of Job. The armor is exceedingly heavy and is said
to be impenetrable to any weapons but bullets. The crocodile makes
a long tunnel-like burrow thirty to forty feet in length, with an opening below the water level, used as an entrance, and with a large
chamber at the inner end well above the water level. The nest is
large and flask-shaped like that of some tortoises, but with a flat
bottom grooved around the periphery, causing the eggs to lie in a

circular ring. The mother lies over the covered-up nest and takes considerable care of the young after they have hatched.

ORDER SQUAMATA

This order includes two suborders: Lacertilia (lizards) and Ophidia (snakes). These are by all odds the most successful and most dominant of modern reptiles. They are also the most recent among the orders to have made their appearance on the geologic scene. The lizards first appeared in the Jurassic and underwent considerable radiation in the Cretaceous, during which time the great marine lizards arose. The snakes, obviously derived from lizard-like ancestors, appeared no earlier than Cretaceous times. During the entire Cenozoic Age the Squamata have been the most prevalent reptiles and are still very numerous in spite of man's antipathy to them, especially to the snakes.

The diagnostic characters of the order are as follows: The skull has a single temporal opening, corresponding to the upper one in *Sphenodon;* there is in the place where the lower temporal opening of *Sphenodon* lies a deep bay in the skull which might be interpreted as equivalent to the lower opening in *Sphenodon* with the lower arch lost; the quadratojugal is absent and the squamosal much reduced; this leaves the quadrate freely movable, giving the jaw a wider gape; the palate is primitive; the teeth are not in sockets but are fused to inner margins of the jaws; the ribs are single-headed.

Two views as to the ancestry of the lizards have been proposed. According to one theory the lizards were derived from certain primitive Palaeozoic reptiles. One Permian type, *Araeoscelis*, is a small, slender form quite lizard-like in form, which has a single upper temporal opening, like the lizards, but here resemblance to modern lizards ceases. Romer favors the view that the lizards have come off from the same general stock that produced the rhynchocephalians, both of which may have been derived from the primitive eosuchians, which date back to the Upper Permian. The many resemblances of lizards to *Sphenodon* support this view. If, however, the Squamata and the Rhynchocephalia had a common ancestor they must have diverged before the Mesozoic was well under way.

SUBORDER LACERTILIA (LIZARDS)

It is not so simple as one might think to distinguish lizards from snakes. One might assume that all lizards have legs and all snakes are limbless, but this rule does not hold, for some lizards are entirely limbless and some snakes have rudimentary hind legs. The chief distinctions between the two types consist of the added peculiarities of snakes that will be discussed a little later.

There are many taxonomic families of lizards and these are sometimes grouped into four superfamilies: 1. Kionocrania, including most of the primitive forms such as geckos, agamids, Gila monster, glass snakes, skinks and some Old World true lizards; 2. Amphisbaenia, a group of burrowing forms, often limbless; 3. Platynota, a group of large forms such as the monitors; 4. Rhiptoglossa, the chameleons.

The lizards, as has been said, are a highly successful, relatively recently evolved group. Like other such groups they have undergone unusually extensive adaptive radiation. In presenting an account of the natural history of some representative lizards we shall have in mind mainly their adaptive features. It will be noted that apparently the primitive habitat of lizards is the dry-land surface. Swift running types were probably the first to evolve. From the ground surface some of them went downward, becoming burrowing, subterranean forms. Many other types became climbing, arboreal forms or else climbers on smooth, rocky surfaces. Some of the arboreal forms tended to become volant (flying) forms, but their success in aerial locomotion was not great. Still others became more or less aquatic, and one species is now marine in its feeding habits. Large numbers of lizards have become desert forms, some of which have adopted the ant-eater type of specialization. The following account of some of the best known forms of lizards does not follow systematic lines, but rather ecological ones.

The geckos are practically cosmopolitan within the warm temperate countries. In the United States they are confined to our southwestern Pacific regions. They are wonderful climbers. By means of adhesive pads on the toes they are able to ascend the smoothest surfaces such as walls, ceilings, or even window-panes. Adhesion is accomplished by the vacuum-cup principle, but the "cup" consists of a complicated system of lamellae. They feed on all sorts of small animals, especially insects and spiders. They are absolutely harmless to man in spite of an undeserved reputation for venomousness. Their chief defense consists of an extremely loosely articulated tail, which comes off with great readiness when seized. When cornered and in grave danger they wag the tail over the body, appearing to offer it for seizure. The enemy is usually satisfied with the detached tail and the tailless gecko proceeds to regenerate another tail, which fortunately it is able to do very readily. This easy loss of the tail seems to be characteristic of most, if not all lizards.

Lacerta viridis (Fig. 141, B) the common European "wall lizard" is an excellent example of generalized lizard. It is a small type with long slender proportions, is a beautiful green above and yellow below. It runs very swiftly upon the ground and over rocks and hides in thickets and under any available shelter. From some such generalized type as this all of the more specialized types have probably radiated.

Sceloporus spinosus (Fig. 141, E), one of the commonest American lizards, is a good example of an arboreal type, though it has also a strong liking for the ground if thickets are available. It is a rusty-colored lizard, harmonizing wonderfully with the bark of the mesquite and other trees which it haunts. During the heat of the day it lies basking on the trunk or exposed branches of trees, and retires to holes in trees or among the roots at night. In the winter it hibernates in shallow holes in the ground or under stones or other shelters. During the cool of the day it is actively in search of food, which consists mainly of tree-inhabiting insects. In the breeding season the male takes on a steely blue sheen about the throat and head. The courtship and mating activities are rather striking. The male stands in front of the female with his brilliant throat inflated and thus displayed to the utmost; then raises himself up and down on the fore legs with a quick rhythm. This the female seems to watch as though fascinated and is soon won. The nest is dug in loose soil in the form of a fairly deep tunnel in a sloping bank. Excavation of the nest is accomplished with the hind feet, as in tortoises. The eggs, which are much like tortoise eggs in appearance, number a dozen or more, and when laid are in a stage equivalent to about a 72-hour chick.

Draco volans (Fig. 141, C), the flying dragon, is the best example of the volant (flying) type of lizard. The body is dorso-ventrally depressed and the skin is stretched out into two fan-shaped, folding membranes, which are supported on five or six of the greatly elongated ribs. On the neck are three hooks which probably enable the animal to secure a hold when alighting from a flight. The wings are mere glider planes and do not in any sense serve as propellers. Only short soaring leaps from branch to branch or between adjacent trees can be accomplished. When the animal is at rest the "wings" are

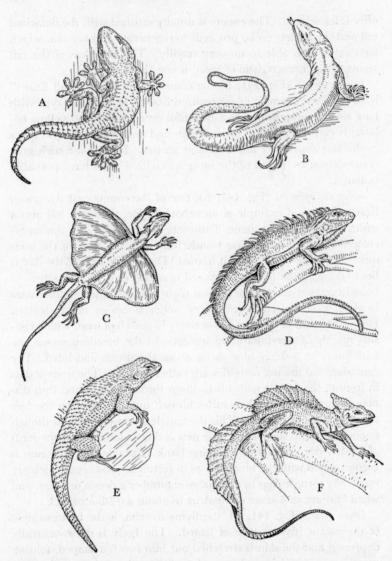

Fig. 141. Group of Lacertilia, I. A. Wall gecko, *Tarentola mauritanica*.
B. *Lacerta viridis*. C. *Draco volans* (flying dragon). D. *Iguana tuberculata*. E.
Sceloporus spinosus. F. Helmeted basilisk, *Basiliscus americanus*. (All redrawn,
A, B, and F, after Lydekker; C and D, after Gadow; E, after Ditmars.)

folded against the sides. These lizards are natives of Indo-Malayan
countries. Not much is known about their habits, but it is said that
they live among gorgeous flowers whose colors they closely approxi-

FIG. 142. Group of Lacertilia, II. A. Horned toad, *Phrynosoma cornutum.*
B. Gila monster, *Heloderma horridum.* C. *Anguis fragilis* (the glass snake). D. Cape
monitor, *Varanus albigularis.* E. Galapagos sea-lizard, *Amblyrhynchus cristatus.*
F. *Moloch horridus.* (All redrawn, A, after Gadow; others after Lydekker.)

mate. Doubtless this camouflage aids the lizard in securing insect
food.

Phrynosoma cornutum (Fig. 142, A), a horned toad, is chosen as a
desert type. Of course this animal is not a toad at all but a short,

flat, spiny lizard, with greatly reduced tail, a character that evidently suggested the name "toad" for it. They live in the semiarid regions of the southwestern states and in Mexico. The only water they seem to take is in the form of dewdrops, and they are capable of living for a long time without any water, growing flatter and lighter as desiccation progresses. Their chief food appears to be ants, though other small insects are not unwelcome. They are fond of basking in the hottest sun during the day, but when night approaches they bury themselves in the sand while still warm from the sun, leaving only the top of the head and the horns exposed. The nostrils are provided with valves to prevent the inhalation of the fine sand. They are colored a dull sandy gray, and this, together with their rugose appearance, makes them very inconspicuous against the usual desert background. One curious habit which the writer had heard of with considerable skepticism and only believed when he saw it with his own eyes, is that of squirting a tiny stream of blood out of the eye, when cornered and in danger. The blood is expelled from the inner corner of the eye and can be shot to a distance of two feet or more. What advantage is gained by this curious habit no one seems to know. The horned toad is a docile little creature and is easily tamed. Of all animals that the writer has experimented with, they are the most readily hypnotized by turning them on the back and pressing gently but firmly against the ventral surface.

Anguis fragilis (Fig. 142, C), a European "slow-worm" or "blindworm," is also called in some sections of the country the "glass snake." These lizards are true fossorial or burrowing types. They are limbless forms, representing the climax of degeneration among the Lacertilia. There is a current legend of the southern states that an allied species of glass snake can be shattered by a blow into a number of pieces and that these pieces get together again into an entire animal, which then goes on its way rejoicing. The truth underlying the legend is that, like other lizards, the tail is quite brittle and readily knocked off by a blow from a stick. Both animal and tail wriggle about vigorously after such violent treatment, but only the tailless body is able to resume the journey.

Basiliscus americanus (Fig. 141, F), the American basilisk, may be chosen as an amphibious type. It is a large, conspicuous lizard about a yard in length. It is characterized by a very pronounced dorsal crest, which looks like a fin, a secondary sexual character limited to the males. They lie on the branches of trees overhanging the water and at the slightest danger drop off into the water and, according to reliable observers, actually run on the surface of the water, using the large feet and lashing tail to keep them from sinking.

Amblyrhynchus cristatus (Fig. 142, E), the sea lizard, is as near an approach to a true aquatic type as the Lacertilia afford. These rather large, heavy-bodied lizards inhabit certain rocky shores on the Galapagos Islands. They are great swimmers, using the flattened, finned tail as a propeller. They habitually feed upon the seaweeds that abound beyond the breakers, and they have to weather the waves in order to secure their food. Often they prefer the really dangerous breakers to their enemies on land, and seek shelter in the sea.

Moloch horridus (Fig. 142, F) is one of the strangest of lizards. Its integument is remarkable for its heavy spines. This animal has been described as a lizard ant-eater and its peculiarities are considered to be primarily adaptations for the ant-eating life. It certainly seems to be well protected to withstand the attacks of ants. One peculiar feature of the integument has attracted considerable attention; for the skin is said to be hygroscopic, capable of absorbing moisture from the air. This strange lizard rivals in bizarre appearance the most fanciful monsters of long ago. Only its small size redeems it from utter frightfulness of aspect.

The only venomous lizards are several species of Gila Monsters (Fig. 142, B), belonging to the genus *Heloderma*, large, heavy-bodied lizards of the arid lands of our southwest and Mexico. They have fang-like recurved teeth, which are so grooved as to form ducts for the poisonous secretion of the labial glands. The Gilas are conspicuously marked with contrasting black and orange patches and are often cited as examples of warning coloration, a common phenomenon among venomous reptiles.

The largest living lizard is the monitor (Fig. 142, D), *Varanus salvator*, a species that reaches a length of seven feet or more. Apart from its great size the monitor is a very generalized lizard, differing but little in proportions from the primitive lizard-like reptile, *Varanops*, which lived in Permian times. In southern China and the Malaysian region, where this lizard has its home, it is hunted by dogs and used for food.

The largest American lizard is *Iguana tuberculata* (Fig. 141, D), a native of South and Central America. The Iguana reaches a length of five or six feet. Its habits are much like those of the basilisk.

The chameleons are the most highly specialized of the lizards. The body is laterally compressed, the tail prehensile, the toes are parted in the middle into two groups used for grasping, after the manner of forceps, a group of three being opposed by a group of two. Most of them are African or Madagascan, though one species (*Chamaeleon vulgaris*) extends into southern Europe.

As an example of extreme arboreal specialization the group is of unusual interest. Two characters of chameleons have become notorious: their ability to change color and their habit of "shooting" insects with their tongues. Accounts of their color versatility are exaggerated, but the fact remains that they are probably among the most effective color changers known, having a range from very light gray to leaf green, and the change can be made in a few seconds. The tongue is capable of "shooting" a fly at a distance of seven inches and the aim is unerring. Probably the aim is improved by the curiously modified eyelids which are grown together with the exception of a mere pin-hole in the center. Apparently the tongue aims at the exact point of focus of the two eyes.

An excellent account of the activities of the chameleon is given by Gadow, accompanied by a composite illustration (Fig. 143).

"It is most interesting to watch them stalking their prey. Suppose we have introduced some butterflies into their roomy cage, which is furnished with living plants and plenty of twigs. The chameleons, hitherto quite motionless, perhaps basking with flattened out bodies so as to catch as many of the sun's rays as possible, become at once lively. One of them makes for a butterfly which has settled in the furthest upper corner of the cage. With unusually fast motions the chameleon stilts along and across the branches and all seems to go well, until he discovers that the end of the branch is still 8 inches from the prey, and he knows perfectly well that 7 inches are the utmost limit to a shot with his tongue. He pauses to think, perhaps with two limbs in the air, but stability is secured by a judicious turn of the tail. After he has solved the puzzle, he retraces his steps to the base of the branch, climbs up the main stem, creeps along the next branch above and, when arrived at the 7 inch distance he shoots the butterfly with unerring aim. The capacity of the mouth and throat is astonishing. A full grown chameleon will catch, chew, and swallow the largest moth."

While we may object to the statement that a chameleon "pauses to

FIG. 143. Chameleons. *C. vulgaris*, showing various attitudes; *C. pumulis* in upper right-hand corner. (From Gadow.)

think" or "knows perfectly well," we can not but admire the vividness of the verbal picture here presented.

SUBORDER OPHIDIA (SNAKES)

While it is customary to regard the lizards and snakes as two suborders of the order Squamata, some leading herpetologists now feel that, while there can be no doubt that snakes have been derived from lizards, they have become so specialized and so distinct from lizards as to deserve full ordinal status. Snakes are the latest product of evolution of the class Reptilia. It might be said that, without the snakes the old, once dominant class would be almost overwhelmed by mammals and birds, but the snakes save the day for their class, for they give the mammals and birds plenty of competition. The snakes apparently got their start in late Cretaceous times, and are therefore contemporaneous with placental mammals.

According to some writers, snakes are regarded as extreme limbless eel-type degenerates, but a more significant view of them is that they represent an advanced type of specialization for swallowing large prey whole, and that the loss of limbs, especially the fore limbs, the greatly elongated trunk, the readily dislocated jaws, and even the hollow fangs and the associated venom, are all progressive adaptations for this peculiar mode of feeding. In general, it may be said that the snakes differ from the lizards mainly in these feeding adaptations.

The snake head is usually rather small, sometimes excessively small as compared with the body, but, in spite of this, the mouth can be greatly distended by several peculiar mechanisms. Thus the two halves of the lower jaw are jointed in front by an elastic ligament that permits the two bones to stretch far apart. The quadrate bone is very loosely suspended from the squamosal, permitting jaw distension by dislocation, and there are several other parts of the jaw apparatus that favor enlargement of the mouth. The lack of the pectoral girdle makes it much easier for large objects to pass down the oesophagus, and thus the loss of limbs becomes an asset. The development of fangs and venom in several families of snakes is interpreted as a peculiarly efficient adaptation for the capture and killing of large prey that could not be caught unless killed by poison. Snakes that thus kill large prey do not at once try to swallow it, but follow it to the place where it dies and then engulf it at leisure. Thus we see that almost all of the snake's peculiarities tie up with its feeding specialty.

Some additional peculiarities of snakes need mention. As an adaptation to terrestrial locomotion without legs, the ventral scales are curiously modified. These scales are broad and band-like. Each locomotor scale is provided with muscles that erect and depress it as the needs of traction require. When moving slowly and smoothly along over irregular ground the scales act as legs, in that they first stand erect, take hold of the substratum and then push backwards. The serpentine movement of a snake consists of alternate lateral curving and straightening of various parts of the long body. This would not do any good as a mode of locomotion unless the tread surface were able to grip the ground, permitting the flexed portions to hold when the body is extended. The band-like scales, when erected act as a non-skid tread, preventing back slip and favoring forward motion.

The hind legs of snakes, although their presence would not interfere with swallowing large prey, are also greatly reduced or absent, but they were evidently lost later than the fore legs. As a matter of fact, quite well-developed vestiges of the hind legs, and even the pelvic girdle, are characteristic of the two most primitive families of snakes, the boas and pythons. In these snakes at least the claw of one digit may protrude from the surface, but the rest of the limb is buried beneath the skin.

The eyes of snakes are lidless, but each eye is protected by a watch-glass-shaped membrane, which is transparent and is shed when the rest of the skin is moulted. During moulting the skin covering the eye becomes opaque and the snake is blind for a time.

The viscera are extremely elongated and every organ partakes of this elongation. In all snakes except boas and pythons, which are in many other respects relatively primitive, one lung is lost and the remaining one greatly elongated. This too is evidently part of the adaptation for swallowing large prey.

According to Gadow, "Snakes are intelligent creatures; some become quite affectionate in captivity, but most of them are of a morose disposition, and they do not care for company." So far as the average man is concerned this feeling is mutual; for the first human reflex is to kill a snake on sight. Whether this is the result of tradition or is a residual instinct dating back to the arboreal period of man's ancestry, we can not say. This much should be said for the snakes, however, that most of them deserve nothing but kindly treatment, since they are far more beneficial than many animals that have a much better reputation. It would appear that the few venomous snakes have given a bad name to the whole group.

Snake Venom. — Many snakes, but a small percentage of the whole group, are more or less venomous, but as a rule they are much less deadly than they are supposed to be. Unfortunately there is no simple criterion for distinguishing the poisonous snakes from the non-poisonous. One merely has to acquaint himself with the habitat and appearance of the various snakes native to the country in which he resides or in which he is sojourning. The poison is secreted in a pair of enlarged, specialized salivary glands, homologous with the parotid glands of the mammals. A duct leads from these glands to the hollows of the paired grooved or tubular fangs. The strike of the snake presses upon the gland and causes the poison to exude from the tip of the fang into the deepest part of the wound. The whole apparatus acts like a hypodermic needle. Fortunately for us there are only five kinds of venomous snakes in the United States: coral snakes, water moccasin, copperhead, rattle-snakes, and opisthoglyphs.

There are two species of coral snakes both belonging to the genus *Elaps;* both are native to the southern states. They are extremely conspicuous owing to the vivid contrasting bands of red, black, and yellow, another example of the so-called warning coloration. The coral snakes are extremely poisonous, but their biting equipment is said to be so constructed that they can not open the mouth wide enough to bite anything but a small part, such as a finger, of a human being.

The water moccasin (*Agkistrodon piscivorus*), the so-called "cotton mouth," is a large, heavy, aquatic species that reaches a length of five or six feet. It is really a kind of rattle-snake without a rattle. This snake has the reputation of being by far the most venomous of all North American snakes, but it is very unusual for a human being to be bitten by it, and fatal cases are rare.

The copperhead (*Agkistrodon contortrix*) ranges from Massachusetts to Florida and west to Texas. It also is a kind of rattler without any rattle.

The true rattle-snakes comprise a number of species belonging to the genus *Crotalus* (Fig. 144, C). Of these the Texas rattler is much the largest and that of Canada the smallest. The largest known specimens reach a length of seven feet and are stockily proportioned. The bite is serious, but seldom fatal for a healthy individual. The rattle of the "rattler" is a curious structure, made by leaving the end of the moulted skin attached to the tip of the tail, each moult adding a new ring to the rattle. The rattling sound, which is more like

Fig. 144. Group of Ophidia. A. African python (*Python seboe*) swallowing a bird. B. Cobra, *Naja tripudians*. C. *Crotalis durissus* (rattlesnake). D. Banded sea-snake, *Platurus laticaudatus*. (Redrawn after Lydekker.)

a shrill hiss, is made by quivering the tail, a movement of excitement or fear rather than purposeful warning signal. Nevertheless it is a sound that, even when heard for the first time, causes one to "bring up all standing" and watch one's step. Give a rattle-snake half a chance and he will run away without attempting to attack.

ADAPTIVE RADIATION AMONG THE SNAKES

Although somewhat limited in their adaptive versatility by the lack of limbs, the snakes show quite a wide range of specialization for the various life zones. The more generalized types are the common ground snakes that hide among rocks and in holes in the ground, using these merely as retreats in time of danger or for hibernation.

A great many arboreal types have been developed. The body of tree-dwelling snakes is peculiarly modified for this habitat. The body is laterally compressed with an ability to extend itself far into space in reaching from branch to branch, while anchored firmly by the prehensile tail. The Boidae (boa-constrictors) are typical examples of arboreal snakes. These large, rapacious creatures secure their prey by dropping upon it out of trees and crushing it to death within their powerful coils. The largest of these snakes are upwards of twenty feet long, about six inches in diameter, and are said to be capable of crushing a tiger or a stag. They are unable, however, to eat such large prey, their limit being rabbits and fairly large birds, which they are able to swallow whole without difficulty. There are several types that are more highly specialized for arboreal life than the Boidae. Among these are the members of the family Colubrinae, which are characterized by their great length and slenderness, and by the great flexibility of the prehensile tail.

Another adaptive type is that which is native of the arid regions and which has adopted the burrowing habit to protect itself against the extremes of temperature so characteristic of desert regions. The chief food of some burrowing snakes consists of earthworms. A specialized burrowing type is represented by the genus *Typhleps*, of which there are about one hundred species. They dig typical burrows in the ground in which they spend much of their time.

The marine snakes are fine examples of a purely aquatic type, that never, except for giving birth to young and caring for them, come out of the water. The species *Platurus laticaudatus* (Fig. 144, D) illustrates the structural and functional adaptations for marine life. They are laterally compressed especially in the tail region, with dorsal and ventral fin-folds and a paddle-like tail fin. Their mode of swimming is precisely like that of eels. They are extremely venomous. They are viviparous, the female of some species coming ashore to give birth to her young among the rocks. The new-born young are about two feet long and at first much less specialized for aquatic life than the adults.

The cobra (Fig. 144, B), *Naja tripudians*, is perhaps the king of all the snakes, and with a description of its habits we shall bring this brief account of snakes to a close. The cobra is a native of India,

China, and Malaysia. Very large specimens reach a length of six feet. It is not for their size, however, that the cobras are so noteworthy, but for their striking appearance, their venomousness, and their sacredness. They are distinguished by the huge hood or neck swelling, upon which appears a color pattern resembling a death's head or a pair of spectacles, depending on the strength of one's imagination. They are an almost invariable accompaniment of the typical Indian conjurer, who charms them and makes them dance to his weird music. The dance is done by erecting the head with inflated hood and by waving it back and forth to the rhythm of the music. The cobra is by nature docile and has no inclination to bite; but when it does strike it is a serious matter, and the number of victims of cobra bite every year is appalling. Some of the natives possess snake stones, a sort of porous material that appears to have the property of drawing out the poison. The owner of such a stone is deemed by his acquaintances to possess a priceless talisman. In India the cobra is considered a sacred animal and, on that account, no systematic campaign of extermination has been started against it.

In concluding this chapter on reptiles it may be said that no account of development has been given, for the reason that reptilian and avian embryology are so similar that the account given for the bird at the end of Chapter XIX will do duty for the reptilian type of development also.

CHAPTER XVIII

CLASS AVES (BIRDS)

DISTINGUISHING CHARACTERS OF BIRDS

There is not the slightest difficulty in distinguishing a modern bird from any other animal, but it is not so easy to set down in black and white what are the distinguishing characters of birds. The only clean-cut possession of birds not shared by some other vertebrate type is that of **feathers.** The fore limb is also, in its present condition, very much modified and specialized as a propeller-plane, but in the fossil birds *Archaeopteryx* and *Archaeornis* the limb, apart from the feathers attached to it, is typically reptilian.

Many characters that might easily be regarded as purely avian turn out to be shared by various groups of reptiles. Birds share with dinosaurs bipedality, hollow bones, simplified hind legs with mesotarsal articulation, the fingers of the fore limb reduced to three, and a prelachrymal fossa. They share with pterosaurs and ichthyosaurs the sclerotic plates of the eye; with pterosaurs, the specialized structure of the cerebellum; with the Ruling Reptiles in general, the diapsid condition of the skull; with bird-like dinosaurs the tetraradiate type of pelvis; with *Sphenodon*, the uncinate processes of the ribs; with chameleons, the air-sacs of the lungs; with many reptiles, such as turtles and numerous dinosaurs, the lack of teeth and horny beak (some of the fossil birds, however, had typical reptilian socketed teeth).

Birds also share with mammals their warm-blooded (homoiothermous) character. It is, however, impossible to be sure that some of the extinct reptiles, such as pterosaurs and some of the dinosaurs, were not also more or less warm-blooded, and it is suspected that some of the mammal-like reptiles were warm-blooded. Birds share with the mammals and the crocodiles the four-chambered heart, but, so far as we know, the dinosaurs may have possessed this character. Birds and mammals have both lost one of the systemic arches, the birds retaining the right arch, mammals the left. Most birds have a single left ovary and oviduct, but some modern hawks have these structures about equally developed on both sides.

In view of all these correspondences between birds and reptiles it may well be asked why we do not simply class birds as a specialized group of flying reptiles with the rank of an order or at best a subclass. Some writers, in fact, have gone so far as to call birds "glorified reptiles." We believe, however, that the birds should be judged on the basis of their unique combination of many peculiarities, even though some of these are shared by other types. No other group of vertebrates possesses all or even a large number of these characters. This fact may be regarded as of sufficient importance to warrant the assignment of the birds to a separate taxonomic class.

For convenience we may offer a list of avian characters, even though many of them are not unique for birds, and some of them are not found in all birds:

1. Feathers.
2. No skin glands except the oil glands on the tail and occasional glands on wattles.
3. Fore limb modified for wings, with only three digits.
4. Warm-blooded (homoiothermous).
5. Four-chambered heart.
6. Single right aorta.
7. Lung air-sacs.
8. Hollow bones.
9. Metanephros.
10. No urinary bladder.
11. Single left ovary and oviduct.
12. Ribs with uncinate processes.
13. Eyes highly specialized, with sclerotic plates.
14. Greatly elongated pelvis, tetraradiate in form.
15. Hind limbs with mesotarsal joint (to be explained later).
16. Extensive fusion of vertebrae in the trunk region, and fusion of vertebrae with the pelvic girdle.
17. Greatly reduced tail.
18. Lack of teeth, the latter displaced by a horny bill, except in some extinct types.
19. Scales (corneoscutes) on lower leg and feet.
20. Eggs and embryonic membranes essentially reptilian, but eggs are incubated by heat of parent body.
21. Parental care highly developed.

22. Diapsid skull.
23. Prelachrymal fossae.
24. Cloaca.
25. Several bones in lower jaw, as in reptiles.
26. Single occipital condyle, as in most reptiles.

Another way of getting before the reader a rather vivid characterization of a bird is to consider the latter as a heavier-than-air flying machine, a monoplane with propeller-planes, a type of motor mechanism that man has as yet failed to invent. Let us compare and contrast the flight adaptations of the bird with a typical aeroplane.

THE BIRD AN AUTOMATIC AEROPLANE

The essential features of a heavier-than-air flying machine are: 1, Planes or wings; 2, great and sustained motor power, including

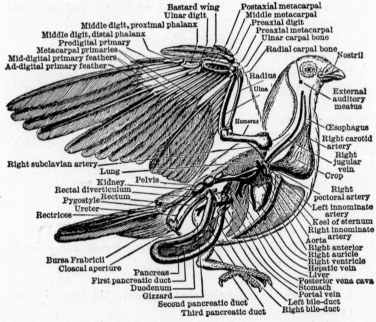

Fig. 145. Anatomy of the pigeon. (From Marshall and Hurst.)

fuel, engine, propeller; 3, minimum weight consistent with maximum rigidity of framework; 4, steering and balancing devices, including rudder, ailerons, stabilizers. Let us consider the ways in which the bird meets these requirements.

1. Planes, or Wings. — The wing of the bird (Fig. 145) is a complex of several structural elements consisting of a framework of bones, muscles, nerves, blood vessels, and feathers. The bony framework is that of a modified fore limb of which the human arm is a good prototype. The humerus is large and has heavy ridges for the attachment of the huge pectoral flight musculature. The radius and ulna are largely unmodified, though the ulna is larger than the radius and has a larger than usual head for muscle attachment. The wrist, hand, and finger bones are highly modified both through loss of whole bony units and by the fusion of the remaining bones into strong complexes. The thumb, or pollex, is reduced to a small rudiment, the index finger is the largest, the third digit fairly well developed, but there is no trace of the fourth and fifth digits. (The phalangeal part of the fore limb is reduced almost to a one-fingered condition.)

Of the wing muscles those of the upper arm are very large and powerful, those of the lower arm much reduced, and those of the hand atrophied. The only movements of the wings are those of elevating, depressing, extending, and flexing. The real flight muscles are the chest muscles, or pectorals, massive groups of fine-grained striated fibers, which are inserted upon the keel of the sternum. These muscle masses, which are capable of prolonged exertion without fatigue, correspond to the cylinders of the aeroplane motor.

The wing feathers are the main factors in giving large planing surface to the wing. A feather (Fig. 146) from the morphological standpoint, is sometimes regarded as no more nor less than an elaborately subdivided scale, rolled up into a cylinder proximally and expanded into a flat vane at the distal end. The quill is a residue of the embryonic rolled-up stage. The vane is composed of a number of subdivisions called barbs, each of which is subdivided into minute barbules which are hooked to the barbules of adjacent barbs so as to give stability to the vane and to make the whole feather a coherent, springy plane. A single row of large flight feathers grows out from the back of the arm and hand, each partly overlapping its neighbor. Several rows of so-called coverts overlie these like shingle rows. The overlapping arrangement of all the feathers contributes greatly to make the wing a fairly rigid, but

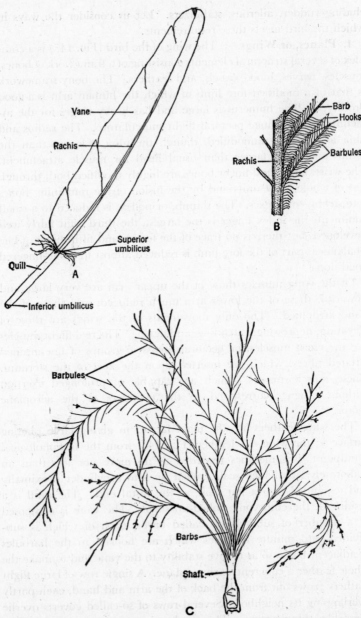

FIG. 146. Feathers. A. Flight feather of pigeon. B. Portion of same feather showing details. C. Down feather, with most barbs not filled in. (From Messer.)

sufficiently flexible plane, which is better adapted for the purpose than the perfectly rigid planes of man-made machines. The wing differs also from the plane in that it is jointed and capable of being folded away when not in use, or of regulating its exposed surface by flexures.

2. **Power.** — The secret of great and sustained power lies in the capacity to convert chemical energy into mechanical motion through rapid and complete combustion of fuel. In the aeroplane, gasoline is the fuel, the electric spark is the combustion agent, and oxygen the combustor; in birds carbohydrates, etc., constitute the fuel, the nerve impulse is the spark, and oxygen the combustor; the wing muscles, especially the pectorals, are in flying birds extremely massive, which means that a great abundance of energy is always available; the nervous system is highly efficient; and the supply of oxygen is ensured by the extraordinary development and unique structure of the lungs and air-passages, as well as by the adequate blood supply and its circulation. The lungs proper are not unduly large, but their capacity is greatly increased by the addition of large air-sacs, that branch off from the lungs. These air-sacs fill all of the coelomic spaces and even send fine branches into the hollows of the bones. By this scheme three functions are subserved: that of sending oxygen directly to many tissues, that of lessening the weight of the body, and that of adding buoyancy, for warm air has lifting power. The lungs, moreover, differ from those of reptiles or mammals in that a through draft of air is made possible through a system of excurrent bronchi, passages that carry used air out of the lung alveoli without interfering with the fresh air that enters through the incurrent bronchi. Thus the bird's oxygen supply is much better provided for than that of any other vertebrate, and in some respects approximates that possessed by the flying insects. Adequate oxidation is further provided for by the large heart (Fig. 150) and by voluminous blood vessels, both of which are proportionately to body weight more generous in their blood-carrying capacity than those of other vertebrates.

The high temperature of the bird is another important element in its power plant. Obviously, the higher the temperature, the more rapid and complete the combustion. The bird's temperature is considerably higher than that of mammals, as any one knows who has felt the skin of a live fowl. In the best fliers it runs up to 110° or 112° F., even when the birds are at rest. Two elements are concerned in maintaining the characteristic avian temperature: a vaso-motor system, similar to that of mammals, and an unusually effective non-conducting coat of feathers, which prevents surface loss of heat; and no known material does this more effectively than the feather coat of a bird, especially when the feathers are arranged as they are in nature. With this equipment the bird is able to endure the intense cold of the upper atmospheric strata without undue loss of heat and without the least danger of freezing.

The alimentary system (Fig. 145) is also proportionately effective. It must be, for it is the fuel refinery. Crude power materials are taken into the crop or storage tank, are gradually fed into the grinding mill (gizzard) and passed into the stomach proper, and subsequently into the intestines, in such a condition that digestion, or the final refining of the fuel, is rapid and complete. Much might be said of the efficiency of the excretory apparatus, but this may be assumed.

The mechanics of propulsion is difficult of explanation because of its extreme complexity, but this much may be said: the wing stroke is practically like the arm stroke in swimming the breast stroke. It must do two things: prevent the body from falling, and give a forward impulse. The stroke must therefore be downward and backward; but a forward and upward movement, like the recovery stroke in swimming, alternates with the power stroke. The possibility of effective and rapid propulsion depends on the relatively frictionless character of the recovery stroke. This is accomplished by bringing back the wing edgewise to the resistance of the air. Many birds make progress by planing up and down the air currents with nearly rigid wings. In this phase of flight man has almost equaled the bird.

3. Lightness and Rigidity. — Many elements combine to make the bird a model of mechanical perfection in this respect. The skeleton (Fig. 149) exhibits instances of the use of nearly all of the recognized architectural principles designed for getting the most strength and rigidity out of the least material. The T and I beam principles are used in many of the bones, the most striking example being the sternum, an ideal T beam. Many of the bones are broadened and flattened; there is much overlapping, as in the uncinate processes of the ribs; and there is very extensive fusion of adjacent bones, with resultant increase of rigidity. The vertebral column, with the exception of the cervical region, is practically rigid, extensive fusions having taken place between the vertebrae themselves, and between the latter and the bones of the pelvis. The bones of the skull are almost paper-thin, but are so fused into a unit as to make a practically sutureless brain-box. A large number of bones are lost, especially in the wings and legs, and those that remain are filled with air instead of with bone-marrow. Thus the skeleton of the birds is, among vertebrates, much the lightest for its size, yet the strongest, for it must be to withstand the racking strains incident to flight.

In a sense the bird is also partially a balloon in that quantities of hot air are carried, not only in the extensive air-sac system, but also enclosed between the body and the feathers and among the innumerable feather interstices. Nearly half of the contour volume of a bird is air-filled.

4. Steering and Balancing Devices. — The tail (Fig. 145) with its feathers (rectrices) is a rudder which may be used as well for vertical as for lateral steering. Elevating the tail produces an upward slant, depression a downward turning. Tilting from side to side gives lateral steerage. Expanding the feathers like a fan, or closing them together, increases or decreases the effectiveness of the rudder. Balancing devices are used especially in soaring, when irregular wind currents strike the outspread wings and tend to capsize the vessel. To equalize irregularities of air pressure on the two wings, the bird may decrease the surface of the wing by partially flexing it at elbow or shoulder, or by twisting the tip of the wing so as to spill off the excess wind. Part of the stabilizing equipment consists of the flexible ends of the feathers which bend upward and spill off the air, much after the fashion of the ailerons on an aeroplane. In the bird no elaborate stabilizer is necessary, for each individual is an automaton, with an effective system of balancing reflexes ever on the alert.

Any more extensive discussion of the flight adaptations of the bird would lead us into a technical exposition quite out of place in the present volume. Enough has been presented to impress the reader with the fact that almost all of the characters that distinguish a bird from a reptile are essential elements of its flying equipment. Unless therefore these characters were evolved in connection with flight they are meaningless; for no other set of conditions could have called forth this peculiar combination of characters.

GENERAL ANATOMY OF BIRDS

While most of the anatomical characters of the bird have already been considered in one way or another, or have at least been listed, it seems necessary to present at somewhat greater length a formal description of some of the most important systems of a typical bird.

Feathers. — Nowhere in the animal kingdom do we find structures so marvelously adapted in so many details for the functions

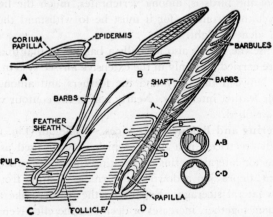

Fig. 147. Four stages in the development of a feather. A, B, C. Down feather. D. Contour feather still in sheath. A–B and C–D, sections of a young contour feather at levels indicated in D. (From Neal and Rand, after Bütschli, courtesy of P. Blakiston's Sons & Co.)

they subserve as do feathers. While most authorities regard feathers as homologous with reptilian scales that have become elaborately subdivided and specialized, there is some ground for taking exception to this view. Studies of the feathers and scales on the legs of the ostrich have led some investigators to believe that feathers were evolved in connection with scales but not directly from them. Paleontology is silent on this point, for the earliest birds known had already evolved the feathers in essentially the modern form.

The grown-out feather, like a hair or a corneous scale, is a dead structure composed of keratin. An individual feather appears in the embryo as a conical papilla (Fig. 147, A) of the skin with an epidermal layer on the outside and a core of dermis (corium). The papilla elongates into a cylinder and its base becomes invaginated rather deeply into the dermis, forming a follicle (Fig. 147, B, C). The innermost layer of epidermis differentiates into a series of longitudinal thickenings, two adjacent ones becoming the rachis or quill of the feather, the others becoming the barbs. All these elements are at first arranged somewhat parallel to each other and form a cylinder with the outer layer of epidermis forming a sheath (Fig. 147, D).

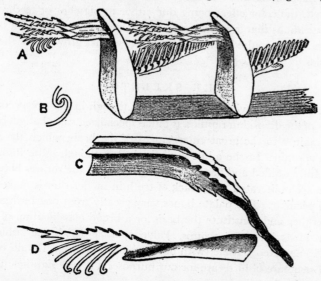

FIG. 148. Details of structure of feather. A. Small portion of feather with pieces of two barbs, each having to the left three distal barbules, and to the right a number of proximal barbules, many of them belonging to adjacent barbs. B. Hooklet of distal barbule interlocking with flange of proximal barbule. C. Two adjacent proximal barbules. D. A distal barbule. (From Parker and Haswell, after Pycraft.)

The barbs are attached serially to the two sides of the rachis, but lie nearly parallel to it until the sheath is shed. Then the barbs spread out laterally on the two sides of the rachis in one plane, and thus form the vane of the feather. Each barb is in itself a complex structure something like the feather itself, for each barb has on each side of its central axis a series of distal barbules, each of which is provided with a group of hooks, or hamuli (Fig. 148). These hooks are so arranged that they grasp the peculiarly shaped edges of the proximal barbules of the adjacent barb, thus serving to connect all the elements of the vane into a very light but strong plane.

Various kinds of feathers are recognized: flight feathers on the wings (remiges), steering feathers on the tail (rectrices), wing coverts, contour feathers, filoplumes, and down feathers in the young.

The feathers are arranged in definite islands, or tracts, on the body surface. These are called pterylae. The shape and extent of these tracts vary systematically in different types of birds and are often of great taxonomic importance. Feathers are frequently brilliantly colored, the color effect being due either to pigment or to the surface striations that give prismatic effects, or to both of these at once. Feathers are moulted periodically and new ones grow out of the old follicles.

THE SKELETON

Skull. — The avian skull (Fig. 149), though in most respects like those of the diapsidan reptiles, is much specialized, the changes being due mainly to the great enlargement of the brain which the skull must contain. In the adult skull the bones, though quite thin, are very fully ossified and are so fused together that the sutures between them are obliterated. The lack of teeth in modern birds makes the skull peculiar. The palate bones vary greatly from one bird group to another and constitute the basis for a broad classification of carinate birds into two groups, Palaeognathae (with old-fashioned palate) and Neognathae (with new-fashioned palate). Details of the skull structure of birds are for our purposes not very significant and will not be described.

Vertebral Column. — The individual vertebrae are elaborately shaped with deep hollows and supporting flanges. The articulation of the centra is peculiar, being saddle-shaped, or heterocoelous. The first two vertebrae, as in reptiles, are the atlas and axis. There are 14 cervical vertebrae, the third to twelfth having the very short ribs fused with them and the last two having small free ribs. There are 5 thoracic vertebrae, the first 4 being fused together and the last fused with the first lumbar vertebra. There are 6 lumbar vertebrae, all fused together and the last fused with the first 5 caudals, which are likewise ankylosed. Thus there is a greatly elongated, solid sacrum composed of 12 vertebrae, including 1 thoracic, 6 lumbar, and 5 caudal. This whole complex is fused firmly with the ilia of the pelvic girdle to form a strong support for the legs, which need a particularly strong base because the bird's body is held horizontally, the legs are set far back near the hind end, and there is no anterior support as in quadrupeds. Behind the first 5 caudal vertebrae come 6 free caudal vertebrae, giving the tail a chance to move; and the last 4 caudal vertebrae are fused to form the pygostyle.

Pectoral Girdle and Wings (Figs. 145 and 149). — This is composed of the scapulae and fused clavicles, the latter united in the middle to form the "wish-bone," and the very large keel-shaped

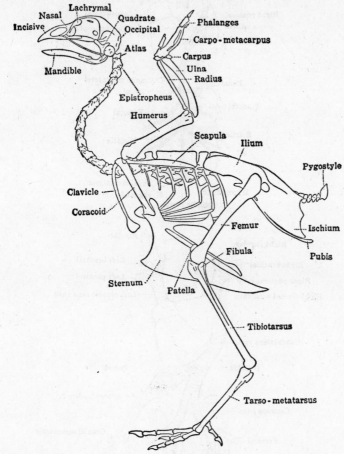

FIG. 149. Skeleton of a fowl. (From Hegner, after Bradley.)

sternum to which the massive pectoral muscles are attached. The wing skeleton consists of the humerus, radius and ulna, radiale and ulnare (the proximal carpals), and the metacarpals fused with the distal carpals to form the carpo-metacarpus. There are but three digits, the first represented by but one bone and constituting the short "bastard wing," or thumb wing. The second digit has two

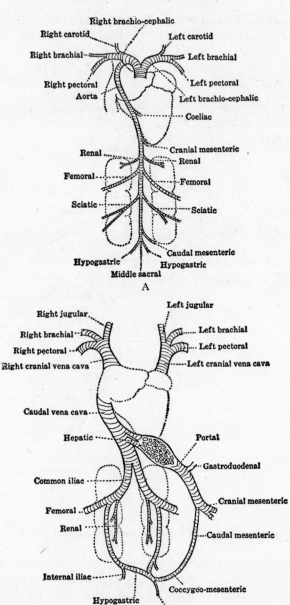

FIG. 150. Circulatory system of a bird. A. Arterial system. B. Venous system.
(From Hegner.)

joints and the third only one. The second and third digit bones are fused.

Pelvic Girdle and Limbs (Figs. 145 and 149). — The whole pelvic girdle, as was said, is strongly fused by the ilia to the backbone, and in the adult bird the ilia are fused to the ischium and pubis. The ilia are very long and extend over a large part of the trunk. The acetabulum, or socket into which the head of the femur fits, is perforated. Both ischium and pubis extend backward parallel to each other, as in the "bird-like" dinosaurs.

The hind limb is peculiar and resembles those of dinosaurs. The femur is short and thick. A knee-cap (patella) covers the front of its distal joint. The second joint is composed of the large tibia with small fibula and the proximal tarsal bones fused with it. The whole bone is called the tibio-tarsus. The distal tarsals are fused with the proximal metatar-sals to form the single tarso-metatarsus. There are four digits, the one equivalent to our little toe being absent. The first toe extends backwards in many birds and is used for grasping a twig in perching. The only two mov-able joints in the leg are at the knee and at the joint peculiar to birds and dinosaurs, the meso-tarsal joint.

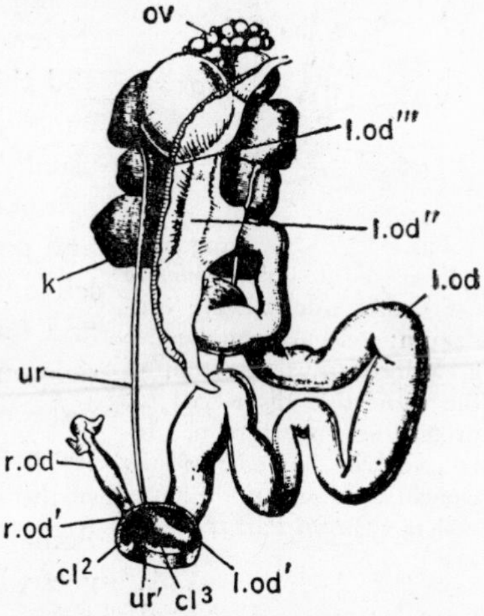

Fig. 151. Female urogenital system of a bird (*Columba livia*). cl², urodaeum; cl³, proctodaeum; k, kidney; l.od, left oviduct; l.od', its cloacal aperture; l.od'', its coelomic funnel; l.od''', its coelomic aperture; ov, ovary; r.od, right oviduct; r.od', its cloacal aperture; ur, ureter; ur', its cloacal aperture. (From Parker's *Zootomy*.)

VASCULAR SYSTEM

The circulatory system (Fig. 150) is in most respects reptilian, but has some special features. The heart is fully four-chambered and there is a single sys-temic arch, the right aorta. The right auricle receives all the venous blood directly from superior and inferior vena cavae, without coming through a sinus venosus. The blood passes from right auricle to right ventricle, to the lungs, back to left auricle, to the left ventricle and out through the right aorta. Hence, apart from the direction of the single aortic arch, the heart arrangement is much the same as in mammals. There is no renal portal system, for the veins leading from the caudal region do not give off branches into the kidneys. There are very large pectoral arteries and veins to supply the enormous wing musculature. In other respects the circulatory system does not differ greatly from that of a reptile.

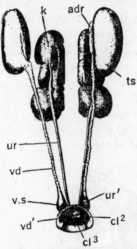

Fig. 152. Male urogenital system of a bird (*Columba livia*). adr, adrenal; cl², urodaeum; cl³, proctodaeum; k, kidney; ts, testis, that of the right side displaced; ur, ureter; ur', aperture of ureter; vd, vas deferens; vd', its cloacal aperture; v.s, seminal vesicle. (From Parker's *Zootomy*.)

UROGENITAL SYSTEM

The kidneys (Figs. 151 and 152) are metanephric and are trilobed. The ureter empties directly into the cloaca and there is no urinary bladder. In the female (Fig. 151) the right ovary is usually vestigial and there is only one oviduct, the left; but in some hawks and possibly other birds, both right and left ovaries and oviducts are present and functional. In most birds the vasa deferentia (Fig. 152) from the paired testes empty directly into the cloaca and the sperms are introduced into the cloaca of the female without the aid of a penis. Some birds, however, such as ducks and geese, have a long and more or less spiral penis. The eggs of birds are essentially like those of reptiles, as are the embryonic membranes.

NERVOUS SYSTEM AND SENSE ORGANS

The **brain** (Fig. 153) is larger in relation to body size than that of any reptile. The cerebral hemispheres are much larger than in reptiles. The enlargement is not due to increased cortex, as in mammals, but to the massive corpus striatum, composed of bundles of fibers. The cerebellum is very large and complex, with a median portion called the vermis and two lateral ones, called flocculi.

In general, the sense organs of birds are much as in reptiles, with some minor differences. The eyes are very large and efficient. Projecting into the posterior chamber of the eyeball is a curious vascular

structure, the pecten, which forms near the spot where the optic
nerve and artery enter the eye. A similar structure, but less specialized, is found in some reptiles. The function of this conspicuous
structure is unknown. In addition to being able to change the shape
of the lens for purposes of accommodation, the bird can also change
the shape of the front part of the transparent cornea by means of a

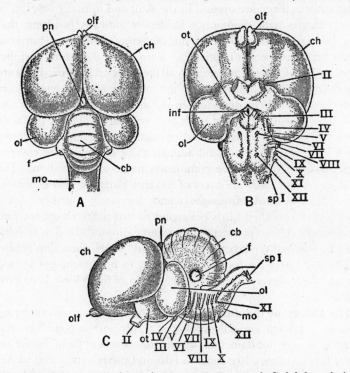

FIG. 153. Brain of bird (pigeon). A, dorsal; B, ventral; C, left lateral view;
cb, cerebellum; f, flocculus; inf, infundibulum; mo, medulla oblongata; ol,
optic lobes; ot, optic tracts; pn, pineal body; II–XII, cerebral or cranial nerves;
sp I, first spinal nerve. (After Parker.)

striated muscle (Crampton's muscle). The auditory part of the membranous labyrinth, the cochlear part of the sacculus, is better
developed than in reptiles but not so well developed as in mammals,
for it is only slightly curved, not spiral. The sense of smell is very
poorly developed, at least in most birds. The olfactory lobes of the
brain are extremely small. Thus the dominating senses of the bird
are those of sight and equilibrium.

The other systems have been sufficiently discussed in other connections.

ORIGIN AND ANCESTRY OF BIRDS

There can be little doubt that the birds are no more than specialized derivatives of the great archosaurian superorder of Mesozoic reptiles. They are diapsid in the skull and in many ways show close affinities with dinosaurs. Evidences indicate, however, that they have not descended from the dinosaurs themselves, but constitute an independent offshoot from the thecodont reptiles (Fig. 123), which were ancestral to all the other archosaurs. Birds are like the ornithischian dinosaurs in the structure of the pelvis, but are more like saurischian dinosaurs in the structure of both arms and legs. Early fossil remains of birds are very scarce. This is probably due to the fact that birds could more readily escape floods and therefore were less likely than land animals to be drowned and covered with aquatic sediment, the commonest mode of fossilization. The most important fossil ancestors of modern birds are two genera of very primitive birds, *Archaeopteryx* and *Archaeornis*, together with a few primitive toothed birds belonging to two different orders, and the fossils of relatively recent ratites and carinates. In lieu of sufficient transitional types between reptiles and birds, discussion of bird origins has taken the form of theories as to how flight got started among birds. Several theories of the origin of flight have been proposed.

The theory of the cursorial origin of flight was advanced by Nopcsa, a Hungarian paleontologist. This author considers that there is a very fundamental distinction between flight based on membranous planes, like those in bats and pterodactyls, and planes made up of feathers; for the former involves marked adaptations of the hind limbs, whereas the latter involves only the fore limbs and leaves the hind limbs unchanged. The hind limbs of birds are essentially homologous with those of the cursorial dinosaurs. It is therefore argued that the origin of flight involved changes in the fore limbs only and that the beginnings of flight occurred while running efficiency was at its height. The conclusion is that the first birds arose from some long-tailed reptile, a hypothetical pro-avis (Fig. 154), that sped over the earth on its strong hind legs, stretched out its fore limbs for the sake of maintaining balance and probably flapped these limbs to aid the speed of running. These flapping fore limbs, or pro-wings, developed more surface, partly by flattening out and partly by the backward growth of the scales of the posterior margin. Similar large scales are supposed to have developed laterally on the tail. The evolution of these specialized flight scales into feathers is thought to have been a mere matter of a continued increase in size and numbers, accompanied by regional specialization; for, accord-

FIG. 154. Restoration of a hypothetical pro-avis, supposed cursorial ancestor of birds. (From Lull, after Nopcsa.)

ing to this theory, a feather is regarded as no more nor less than a specialized scale. The gradual modification of the remaining body scales into feathers would be the logical sequence of events, and the long list of flight adaptations would appear as correlated variations. The first steps in flying would be prolonged leaps, aided by the flapping pro-wings; then short soaring flights would be made, followed by longer flights accomplished by energetic flapping of the wings alternating with periods of soaring. While rather plausible in some ways the theory of the cursorial origin of flight has not gained general acceptance.

The theory of the arboreal origin of flight has met with more widespread approval. Two phases of this general theory have been advanced: the pair-wing theory, and the four-wing theory.

The *"pair-wing" theory* is derived directly from a study of the characters of *Archaeopteryx* (Fig. 155, I). The long-clawed, prehensile, probably climbing wing-fingers of this ancestral bird point toward an arboreal habitat. *Archaeopteryx* is believed to have been not a true flyer, but merely a soarer or glider, capable of only short passages from limb to limb, or from tree to tree. The lack of any foundation for a strong flight musculature argues against the possibility that the creature could have taken any long flight in which propulsion by means of wings would be necessary.

The *"four-wing" theory* of Beebe is the most recent theory dealing with the origin of flight. This author made the remarkable dis-

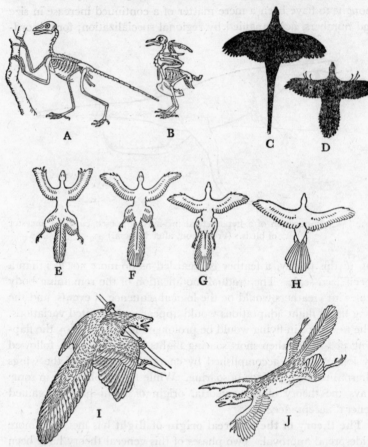

FIG. 155. Group of figures to illustrate theories of the origin of flight. A. Reconstruction of skeleton of *Archaeopteryx* compared with that of a pigeon, B. C, D. Silhouettes of pheasant (left) and *Archaeopteryx* (right) to illustrate two-wing theory of origin of flight. E, F, G, H. Four stages in the hypothetical evolution of the two-winged from the four-winged bird. I. Restoration of *Archaeopteryx*, after Heilmann. J. Tetrapteryx, the hypothetical four-winged ancestral bird of Beebe. (Redrawn after Osborn, *Origin and Evolution of Life*.)

covery that vestigial flight feathers occur on the thighs of a number of species of modern birds. Traces of similar feathers were found on the thighs of *Archaeopteryx*. These discoveries led to the conclusion that the first flyers had wings on both arms and legs (Fig. 155, J) and used both sets in gliding from trees to the ground and from tree to tree. Later the wings of the legs degenerated as the tail feathers took up the duty of acting as a posterior plane, and the arm-wings increased in size and effectiveness as motor organs, as shown in Fig. 155, E, F, G, H.

Gregory's *compromise theory* of the origin of flight is perhaps more nearly acceptable than any of those hitherto given, and is herewith presented in his own words:

"The pro-aves were surely quick runners, both on the ground and in the trees, but it is not clear whether the upright position was first attained upon the ground or in the trees. They very early acquired the habit of perching upright on the branches, as shown by the consolidated instep bones, grasping first digit, and strong claws of *Archaeopteryx*. Their slender arms ended in three long fingers provided with large claws which were at first doubtless used in climbing. These active pro-aves contrasted widely in habits with their sluggish remote reptilian forebears. In pursuit of their prey they jumped lightly from branch to branch and finally from tree to tree, partly sustained by the folds of skin on their arms and legs and later by the long scale-feathers of the pectoral and pelvic 'wings' and tail. That they held the arms and legs perfectly still throughout the gliding leap appears doubtful, for all recent animals that do that have never attained true flight. I cannot avoid the impression that a vigorous downward flap of the arms even before they became efficient wings, would assist in the 'take-off' for the leap, and that another flap just before landing would check the speed and assist in the landing."

Diving Origin of Flight. — So far as the writer is aware, no one has proposed a theory of flight involving the idea that flight may have originated in connection with soaring over the water and diving after fish. Yet there are certain considerations that strongly support such a conception. According to this view the pro-aves used the fore limbs, together with their membranes and elongated scales (possibly also the similar structures of the legs), as planes to aid in diving. The value of such accessories is obvious, the dive being more definitely directed, the descent made flatter so as to carry the diver farther out from shore, and the force of the plunge eased up sufficiently to avoid shock. If the wings were flapped more or less a longer glide out over the water could be made, and possible circling movements could be taken over the water while searching for fish. It would appear therefore that the pro-wings as planes in diving would serve as useful a function as in running or leaping from bough to bough.

We would then have to suppose that some of the archaic diving birds, such as the penguins, underwent a specialization of the primitive wings, using them for under-water "flying"; that others, such as the grebes, never developed them into fully effective organs of flight; while still others, such as the loons, became good flyers though still retaining their diving propensities. According to Dr. Coues, the loon practically flies under the water, using the wings as well as the feet as propellers. The strong flying sea birds would then be derived from ancestral diving types that had gradually perfected their flight; while land birds of all sorts would be derivatives of the sea birds. There are, in fact, many evidences that the sea is the ancestral home of the birds and that they have invaded the land in comparatively recent times. If one turns to Chapter I, where the orders of carinate birds are listed, he will note that all of the most primitive orders of birds are divers or at least aquatic, while the most specialized orders are arboreal. If this classification represents an approximation to the phylogenetic order, the arboreal birds, instead of being the most primitive (as the theory of arboreal origin of flight maintains), are a modern product, and life in the trees is a relatively modern habit.

Archaeopteryx, of course, seems to militate against the diving origin of flight, for it is assumed to be a climbing arboreal bird. But might not climbing be equally appropriate as an aid in scaling cliffs after diving and swimming in the water? Moreover, the teeth of *Archaeopteryx* would be of great service in seizing fish. On the whole, then, the existence of *Archaeopteryx* is no more a barrier to the acceptance of the diving than of the arboreal origin of flight; while other considerations appear to make the former more probable than the latter.

GENERAL CLASSIFICATION OF BIRDS

Among the many different classifications of the Class Aves we have chosen as most simple and logical the following:

CLASS AVES

    Grade I. Archaeornithes, including *Archaeopteryx* and *Archaeornis*.

    Grade II. Neornithes, including all other birds.

Section 1.   Odontormae
   Order Ichthyorniformes
Section 2.   Odontolcae
   Order Hesperornithes
Section 3.   Ratitae (6 orders)
Section 4.   Carinatae
  Group *a*.   Palaeognathae
   Order Tinamiformes
  Group *b*.   Neognathae (15 orders)

A more complete classification of birds appears at the end of Chapter I.

In the present chapter we shall deal with birds of the grade Archaeornithes and with the two entirely extinct sections of the grade Neornithes (sections Odontormae and Odontolcae), leaving the Ratitae and Carinatae to be dealt with in a separate chapter.

ARCHAEORNITHES

Birds of this primitive type are represented by two fossil skeletons with feathers, one assigned to the genus *Archaeopteryx* (Figs. 155, 157), the other to a separate genus, *Archaeornis*. Formerly the two were regarded as members of the same genus, but experts found them unlike in several important respects and have given each a separate generic status.

Fortunately the two fossils are practically complete and well preserved. They came from the Jurassic lithographic rocks of Germany, in which the clear outlines of even such fragile structures as the feathers are clearly etched (Fig. 156). All birds exhibit many reptilian characters, but these ancient birds, about the size of crows, had retained many additional reptilian features. In fact, it is admitted by some paleontologists that, had the feathers not been preserved, there would be little to distinguish these birds from some of the smaller primitive dinosaurs.

The skull (Fig. 157), although already bird-like in being expanded and larger than that of a reptile and with considerable fusion of bones, had a full set of socketed teeth and no horny beak. The tail was very long and slender with 21 separate vertebrae, each with a pair of remiges attached. The backbone was very primitive, with little or no fusion of vertebrae and with separate cervical ribs on all neck vertebrae. The vertebrae were of the primitive amphicoelous type and showed no indication of the saddle-shaped articulation characteristic of modern birds. The arms were but little modified for flight. Three long, separate, clawed fingers suggest their use in climbing. Feathers were attached only to the fore arm, not to fingers

FIG. 156. Subclass ARCHAEORNITHES. Fossil remains of *Archaeopteryx* showing *claws on digits of fore limbs* and *long tail with feathers on either side*. About 20 inches long. (Courtesy, U. S. Nat. Mus.)

as in modern birds, giving a relatively small plane. The sternum was small, keelless, and could not have supported a large pectoral musculature. Hence these "birds" could not have had the power of active flight. At most, they could have fluttered or planed from tree to tree or soared for a fair distance from a height such as the top of a tree or a cliff.

The hind legs, like those of dinosaurs, had the fibula fused with the tibia and the mesotarsal joint as in modern birds. The pelvis was bird-like and the ilia were fused to only six vertebrae, which constituted the sacrum. There was a complete set of abdominal ribs, or gastralia, a primitive reptilian character. It is rather remarkable,

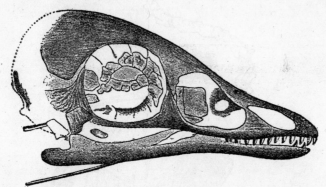

Fig. 157. Skull of *Archaeopteryx*, showing teeth and sclerotic plates. (From Headley, after Dames.)

in view of the fact that some of the dinosaurs had hollow bones, that these primitive birds lacked that avian feature. *Archaeopteryx* and *Archaeornis* are classic connecting-link types and prove conclusively that birds are descendants of reptiles. It would be difficult to imagine a more impressive connecting-link between reptiles and birds than that afforded by *Archaeopteryx* and *Archaeornis*.

It need hardly be said that these primitive reptilian birds are very sharply marked off from all other birds and fully deserve their assignment to a separate subclass.

PRIMITIVE EXTINCT NEORNITHES

There is a good deal of difference of opinion as to the taxonomic position of these ancient birds. Some authorities prefer to class at least *Ichthyornis* as an order of Carinatae. Others combine the two types into one superorder, Odontognathae. We shall regard them as representatives of two distinct sections of Neornithes, each of equal rank with section Carinatae and Ratitae.

As a representative of the Section Odontormae there is but one

genus, the Cretaceous bird, *Ichthyornis* (Fig. 158), which represents
the order Ichthyorniformes.   The bird differs most sharply from

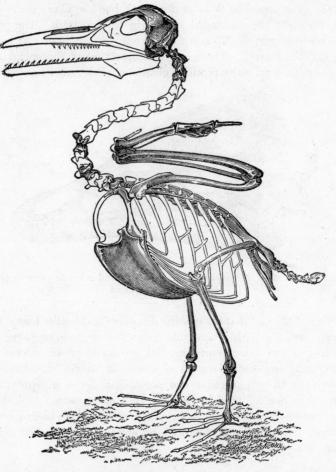

FIG. 158. *Ichthyornis victor*. Restored skeleton. (From Parker and Haswell, after
Marsh.)

carinate birds in having typical reptilian teeth. In other respects it
was not unlike a modern tern in size and general form. Possibly it
was similar to the tern in habits.

The Section Odontolcae is represented by an odd bird, *Hesperornis* (Fig. 159), showing many indications of being greatly specialized as a diver, also belonging to Cretaceous times. This bird

was also provided with a full set of teeth. It was rather large, about the size of a loon and probably with similar habits. It is even more

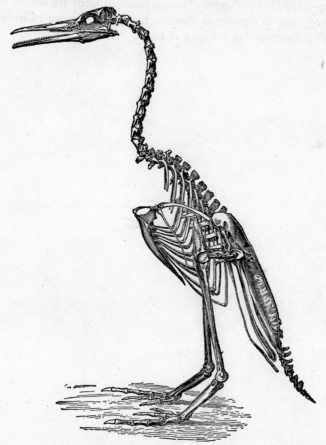

FIG. 159. *Hesperornis regalis*. Restored skeleton. (From Parker and Haswell, after Marsh.)

specialized as a diver than are loons, for the pelvis is extremely long, the legs set very far back and evidently bending outward at the mesotarsal joint so as to act like stern propellers. The wings had evidently been reduced to a vestige, only a slender humerus being preserved. The lack of a keel on the sternum further suggests greatly reduced wings.

All other fossil birds are Cenozoic. Hence about all that we have in the way of Mesozoic fossil birds are the four types just discussed. Paleontologists are doubtless on the *qui vive* for any other links in this abbreviated bird pedigree. Though fossils of birds are scarce, what we have are so significant that we hardly need more in order to establish the reptilian ancestry of birds.

CHAPTER XIX

BIRDS OF TODAY

INTRODUCTORY STATEMENT

Birds of the present period constitute an extraordinarily successful and highly diversified group, comparable in many ways with the teleost fishes. Birds appear to be a climax group, at the height of their evolutionary career. They have undergone very extensive adaptive radiation, being specialized as expert divers, waders, runners, soarers, distance fliers, ground burrowers, cave-dwellers, and tree-dwellers. Some are carnivorous, others insectivorous, others graminivorous, and still others omnivorous.

Among the most specialized parts of the body are feathers, beaks, and feet (Figs. 160 and 161). In some birds, as in penguins, the feathers are short and much like scales; in others they are soft and plumy; and there are all sorts of specialized and elaborated tufts or groups of feathers that are characteristic of particular groups. The coloration of feathers may be plain white or black, but more often the feathers in different parts of the body are colored differently, producing various patterns more or less strikingly elaborate.

Beaks of birds also show a very wide range of specialization. Various types of beaks are shown in Figure 160, and these varieties of beak are adapted to the diverse feeding habits of the different groups illustrated.

The feet of birds (Fig. 161) are as adaptively specialized as are the beaks, and are utilized for different modes of locomotion, perching, and feeding. We note the specialized running foot of the ostrich, the swimming foot of the duck, the diving foot of the grebe, the wading foot of the stork, the seizing talons of the falcon, the climbing foot of the woodpecker, and various kinds of specialized perching feet.

Many birds exhibit pronounced sexual dimorphism, the males usually being the more highly colored and with more elaborate plumage than the female, and possessing masculine head-furnishings, spurs, and other excrescences, while the female is more modest in color and resembles the background. Is it more important for females to be concealed from enemies than for males? Various theories as to the adaptive significance of sexual color dimorphism

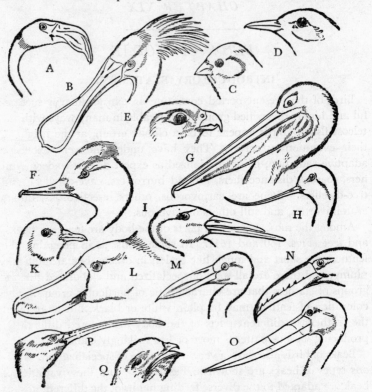

FIG. 160. **The most important forms of birds' beaks.** A. Flamingo, *Phoenicopterus*. B. Spoon-bill, *Platalea*. C. Yellow bunting, *Emberiza*. D. Thrush, *Turdus*. E. Falcon, *Falco*. F. Duck, *Mergus*. G. Pelican, *Pelicanus*. H. Avocet, *Recurvirostra*. I. Black skimmer, *Rhynchops*. K. Pigeon, *Columba*. L. Shoe-bill, *Baloeniceps*. M. Stork, *Anastomus*. N. Aracari, *Pteroglossus*. O. Stork, *Mycteria*. P. Bird-of-paradise, *Falcinellus*. Q. Swift, *Cypselus*. (From Hegner, after Sedgwick's Zoölogy: A, B, C, D, K, after Naumann; G, I, M, O, after règne animal; L, after Brehm.)

in birds have been offered, but this is hardly the place to discuss them.

A large part of the present chapter deals with the taxonomic divisions of modern birds and the natural history of many of the best-known types. In a relatively short course in vertebrate zoology it may be necessary to omit these sections of the book. It is felt, how-

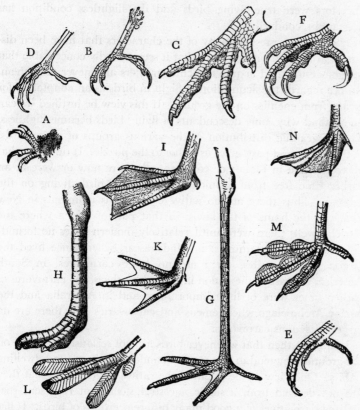

FIG. 161. The most important forms of birds' feet. A. Clinging foot of a swift, *Cypselus*. B. Climbing foot of woodpecker, *Picus*. C. Scratching foot of pheasant, *Phasianus*. D. Perching foot of ouzel, *Turdus*. E. Foot of kingfisher, *Alcedo*. F. Seizing foot of falcon, *Falco*. G. Wading foot of stork, *Mycteria*. H. Running foot of ostrich, *Struthio*. I. Swimming foot of duck, *Mergus*. K. Wading foot of avocet, *Recurvirostra*. L. Diving foot of grebe, *Podicipes*. M. Wading foot of coot, *Fulica*. N. Swimming foot of tropic-bird, *Phaëton*. (From Hegner, after Sedgwick's Zoölogy: B, C, D, F, N, from règne animal.)

ever, that many persons are amateur ornithologists and would appreciate our attempt to present an abbreviated taxonomic survey of this most interesting group.

RATITAE (FLIGHTLESS BIRDS)

There is a traditional problem concerning the Ratitae as to whether they are descended from ancestors that had never developed powers of flight but had been runners from the first, or whether their ancestors were true flying birds and the flightless condition has appeared secondarily.

The ratites possess so many of the characters that have been discussed as adaptations for flight that it seems hardly conceivable that their ancestors had acquired such characters and never used them. Romer regards the acquisition of flight in birds as an adaptation for escape from enemies on the ground. If this view be justified we can understand why some descendants of flying birds became flightless. The geographic distribution of the various groups of ratite birds, both present and past, gives us a clue to the puzzle. It turns out that all ratites live in islands or continents that are now or were at an earlier time free from formidable enemies of birds living on the ground. Thus there are no native carnivorous mammals in New Zealand, the home of the kiwis; in that part of Africa where the ostrich dwells there were until relatively modern times no formidable carnivorous mammals; in Madagascar, where once lived the largest known ratites, there are no large carnivores; in South America, at least in the region inhabited by rheas, the carnivores of earlier times were of little importance; and in Australia and the Malay Archipelago where emeus and cassowaries live, there are no large indigenous carnivores.

It appears then that whenever birds are not seriously menaced on the ground they tend to give up flight and reassume ground-dwelling habits. One view of the origin of the ratites in general is that they are not derived from a single ancestral stock, but represent specialized derivatives of a good many different groups of birds. It has been noted that poor fliers have arisen in several groups. The recently extinct dodo was flightless, the tinamous are poor fliers, and various other inferior fliers among carinate birds are well known. Might the various kinds of ratite birds have been derived independently from as many different ancestral stocks?

This seems hardly likely in view of the following facts. All of the ratites have retained the primitive type of palate, possessed by no carinate bird except the tinamous. Also all the ratites agree in another respect, that the males rather than the females incubate the eggs. It is quite improbable that this combination of peculiar features has developed independently in a number of separate ancestral stocks. It is more than probable then that all the present and extinct ratites evolved from a Tertiary group of flightless birds that became widespread over the world before the carnivorous placental mammals became a menace, that in most parts of the world the ratites were exterminated by the on-coming placental carnivores, but that in some regions that were cut off as isolated land bodies before the placental carnivores reached them, the ratites were able to persist.

Let us now deal separately with the orders of ratites, survivors and those recently extinct.

The Ostriches or Camel-birds (Struthioniformes). — These largest of living birds are more highly specialized as runners than are any others. The foot is a hoof-like running appendage with only two toes, with heavy claws on the short stout toes. Beneath, the foot is heavily padded with callouses. The beak is short and broad but is split back far enough to give a wide gape to the mouth. The head is comparatively small; the neck is very long and flexible. The plumes of commerce are homologous with the flight and steering feathers of the flying birds, but the barbs are not attached to one another as in the flat vane of the typical feather.

There is some difference of opinion as to how many species of ostriches exist. Some authorities recognize only one species, *Struthio camelus* (Fig. 162, D); others distinguish two additional species which they call *S. australis*, and *S. molybdophanes*. It seems advisable to treat these doubtful "species" as varieties and to deal with only one species of ostrich.

Ostriches are confined to Africa, Arabia, and Mesopotamia. They live in arid or desert country, thriving in the Sahara Desert and similar environment complexes. They are able to make good progress in the sand, for the foot is very much like that of the camel. On hard soil they are probably the swiftest runners known, being able to outdistance a good horse easily. They have, however, the unfortunate habit of running in a circle, and thus may be caught by men on horse-back who know how to short-cut across the circle and thus to intercept them. Their stride is said to be fully twenty-five feet and when at full speed the wings are stretched out as balancers and probably partially lift the weight off the ground after the manner of the hypothetical pro-avian cursorial ancestor of the birds.

A single cock has a following of several hens, which lay their eggs in a common nest, a shallow excavation in the sand or dry soil, concealed by débris. The eggs are not left, as is popularly supposed, to be incubated by the sun's heat, but are brooded mainly by the cock. Brooding of eggs is necessary, for the eggs would be chilled and

FIG. 162. Group of ratite birds. A. Rhea, *Rhea americana*. B. The kiwi, *Apteryx australis*. C. Cassowary, *Casuarius uniappendiculatus*. D. Ostrich, *Struthio camelus*. E. Emeu, *Dromaeus novae-hollandiae*. (Redrawn after Evans.)

doubtless killed by the low nocturnal temperatures characteristic of deserts and arid regions.

When cornered, the ostrich fights viciously, delivering a sidewise kick that would compare favorably with that of a mule. They also bite and peck with the strong beak, but the feet are their main dependence. In captivity they are quite tractable and they are extensively cultivated on farms for the sake of their valuable plumage.

Two stupid traits are popularly attributed to the ostrich: first, that he hides his head in the sand in order to conceal himself from his enemies; second, that he eats tin cans, railroad spikes, and similar non-nutritious articles. The first is a slander on this alert, wary, and decidedly intelligent creature; for competent observers report exactly the opposite behavior, in that when hiding it crouches low among the grasses or underbrush and only raises the top of the head and eyes above the shelter. The second is only partially true, and there is method even in this apparent show of madness; for when the bird is in captivity it sometimes is forced to swallow various unusual articles for food-grinding purposes, in lieu of gravel or more suitable gizzard-filling material.

The Rheas (Rheiformes). — The rheas are much like the ostriches in general appearance and in habits, but are smaller and less highly specialized for running. They have three toes furnished with rather heavy, but typical, claws. The wings are better developed and the feathers less plume-like than in the ostrich. The head, neck, and thighs are feathered. The rheas are popularly confused with the ostrich; in fact *Rhea americana* (Fig. 162, A) is called the "American ostrich." This species lives upon the pampas of Argentine, southern Brazil, Bolivia, and Paraguay. They are swift runners, with a habit of doubling upon their pursuers and occasionally lying down in the long grass with only the head protruding. Often they lie in this position until almost trodden upon, apparently relying implicitly on the efficacy of their concealment. When running at full speed they materially aid their progress by vigorously flapping their wings. Mating and nesting habits are almost identical with those of the ostrich.

The Emeus and Cassowaries (Casuariiformes). — These large birds are characterized by: rudimentary wings; long, limp, bifurcated contour feathers; no plumes; three toes with typical claws; legs proportionately shorter than in the two preceding orders.

There are several species of cassowaries (Fig. 162, C), native to

Australia and to several islands of the Malay Archipelago. They live in wooded country, keeping to the densest parts. They are swift and apparently reckless runners, for they go at breakneck speed through the heavy underbrush, over logs and other obstacles six feet or more high. Rivers are no obstacles, for they are excellent swimmers.

The plumage is much like long, soft fur and is used for weaving rugs and ornaments. The head is quite a striking object, generally blue in color, with flesh-colored wattles and an orange stripe down the middle of the back of the neck. A black shield or casque with green sides adorns the top of the head. This color description gives the suggestion that such a head would be decidedly conspicuous, but our modern knowledge of camouflage would lead us to believe that in the dense woods such a broken combination of colors might be practically invisible. A nest is made of leaves and grass and a few large green eggs are deposited therein. As in the other Ratitae, the cock broods the eggs.

The emeu (Fig. 162, E) is a native of Australia and is not unlike the cassowary in habits and habitat, except that it lives in woods that are less dense. They are purely monogamous, differing in this respect from other ratite birds. The male incubates the eggs that are laid to the number of a dozen or more in a hollow scraped out of the surface soil. The flesh is palatable and the subcutaneous fat is used by the natives for oil.

The Kiwis (Apterygiformes). — The kiwis (Fig. 162, B) are frequently called "New Zealand wingless birds." They are the smallest of the modern ratite birds, unless we include the tinamous whose ratite affinities are in question. The beak is long and slender; the neck and the legs are comparatively short; the wings are more rudimentary than those of any living bird and are completely concealed beneath the long, hair-like plumage; there are four toes, but the hallux is quite short. Five species of the genus *Apteryx* are distinguished. These are distributed on the various islands of the New Zealand group, where they occupy wooded, hilly country. These strange birds live a nocturnal life, hiding in burrows of their own making during the day. The burrows are dug out by scratching movements of their strong feet. They can run much more swiftly than one would expect them to do, considering the comparatively short legs. Their stride measures at least a yard long and involves leaving the ground at every step. When they are cornered they strike viciously with the feet, raising the leg as high as the breast and delivering a downward blow. Their food consists mainly of earthworms, which are best secured at night. The bird seizes the worm with the long beak and gently pulls it out of its hole, using a curious wriggling motion. The name "kiwi" was suggested by their loud, whistling note. The nest, if such it may be called, is an enlarged chamber at the end of the tunnel-like burrow and is made by the female. The male, however, with true ratite chivalry, assumes the main responsibility of incubating the two large eggs.

EXTINCT RATITAE

The Moas (Dinornithiformes). — When British explorers first occupied New Zealand nearly a century ago the skeletons of gigantic wingless birds were found scattered about the plains. These skeletal remains were in such a good state of preservation that it seems probable that there were living moas less than five hundred years ago. It may well be that the last of these birds were exterminated by the Maoris. *Dinornis* was in general appearance not unlike the ostrich, but was very much more heavily built in the legs and had either no wing bones at all or at best the merest rudiments of wings. The birds were somewhat taller than the ostrich, with head and neck much like those of the latter.

The Elephant Birds (Aepyornithes). — These birds probably were living in Madagascar less than two centuries ago. They are believed to have furnished the factual foundation for the mythical "Rocs" of Sinbad the Sailor. They were out of accord with these birds of oriental fiction in that they were incapable of flight and were much less gigantic in size, being only about seven feet in height, though of massive build. The eggs were surprisingly large in size, some of those which are still used by the natives as receptacles measuring thirteen by nine inches and having a capacity of two gallons. This is the largest egg on record, though doubtless some of the extinct giant reptiles had larger ones. No doubt this fine bird was hunted out of existence by the native tribes of Madagascar. Possibly the collecting of their eggs was more destructive to the species than was the slaughter of adults.

KEELED, OR FLYING BIRDS (NEORNITHES CARINATAE)

Nearly twelve thousand species of modern birds belong to this great division, as compared with a dozen or so species of all other living birds. The study of birds has grown into the highly specialized science of ornithology, and a very large number of both professional and amateur naturalists and bird-lovers have been engaged in adding to the already voluminous annals of bird lore and pseudo-lore. A vast literature dealing with the habits, distribution, migrations, and adaptations of birds has accumulated, much of which is worthless, because exaggerated, inaccurate, and superficial. But the authentic literature on all phases of bird life is so voluminous that no one but a specialist can hope to keep abreast of it.

The classification of the carinate birds, though elaborate, is in a fairly satisfactory condition. Only in a few minor points is there radical disagreement among authorities. The subdivision of the carinate birds into orders is a highly technical matter, based on numerous criteria which we can not hope to explain to the general student. The ordinal distinctions sometimes seem rather finely drawn, but there is rather general agreement among the experts as to the majority of the orders. Whether these so-called orders deserve to rank as such is a matter that one hesitates to question, but one sometimes feels that they do not deserve any higher rank than do the suborders of teleost fishes. Be that as it may, we shall yield to the opinion of experts and review the groups of birds in the order listed in Chapter I.

THE TINAMOUS (TINAMIFORMES)

There seems to be less general agreement as to the taxonomic status of these odd birds than about any of the other orders. Some authorities prefer to place them among the Ratitae, for they are described as running birds with poor powers of flight and they also possess the primitive type of palate characteristic of all the ratites. On the other hand, they have a well-developed keel on the sternum and are therefore carinate. As indicated in the formal list of orders of the Carinatae, we shall consider them as an isolated group of this section, a group called Palaeognathae Carinatae, keeled birds with the primitive type of palate.

The tinamous (Fig. 165, A) resemble superficially certain common ground-dwelling birds such as quails, but they are not at all closely related to the latter. Their wings are short and rounded; the sternum and pectoral musculature are well developed; the tail feathers are very much reduced, even rudimentary in some species. They are strong, swift runners and are induced to fly only as a last resort. When they have to fly they make a great commotion about it and are able actively to fly only for relatively short distances. Their mode of flight involves an extraordinary effort that quickly gets them up to some height, from which they soar slowly down to the ground and land after covering sometimes as much as half a mile or more of distance. This seems like a fairly good effort at flight and one may well wonder why they have the reputation for being such poor fliers.

THE PENGUINS (SPHENISCIFORMES)

These curious, highly specialized, marine diving birds (Fig. 163, B) have a wide distribution among the islands and continents of the Antarctic region, some species reaching as far north as South Africa and the Galapagos Islands. They are really flightless birds and might on that account be excluded from the Carinatae, but they have well-developed wings and a fairly good keel to the sternum, the wings being used for "flying" through the water instead of through the air; for the wings and not the feet are the chief organs of locomotion; a unique character among diving birds. The legs of the penguin are set so far back on the trunk that in the water they are used primarily as a rudder, and on land their terminal position makes the bird sit practically upright on the tail. The wings are modified into flippers not unlike those of the whale; they are quite devoid of flight feathers and the bony framework is stiff and inflexible. The swimming stroke, when under the water, consists of alternating rotary sweeps of the two flipper-like wings, which drive the pointed body through the water at a fine speed. Penguins live on fish, mollusks, and crustaceans. They are markedly gregarious, especially during the breeding season, thousands of them being congregated upon the narrow confines of rocky islets and points of land along the sea-shores. From various elevations they are constantly diving into the icy water after their food, emerging wet and glistening, but capable of almost instantly drying their plumage by vigorous shaking of the muscular skin. The penguins and the screamers are the only birds that have the skin completely covered with feathers. In the penguins the feathers are lance-shaped and have flattened shafts; they overlap one another in the most perfect fashion so as to shed effectively all water from the skin. Most penguins lay their eggs on rocky ledges near the water. The egg is shaped like a top and will not roll off the precarious nesting place. Certain burrowing species of the Falkland Islands differ rather

FIG. 163. Primitive carinate birds. A. Loon, or great northern diver, *Colymbus gracialis*. B. Rock-hopper penguin, *Eudyptes chrysocoma*. C. Albatross, *Diomedea exulans*. D. White stork, *Ciconia alba*. E. Red-breast goose, *Bernicla ruficollis*. F. Red kite, *Milvus ictinius*. (B and D after Lydekker, the rest after Evans.)

sharply from the others, in that they lay their eggs in rather shallow burrows. The penguins, it appears to us, are so radically different in structure from both flying birds and ratite birds that they might well be placed in a separate division co-ordinate in rank with the Ratitae and the Carinatae.

THE LOONS AND GREBES (COLYMBIFORMES)

This archaic and quite isolated group of diving birds is placed first among the modern flying birds because they possess a more generalized structure than any other. The loon, or great northern diver (Fig. 163, A), is the example of the order most familiar to dwellers in the northern states and Canada. Its weird, laughing cry is one of the outstanding features of our northern woodland life. The ability of the loon to dodge a bullet by diving is proverbial, even if not true. The coloration of this striking bird is a study in contrasting blacks and whites, with a checkered pattern on the back, white breast, black head, and white and black bands on the neck. On land the loon is quite clumsy and makes poor progress in walking. It really never seems to come ashore except for nesting purposes, when it deposits its two large eggs in a makeshift nest composed of trash accumulated in some slight depression not far from the water's edge. Fortunately, the eggs are of a brownish mottled color and are so nearly in harmony with the background that they are very difficult to detect.

Another species of loon, the Pacific loon, has been studied by Coues, who gives the following realistic description of its behavior in the water:

"Now two or three would ride lightly over the surface, with neck gracefully curved, propelled with idle strokes of their paddles to this side and that, one leg, often the other, stretched at ease almost horizontally backward, while their flashing eyes, first directed upward with sidelong glance, then peering into the depths below, sought for some attractive morsel. In an instant, with a peculiar motion, impossible to describe, they would disappear beneath the surface, leaving a little foam and bubbles to mark where they went down, and I could follow their course under the water; see them shoot with marvelous swiftness through the liquid element, as, urged by the powerful strokes of the webbed feet and beats of the half-opened wings, they flew rather than swam; see them dart out the arrow-like bill, transfix an unlucky fish, and lightly rise to the surface again."

Loons are almost as efficient flyers as they are divers and swimmers; in this respect they are more generalized than are the penguins.

The grebes are somewhat more like penguins than are the loons, though they too are good flyers. They are much smaller than loons and have a much wider distribution, being practically cosmopolitan in their range. The European little grebe, or "dabchick," is an interesting little fellow about nine inches in length. It has attracted a good deal of attention on account of its unique habit of taking its young one under its wing when diving into the water to escape from its enemies on the land or in the air. The American eared grebe is characterized by the presence of conspicuous tufts of feathers on the sides of its head that look like ears. The great crested grebe and the pied-billed grebe, which is an American dabchick, are two other well-known species.

THE PETRELS AND ALBATROSSES
(PROCELLARIIFORMES)

These sea birds are characterized by powers of flight more marked than any other group. Because of their ability to travel great distances with the greatest ease they have attained a world-wide distribution.

The petrels are birds of moderate size, with extremely long, narrow wings and hooked beak. They soar about over the waves and dive into the sea after fish, their main food. The stormy petrel is considered by mariners as a prophet of rough weather when it hovers about ships at sea.

The albatross (Fig. 163, C), is one of the largest of flying birds, considerably larger than a goose. The following vivid word picture of Professor Hutton will serve to acquaint the reader with one of our noblest birds:

"With outstretched, motionless wings he sails over the surface of the sea, now rising high in the air, now with a bold sweep, and wings inclined at an angle with the horizon, descending until the tip of the lower one all but touches the crests of the waves as he skims over them. Suddenly he sees something floating on the water and prepares to alight; but how changed he now is from the noble bird but a moment before all grace and symmetry. He raises his wings, his head goes back, and his back goes in; down drop two enormous webbed feet straddled out to their full extent, and with a hoarse croak, between the cry of a raven and that of a sheep, he falls 'souse' into the water. Here he is at home again, breasting the waves like a cork. Presently he stretches out his neck, and with great exertion of his wings runs along the top of the water for seventy or eighty yards, until, at last, having got sufficient impetus, he tucks up his legs, and is once more fairly launched into the air."

Several less well-known types of birds are also classed in this order: fulmars, shearwaters, and diving petrels.

PELICAN-LIKE BIRDS (PELICANIFORMES)

This group of birds was formerly classed among the Ciconiiformes, but more recently they have been given separate ordinal status. The group includes pelicans, cormorants, man-of-war birds, tropic birds, darters, and gannets. These are mostly sea birds of fish-eating habits. They are all excellent fliers.

Pelicans are familiar large oceanic shore birds. They are very common along both the Florida and the California coasts and from there south. The bill of the pelican is provided with a distensi-

Fig. 164. A cormorant. (From Hegner.)

ble pouch on the lower side, enabling the bird to carry a goodly supply of fish to a beach where they may be eaten at leisure. Pelicans fly about in flocks and perform group movements with military precision, often wheeling and spiraling apparently under the direction of a leader.

Cormorants (Fig. 164) are fairly large, rather ugly, dark-colored birds, with face and throat naked. They are highly skilled fish catchers, competing with pelicans along the southern California coast, but extending much farther north than the pelicans ever go. They sometimes congregate in large numbers on small rocky islands near the coast. In Japan cormorants are tamed by fishermen and used to capture fish. Tethered birds dive, swallow fish, and are forced to disgorge them.

Man-of-war birds, or tropic birds as they are frequently called, are birds of the open sea. They are of course extremely strong fliers and seldom come ashore except for nesting. Darters, or snake birds, are not marine, but frequent deep inlets of the sea and fresh-water lakes. They excel as divers, leaving scarcely a ripple upon the surface when they go down after fish.

STORK-LIKE BIRDS (CICONIIFORMES)

These birds are all long-legged waders. The group includes the herons, egrets, bitterns, boat-bills, shoe-bills, hammer-heads, storks (Fig. 163, D) ibises, spoon-bills, and flamingos. These all have a strong general resemblance. They have very long, straight legs; long, flexible necks, huge bills, and slow, flapping wing strokes. They are so familiar as to need but little description. The spoon-bill is an odd stork-like bird with a spoon-shaped bill with which it captures insects, larvae, fish, frogs, etc. They are largely tropical in distribution. Flamingos are large, extremely long-legged, long-necked birds, with wonderful pink plumage. They are good flyers, but are more characteristically waders. In the breeding season they are decidedly gregarious, building extensive colonies of tall, chimney-like nests of mud, that are hollowed out at the top to receive the eggs. These nests, which look like a lot of tree-stumps, are made high partly to keep the eggs out of reach of the water, for they are built on low ground, and partly because they are of a convenient height for these long-legged creatures to sit down upon. One might imagine the rather precarious situation involved in an attempt of these stilted birds to sit down on eggs in a nest built at the level of the ground. In certain respects the flamingos are transitional between the storks and the geese.

THE GOOSE-LIKE BIRDS (ANSERIFORMES)

This order is divided into two quite well-defined suborders consisting of the screamers and the Anseres proper.

The screamers are quite unlike the goose tribe in general appearance and in habits, and it is only on the basis of skull and skeletal characters that they are classed as Anseriformes. They are about the size of turkeys and have a fowl-like head and bill. They are highly unique in two respects; the ribs are entirely devoid of uncinate processes, which are possessed by all other living birds; and they share with the penguins and ratites the distinction of being the only birds having the entire skin covered with feathers, no apteria or naked areas being present. Some writers consider these two characters so distinctive that they would assign to the screamers rank as a separate order.

The horned screamer is the best known species, characterized by the possession of a forward curving brow-horn about five inches in length. It also has on the anterior margin of each wing two sharp claw-like spikes that could readily do considerable damage to an antagonist. The exceptionally loud screaming note of these strange birds has given them their name.

The remaining members of the order are Anseres, familiar types to everyone. The swans are large birds emblematic of grace of form and movement. The geese proper (Fig. 163, E) are the most generalized members of the order, and are intermediate between the swans and the ducks in their characters, especially in the length of the neck. Some of the ducks are among the most brilliant in plumage among birds. Few handsomer vertebrates exist than the male mandarin duck. The eider ducks are natives of the far north and are the most widely known and highly prized members of the duck family. The mergansers, or fish-ducks, differ from the true ducks in having more slender bodies, long compressed bills, grebe-like necks, and in having the edges of the bill serrated so as to give the impression that they have teeth. On account of their fish-eating habits they are not nearly so desirable for food as are most of the ducks and geese, which are largely graminivorous.

FALCON-LIKE BIRDS, OR BIRDS OF PREY (FALCONIFORMES)

Just as the great carnivores among mammals are designated as the "kings of beasts" so the great birds of prey (eagles, hawks, falcons, etc.) are regarded as "kings among birds." The members of this order are characterized by hooked, raptorial beak, strong talons, large crop, and predaceous habits. So much are the eagles objects of human admiration that they have been chosen as emblems of empire; even our own naturally peaceful commonwealth is proud to be represented by the king of American eagles. The order Falconiformes falls into three subdivisions, represented respectively by: the American vultures; the secretary bird of Africa; and the falcons, kites (Fig. 163, F), eagles, hawks, buzzards, Old World vultures, etc.

The American vultures are large birds with exceptional powers of flight, though somewhat sluggish in habit. The common turkey buzzard is the most conspicuous example of this group and is a familiar part of the scenery in most of our southern states. They are economically of considerable importance on account of their effec·· tive work as scavengers, and on this account there are laws protecting them from marksmen. In spite of their value as sanitary agents they are generally looked down upon because of their disgusting feeding habits and because they have a trick of vomiting upon their adversaries. If the truth were known it would probably be found that the buzzard is a victim of chronic dyspepsia due to the unwholesome character of its food, and that it would accept with gratitude any offerings of fresh meat that might come its way. It is said to eat carrion because its beak is not strong enough to enable it to kill living prey. Perhaps the poor buzzard is more to be pitied than censured. The Andean condor, the California condor, and the king vulture are other familiar members of the present group.

The secretary bird (*Gypogeranus*) is perhaps the strangest of all birds of prey. It is a long-legged bird, rather more like a crane in proportions than like the other members of its order; it stands about four feet in height on long slender legs, upon which it places more reliance for speeding than upon its wings. It is especially fond of snakes, though it accepts lizards, frogs, and insects. Its method of attacking a snake is unique. The snake is incited to strike, and when it does the bird side-steps and receives the blow on the edge of its stiffly extended wing. The force of the blow seems to stun the snake momentarily, and the bird pounces on it, grasps it by the neck with its powerful talons, and kills it.

The remaining subdivision includes the following types: falcons, kites, gyrfalcons, duck-hawks, kestrels, falconets, carrion-buzzards, numerous types of hawks, caracaras, true eagles, hawk-eagles, harpies, harriers, and Old World vultures. Several other less known types might be mentioned, but these will suffice.

The golden eagle may well be allowed to represent the entire collection. This characteristic American bird is nearly a yard long and has a wing-spread of nearly seven feet. It is proverbial for its courage, but one is somewhat taken aback by what Major Bendire says about it: "Notwithstanding the many sensational stories of the fierceness and prowess of the golden eagle, especially in defense of its eyrie, from my own observations I must confess, if not an arrant coward, it certainly is the most indifferent bird, in respect to the care of its eggs and young, I have ever seen." On the other hand, Bendire describes this bird as "a clean, trim-looking, handsome bird, keen-sighted, rather shy and wary at times, even in thinly settled parts of the country, swift of flight, strong and powerful of body, and more than a match for any animal of similar size."

THE FOWL-LIKE BIRDS (GALLIFORMES)

This order is a large and cosmopolitan one and is divided into three suborders: Mesitae, Turnices, and Galli. Two of these are small and the other contains all of the numerous types of game birds.

The Madagascar mesite is the sole representative of the first sub-order, Mesitae. It is decidedly aberrant, having a head and bill more like that of a rail than like that of a game bird. So anomalous is this bird that authorities have classed it variously with the rails, with the cranes, and even with the song-birds.

The Hemipodes, or bustard quails (Turnices), representing the second suborder, are in outward appearance not unlike small quails or partridges, but differ so fundamentally from the latter in skeletal structure that they are placed in a separate division.

The gallinaceous game birds (Galli) comprise a large assemblage of more or less familiar types, most of which need no description. Apart from the game birds proper the Galli include two families of unfamiliar birds, represented by the brush turkeys (Megapodes) of Australia and New Guinea and the curassows and guans (Cracidae) of tropical America.

The true gallinaceous game birds consist of turkeys, guinea-fowls, grouse, partridges, quails, ptarmigans, prairie-hens, bob-whites, pheasants (Fig. 165, B), jungle-fowls, and pea-fowls. The most highly specialized types of Galli are characterized by exceptionally gorgeous plumage, notable examples being the males of the golden and Lady Amherst pheasants, which are native to south China and eastern Tibet. As described by Mr. Ogilvie-Grant, the male of the golden pheasant has the top of the head, crest and rump brilliant golden yellow, the square-tipped feathers of the back and the neck brilliant orange, tipped and banded with steel blue, while the throat and sides of the head are pale rust color, the shoulders and remainder of the under parts crimson-scarlet, and the middle tail feathers black with rounded spots of pale brown; the tail extends twenty-seven out of a total length of forty inches. The pea-fowls are almost as beautifully colored as the finest of the pheasants, but they are too familiar

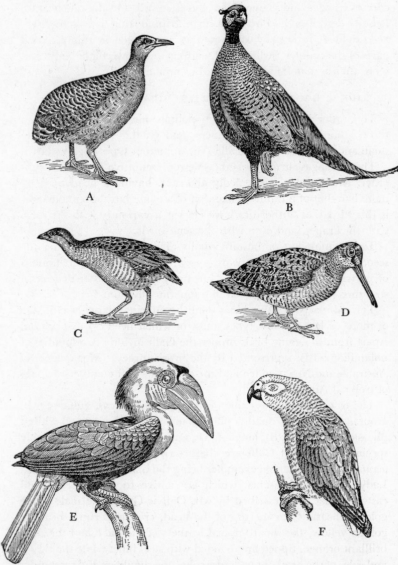

Fig. 165. Representative carinate birds. A. Great tinamou, *Rhynchotus rufescens*. B. Pheasant, *Phasianus colchicus*. C. Land-rail, *Crex pratensis*. D. Woodcock, *Scolopax rusticula*. E. Hornbill, *Rhytidoceros undulatus*. F. Parrot, *Psittacus erithacus*. (Redrawn after Evans.)

to require description. Their native home is in oriental countries, but they have been domesticated and widely distributed by man.

The jungle-fowls deserve special mention because it is from them that the various breeds of domestic poultry have been derived. Four distinct species of jungle-fowl are known, all of them native to the dense jungles of the Indo-Malayan region. Of these it is believed that the red jungle-fowl (*Gallus gallus*) has given rise to all the domestic breeds of poultry. The breed known as the black-breasted game has retained more completely than any of the others the characters of the wild ancestor. The most extreme deviations from the primitive characters of the ancestral species are seen in the Japanese tosa fowl, in which the tail feathers have been known to reach a length of fifteen feet, and the cochins, with their short, plump appearance and feathered shanks.

HOACTZINS (OPISTHOCOMIFORMES)

There is some question as to the right of this small group of birds to full ordinal status. Some authorities class the hoactzins, the sole members of the group, as a family of Galliformes, but others insist that they be assigned to a separate order. The hoactzin, *Opisthocomus cristatus*, is one of the most curious of birds. In the adult condition it is not unlike a small type of pheasant, but it has certain anatomical characters that set it apart from all other birds: the breast bone is wider behind than in front; the keel of the sternum is confined to the posterior part; the crop is extremely large and muscular, invading the space usually taken up with pectoral muscles and the anterior part of the sternum; and the bones of the shoulder girdle are fused completely to one another and to the sternum. The most remarkable features of the hoactzin, however, concern the young bird, which, when newly hatched, has a well-developed clawed thumb and index finger on the wing, reminding one of the condition in *Archaeopteryx*. By means of these wing-digits and the feet which are extraordinarily large and strong for a young bird, these youngsters are able to clamber about among the branches and hunt for their own food. They are really practically quadrupedal in the use of both pairs of limbs in climbing. It is believed by some writers that the juvenile characters of the hoactzin are reminiscences of an Archaeopteryx-like ancestry. Inasmuch, however, as they belong to one of the more highly specialized groups of birds, and inasmuch as no other known type of bird exhibits similar juvenile characters, it seems more likely that these characters are adaptive, juvenile specializations.

THE CRANE-LIKE BIRDS (GRUIFORMES)

The majority of the members of this order are waders, but some, such as the bustards and the wekas, are decidedly terrestrial. The group does not hold together as well as some of the others, and probably should be divided into two orders. Seven families are distinguished, represented by the following types: rails (Fig. 165, C), gallinules, and coots; bustards; the kagu; sun-bitterns; and finfoots.

The common sandhill crane is probably the most abundant and conspicuous example of the larger Gruiformes in America. Coues, much impressed by their appearance in migration flight, writes of them as follows:

"Such ponderous bodies, moving with slow-beating wings, give a great idea of momentum from mere weight — of force of motion without swiftness; for they plod along heavily, seeming to need every inch of their ample wings to sustain themselves. One would think they must soon alight fatigued with such exertion, but the raucous cries continue, and the birds fly on for miles along the tortuous stream, in Indian file, under some trusty leader, who croaks his hoarse orders, implicitly obeyed."

The great bustard is the largest European bird, being about forty-five inches long and weighing nearly thirty pounds. In general appearance it is not unlike a goose, but has a head and bill more like that of a crane. Sun-bitterns are rather small birds something like a combination of a rail and a heron, but with rather short legs, a very thin neck, and large head with long, pointed bill. When at rest the head is sunk down on the body so as to give it the appearance of being practically neckless. The finfoot tribe consists of birds about whose relationship there is a good deal of controversy; some authorities placing them among the grebes, on account of the grebe-like head and bill. The rails (Fig. 165, C) are rather ordinary birds, so far as appearance goes; but they are of interest because they are believed to be intermediate between the two orders, Galliformes and Charadiiformes. In general appearance they remind one of both the quail and the plover.

PLOVER-LIKE BIRDS (CHARADIIFORMES)

This group includes the plovers, snipes, sand-pipers, woodcocks, avocets, phalaropes, curlews, jacanas, etc., all belonging to the suborder Limicolae; the gulls, terns, noddies, skimmers, auks, puffins, murres, etc., to the suborder Lari; and the sand grouse, belonging to the suborder Pterocles. Formerly the pigeons were included in this order, but have recently been granted separate ordinal status.

The Limicolae are marsh and shore birds, with fairly long neck, long slender bill, legs moderately long and slender, short tail and wings, and plumage streaked and of inconspicuous patterns. They usually nest on the ground and the young are capable of running very soon after hatching. Most of them are birds without any outstanding characteristics that might capture the attention. As an example we may well select the American woodcock (Fig. 165, D), a species native to the Mississippi valley. This bird has an unusually long bill, which it uses largely for unearthing earthworms from their burrows. It is said that a woodcock will eat half a pound of worms in a day. It is mainly nocturnal and when flushed in the daytime appears to be dazzled by the light. The jacanas are strange-looking tropical birds, characterized by enormously long toes and claws, by means of which they are able to walk about with ease over the lily-pads, after the fashion of a man on snow-shoes.

The Lari are the gulls and their allies, a group almost too familiar to require description. They are aquatic, mainly oceanic, in habitat, are of medium size and have unusually long, pointed wings. Besides the gulls, terns, noddies and such typically gull-like birds the suborder includes the auks, the puffins, and the murres. The puffins, or sea-parrots, are the most grotesque members of the entire order. They have a brilliantly colored, laterally compressed bill; and their body-form and attitude remind one of that of the penguins. The great auk, a recently extinct species, is of considerable interest. Of it Knowlton says that "its sad and untimely fate has invested it with a pathetic, not to say melancholy history." It used to be extremely abundant on the islands north of Scotland and near Newfoundland, but it was slaughtered by the millions, largely for its feathers. The eggs were also collected so that nothing is now left of that fine species but heaps of bones scattered about the lonely islands. The last living specimen was seen in 1844.

The Pterocles are the pigeon grouse, or sand grouse, a small group that appears to combine the characters of several orders and whose systematic relations are not at all certain. Outwardly they appear to be intermediate between the grouse and the pigeon.

PIGEON-LIKE BIRDS (COLUMBIFORMES)

This order includes the pigeons, doves, the dodo, and the solitaire. The dodo is a recently extinct, aberrant, not to say grotesque, and gigantic pigeon. A funnier looking bird could not readily be imagined, if we may credit the pictorial records of it made by travelers of the seventeenth century. That these apparent caricatures were founded on fact is evidenced by the bones of the bird found in pools. It was a short, plump bird, with an eagle-like beak and ridiculously inadequate plumage, wings, and tail.

Fig. 166. The rock pigeon, *Columbia livia*. (From Hegner.)

The true pigeons constitute a very large and widely distributed group. Perhaps the most interesting and significant of the species are the rock pigeon, the extinct passenger pigeon, and the great crowned pigeon.

The rock pigeon or rock dove, *Columba livia* (Fig. 166), is the species from which nearly all of the fancy breeds of domestic pigeons have been derived; and when fancy breeds are allowed to interbreed freely, the offspring tend to revert to the characters of the wild ancestor. The common mongrel pigeon of the city streets represents fairly closely the characteristics of the wild rock pigeon. The passenger pigeon a century ago existed in numbers almost incredibly large. Wilson, a pioneer American ornithologist, estimates that in a single flock seen by him near Frankfort, Kentucky, there were over two billion individuals. In describing similar conditions, Henderson says that "the air was literally filled with pigeons, the light of noonday was obscured as by an eclipse," and adds that their wings made "a noise like thunder." "Nothing," says Nuttall, "can exceed the waste and desolation of the nocturnal resorts [of these pigeons]; the vegetation becomes buried by their excrement to the depth of several inches. The tall trees for thousands of acres are completely killed, and the ground completely strewed with massive branches torn down by the clustering weight of the birds which have rested upon them. The whole region for several years presents a continued scene of desolation, as if swept by the resistless blast of a whirlwind." Competent authorities insist that this recently extremely abundant species has been extinct for some decades. The fate of this fine species of bird well illustrates the ruthlessness of man when he begins the process of extermination. The great crowned pigeon, a native of the Solomon Islands, represents the climax of the evolution of the pigeon family. It is a noble-looking bird, as much as thirty-four inches in length, with a large erect, fan-shaped crest of feathers on top of the head which gives it a regal appearance.

CUCKOO-LIKE BIRDS (CUCULIFORMES)

This order includes the cuckoos, plantain-eaters, and road-runners. Formerly it included also the parrots, but these have now been promoted to a separate order.

Of the cuckoos Knowlton says:

"Taking everything into account, the Cuckoos comprise a very remarkable and interesting group of birds, being for the most part birds of shams and pretenses, and ever seeking to convey the impression that they are other than they really are."

We might well call them "camouflage birds," a term that would well characterize these interesting traits. They are certainly great mimics both of the appearance and of the voices of other birds. Some cuckoos place their eggs in the nests of other birds. It is perhaps on account of this peculiar parasitic nesting habit that they are best known. Instead of building a nest of her own, the female lays her eggs on the ground and then carries them in her bill to the nest of other birds. The bird thus imposed upon is likely to react against this intrusion by dumping out the foreign egg, or by building a second story to the nest, thus leaving the cuckoo egg walled up in the basement. Doubtless, however, a sufficiently large number of cuckoo eggs are tolerated by other birds to keep up the normal supply of the various species. This parasitic habit belongs only to the Old World cuckoos, for the American cuckoos build their own nests. The road-runner is an interesting terrestrial cuckoo familiar to the inhabitants of the southwestern United States and Mexico. One sees this long-legged bird pacing along ahead of him on lonely country roads, always keeping a respectful distance ahead, but not offering to leave the road or to fly. The plantain-eaters seem to be in some ways intermediate between the cuckoos and the parrots.

PARROT-LIKE BIRDS (PSITTACACIFORMES)

This order consists of parrots (Fig. 165, F), parakeets, cockatoos, macaws, and love-birds. The group is sharply circumscribed, all members bearing a strong resemblnce to one another. There are over eighty known genera, all unmistakably interrelated. They are usually brilliant in plumage, favoring green, yellow, and brilliant red tints, but are occasionally brown or black. They are climbing arboreal birds that use the bill as an aid to climbing, a unique use for this organ. Perhaps the most striking characteristic of the parrots is their ability to articulate. Though their native language is one of discordant screams, they can be taught to mimic human language with moderate success.

ROLLER-LIKE BIRDS (CORACIIFORMES)

This is one of the largest and most heterogeneous of the avian orders, having affinities with the cuckoo-like birds, on the one hand, and with the sparrow-like birds, on the other. There are seven suborders, most of which are not literally roller-like in appearance.

The Coraciae (true rollers and their allies) include: rollers, motmots and todies, kingfishers, bee-eaters, horn-bills, and hoopoes, a rather heterogeneous collection of types in itself. The common roller (Fig. 167, D) is a native of southern Europe, outwardly resembling many of the typical passerine birds. The horn-bills (Fig. 165, E) are the most remarkable of the Coraciae. They are large birds with enormous bill, used by the male as a trowel in the operation of walling up the female in a hollow tree. Whether the female is a restless sitter and needs thus to be kept on the job, or whether the wall is for her protection while she is confined at her intimate task, it is difficult to say. She is fed, however, by the male, through a small window just large enough for her bill to be thrust out.

The Striges (owls), are a well-defined group, formerly classed with the Falconiformes on account of their predaceous habits, but now known to have closer affinities with the goat-suckers. The great horned owl (Fig. 167, E) is the finest of its kind, a wise-looking, powerful bird of great size, described as a "veritable tiger among birds." It kills quails, grouse, doves, wild ducks, as well as all sorts of small and medium-sized mammals. It hunts at night and hides in

FIG. 167. Types of Coraciiformes, showing generalized and specialized species. A. Trogon or quezal, *Pharomacrus mocinno*. B. Toucan, *Rhamphastus ariel*. C. Hummingbird, *Eulampis jugularis*. D. Common roller, *Caracias garrulus*. E. Great horned owl, *Bubo virginianus*. (All redrawn; A, B, C, after Evans; D and E, after Knowlton.)

hollow trees during the day. The little American screech owl is the commonest and most widely distributed of our owls. Some authorities regard the owls as so distinct that they have given them separate ordinal value and have called the order Strigiformes.

The Caprimulgi (goat-suckers and their allies) include the oil-bird, the frog-mouths, the goat-suckers or nightjars, and the whip-poor-wills. They are all much alike, being characterized by rather compact bodies, very short but extremely wide bill, and deeply cleft mouth fringed with stiff hairs, used to trap insects as they fly through the air. Their flight is swift and practically noiseless. Their mournful nocturnal cries sound like "whip-poor-will," or "poor-will."

Micropodii (hummingbirds and swifts) are the smallest of birds. Of the hummingbirds (Fig. 167, C) much has been written in praise of their beauty. "Glittering fragments of the rainbow," Audobon calls them; while Knowlton characterized them as "gems of the feathered race." Small though they be, they are among the most highly specialized of all birds; and therefore, of vertebrates. They seldom alight, but feed while upon the wing, hovering over a flower, poised as though resting, but continuously beating the air with vibrant wings, whose speed of wing-stroke rivals that of the insects. They are the only birds that can fly straight up or down, backward or forward. Their tiny eggs and nests are objects of intense curiosity among bird-lovers; some of the nests are of the size of a thimble and the tiny eggs are like pearls. Though of miniature size the hummingbirds are pugnacious and full of courage, a pair of them not hesitating to attack such giant intruders as hawks and large snakes.

The swifts are less attractive than their relatives, the hummingbirds, and are often mistaken for swallows. The beak is short and broad, and the wide gape of mouth is like that of the goat-suckers.

The Trogones (trogons) are highly specialized tropical birds of comparatively small size, with long tail, short strong bill, and very elaborate plumage. The quezal (Fig. 167, A) is one of the most attractively colored of the trogons, if not of all birds. Its brilliant plumage of gold, metallic greens and blues, and its gracefully drooping, ethereal plumes give it an almost unearthly beauty.

The Pici (picarian birds) include both familiar and unfamiliar types such as the jacamars and puff-birds, barbets and honey-guides, toucans, woodpeckers, and wrynecks. Of these we must be content to examine only the toucans and woodpeckers. The toucans (Fig. 167, B) with the possible exception of the horn-bills, have the most remarkably specialized beak known. Of them Stejneger says: "The first thing which strikes the observer, when looking at one of the large Toucans, is the enormous size of the bill. It is not only as long as the bird itself, but it does not lack much of equaling the body in bulk; and the observer will most likely make the remark that such an enormous bill must be very heavy. The fact is, however, that the bill is extremely light in comparison with its size, being very thin and filled with light, cellular bony tissue." It is not clear of what value such an enormous bill can be to the bird, for none of its activities appear to be connected with this great structure. In all probability this great bill is an example of an overspecialized structure, much like the enormous horns of the extinct Irish elk, which are believed to have finally caused the extinction of the species.

The woodpeckers and the sapsuckers are among the most familiar of our native birds, and they are especially known for their habit of riddling the bark and wood of trees in their search for insects and larvae, and for their noisy drumming while engaged in this task. The finest of the woodpeckers is the great ivory-billed woodpecker, which has a length of about twenty inches.

The order Coraciiformes is so heterogeneous that it probably needs splitting up. As a matter of fact some of the "splitters" among ornithologists have gone so far as to break up this assemblage into half a dozen separate orders.

THE PASSERINE BIRDS (PASSERIFORMES)

This order, consisting largely of perching birds, is for the Neornithes what the suborder Acanthopterygii is for the order Teleostei; the largest, most varied, most distinctively modern expression of the group. Over five thousand species, or nearly half of all known species of birds, are included within this single order. The list of families, thirty-six in number, is too long to recite, but the reader may get an idea of the scope and variety of the order from the following list of representative types: broad-bills, wagtails, rock-wrens, kingbirds, oven-birds, ant-birds, lyre-birds, larks, pipits, fork-tails, thrushes, robins, warblers, gnatcatchers, mocking-birds, water-ousels, wrens, tits, swallows (Fig. 168, A), martins, wax-wings, shrikes, nut-hatches, greenlets, titmice, orioles (Fig. 168, D), birds-of-paradise, crows, ravens, magpies, starlings, honey-eaters, sun-birds, flower-pickers, creepers, quit-quits, tanagers, weaver-birds, sparrows, finches, buntings, etc.

FIG. 168. Types of passerine birds, showing generalized and specialized forms. A. Swallow, *Hirudo rustica*. B. Lyre-bird, *Menura superba*. C. Lesser bird-of-paradise, *Paradisea minor*. D. Baltimore oriole, *Icterus*. E. House-sparrow, *Passer domesticus*. (All redrawn; C, after Knowlton, the rest after Evans.)

In general, it may be said that the passerine birds are of small or moderate size, of conservative or generalized proportions, and without exaggerations of beak or feet. Some of them, however, have developed a wealth of plumage elaborations. Garrod and Forbes subdivide the passerine birds into two suborders: The Desmodactyli, in which the hallux, or hind toe, is weak and the front toes are more or less united; and the Eleutherodactyli, in which the hallux is the strongest toe and the other toes are free.

The Desmodactyli are the broad-bills, a single unfamiliar type native to oriental countries. They do not differ outwardly from the general standard of passerine birds, and are of interest principally to the systematists.

The Eleutherodactyli, or free-toed Passeriformes, comprise all of the remaining members of the order, and can not receive the proportionate amount of attention in the present volume that their importance deserves. For particulars as to the families of passerine birds and the habits of the numerous genera and species, the reader is referred to the many good treatises on birds. We shall merely call attention to a few of the most conspicuous types.

The birds-of-paradise (Fig. 168, C) are without question the most elaborately plumaged members of the order, and constitute a striking exception to the general rule that passerine birds have conservative plumage. The only birds of other orders that compare with the birds-of-paradise in brilliancy are the long-tailed trogons, or quezals, and the hummingbirds, and none of these types have such elaborate feather structure. On the whole, then, these birds may be said to cap the climax in the evolution of plumage specialization. The great bird-of-paradise is perhaps the most beautiful of the numerous species. Apart from the striking color scheme, the most remarkable specializations consist of a pair of dense tufts of delicate, drooping plumes, that vary from two to three feet in length, arching upward and then falling downward in a veritable cascade of glistening light. Anatomically speaking, this marvelously handsome creature is no more nor less than "a glorified crow," for when plucked he is seen to be as plain and common a bird as is his black cousin.

The lyre-birds (Fig. 168, B) of South Australia rival the birds-of-paradise in elaborate structure of plumage, but are not at all brilliant. They are moderately large birds, about two and a half feet long, with rather long neck, and with fowl-like head and beak. Their only claim to beauty consists of the remarkable lyre-like tail. The sides of the "lyre" consist of two large strong feathers, that curve outward from their base, then curve inward, and again outward, at the ends, in most graceful lines. Two middle feathers, almost as graceful as the frame-feathers, cross each other and droop out beyond the outer feathers; while the remaining feathers are long, slender and comparatively straight, and simulate the strings of the lyre. In color these birds are for the most part of a soft brown, and they are not conspicuous in their natural haunts.

The sparrows (Fig. 168, E) are usually placed last in the systems of classification because they are believed to be the most modern type. They are the most numerous and the most familiar of all birds. They are usually small, inconspicuously colored birds, characterized by strong, hard, conical beak, compact form and comparatively short body, tail, and wings. Possibly the most significant event in the history of modern bird life was the invasion of North America by the English sparrow in 1852. It first landed in Brooklyn and spread from there over the northeastern Atlantic states. In a half century it had spread over a large part of the continent and is now probably the most numerous bird species in the world. The English sparrow is a modernist among birds and leads us to discuss the probable future of the bird tribe.

THE FUTURE OF BIRDS

It will have been noted that most of the orders of birds have some very generalized types and some highly specialized types. One could select from nearly every order a representative that is conservatively proportioned and has simple beak and generalized feet. In each order we also find certain types with exaggerated proportions, overspecialized beak or feet, and highly colored or elaborate plumage. If we may rely on the uniformity of nature, we may expect the events of the past to repeat themselves, and if they do, these specialized birds will become still more elaborate and, unable to reverse the course of specialization, become extinct. It is all well enough to be handsome and brilliant of plumage or unduly long of leg or large of bill, but perhaps the birds thus endowed will pay for it in contributing to the prehistoric fauna of the next geologic age, while the sparrow and his ilk will still dispute with other dominant races the domains of earth and tree and air. It is as much as a bird's life is worth now-a-days to have beautiful or elaborate plumage, for primitive man must have its plumes for the adornment of his primitive mate;

and he gets what the mate desires whether he has to hunt the track-less forests for it, or merely pays an exorbitant milliner's bill. Safety and perpetuity for the bird of today lies in homeliness of aspect, adaptability as to environment and food, and a goodly share of pugnacity and resistance to hardship. Let the modern birds con-sider the sparrow and his ways. He is plain and homely, eats any-thing, lives anywhere, builds his nests in strange and unfamiliar places, using new and untried materials. He can whip anything his own size in feathers, but does not needlessly pick a quarrel, and he can put up with either cold or heat, drought or flood; they all look alike to him. Doubtless in the distant future he will probably dispute for the supremacy of the earth with the mouse, the ant, and super-man.

Man owes much to the passerine birds. They give to him who has a naturalistic bent a keener zest for woodland life. Vast numbers of people find their lives enriched by the study of the haunts and varied activities of the birds. As destroyers of harmful insects the passerine birds are of inestimable value to mankind. It is therefore of the ut-most importance that all agencies organized for the prevention of slaughter of the song-birds and other passerine birds, should receive the united support of every zoologist and lover of nature. Organiza-tions such as Audubon Societies and the various sportsman's clubs are doing much to spread propaganda favoring bird protection. The writer of this volume would like to go on record as unreservedly urg-ing the support of all agencies designed for bringing about the en-forcement of laws forbidding the cruel and senseless slaughter of migrant passerine birds.

MIGRATION OF BIRDS

"The desire to migrate," says Seebohm, "is a hereditary impulse, to which the descendants of migratory birds are subject — a force almost, if not quite as irresistible as the hereditary impulse to breed in the spring." Migrations follow more or less direct paths between winter homes and breeding quarters. Most birds breed in the north and winter in the south. Migration paths follow coast lines, as a rule, and such locations as islands, capes, inlets, and other good landmarks are favorite stopping places. Frequently the same birds stop at the same places several years in succession.

Birds have keen powers of orientation, and a strong homing in-stinct. This is not, as some appear to believe, due to a sixth sense, but to a highly developed place memory, or ability to recognize after a lapse of time elements in a landscape that have been observed one or more times before. If a bird is taken to an entirely new region and released it has great difficulty in orienting itself and only succeeds in getting home if by chance it happens to discover a familiar landmark. Young birds are much less capable of homing than are older birds, and need to follow a leader until they become familiar with the route. Some birds migrate in flocks of great size, others in small numbers or even in pairs. The speed attained by migrating birds may be as high as a hundred miles an hour, but the majority of them scarcely attain half that speed. Even at the rate of fifty miles an hour birds have been known to travel a distance of nearly two thousand miles in two days; for they take little rest while migrating, and are often entirely exhausted when they reach their destination. It is during the migration season that ignorant and lawless pot-hunters take advantage of the large numbers of fatigued birds and shoot them in vast numbers, displaying in so doing a lack of sportsmanship truly lamentable.

CHAPTER XX

EMBRYONIC DEVELOPMENT OF THE BIRD

The reader will doubtless recall that two former accounts of embryonic development have been given in some detail, that of amphioxus and that of the frog. These show two steps in the progressive evolution of chordate development. The present account of the outlines of the embryology of the chick reveals a third important advance in the series of four main types of development. The story of mammalian development presents the last and most advanced type. These four types together constitute a fairly adequate outline study of chordate comparative embryology, and should be studied as a unit.

It will be recalled that much emphasis was placed on the major improvement introduced by the reptiles over the condition present in the Amphibia, namely, the invention of the "land egg," with all that it implies. Only a very brief account of this remarkable innovation was given in the chapter on reptiles. In this place the "land egg" and the modes of its development will be given the attention they deserve as among the most significant evolutionary improvements that have occurred anywhere in the whole history of vertebrate evolution. As has already been said, the egg and development of the bird are almost wholly reptilian in character. Hence the following description applies, except for minor details and finishing touches, to reptiles as well as to birds.

The classic type for the study of avian embryology is the common domestic fowl. Usually the study of the development of the chick constitutes the major part of a separate college course in vertebrate embryology. It would be beyond the scope of this course to present any more than a brief outline of chick development.

Egg and Early Embryonic Development. — The egg of the bird (Fig. 169) is a large and complex structure, consisting of the ovum proper, the albuminous layers, shell membranes, and shell. The ovum, or what is usually referred to as the yolk, is a single food-gorged cell enclosed within a vitelline membrane and with a single

357

nucleus, or germinal vesicle. The active protoplasm of the ovum is largely aggregated in a small region situated at the animal pole of the cell, called the germinal spot, where lies the nucleus. This small mass of hyaline protoplasm is continuous with a thin sheath of protoplasm that surrounds and encloses the entire yolk mass and to a certain extent permeates the body of the yolk.

Immediately surrounding the ovum is a thick viscous layer of albumen that is swathed about the ovum and prolonged on opposite sides into twisted ropes, called chalazae, that suspend the ovum

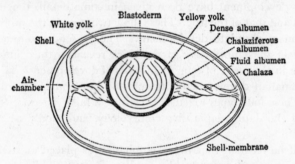

FIG. 169. Diagram of the egg of a bird. (After Bradley.)

from the shell membranes in such a way that it can not come in contact with the shell. Between the chalazal layer of albumen and the shell membrane is a second layer of albumen which is quite fluid in consistency. Surrounding the albumen is the double parchment-like shell-membrane, with an air-space between its two layers at the broad end of the egg. The shell proper is a rather complex structure composed of calcium carbonate; it is porous and more or less pigmented.

Cleavage (Fig. 170) is strictly meroblastic, the first cleavage being merely a furrow, and many furrows are formed before any of the cells are furnished with bottom partitions that cut them off from the underlying yolk. Development proceeds beyond the gastrula stage before the egg is laid. A newly laid egg shows the embryo as an embryonic disc, a small whitish spot at the animal pole, composed of central transparent area (area pellucida) bounded by an opaque ring or germ wall. The pellucid area is two-layered posteriorly, an inrolling of cells having occurred which constitutes the primitive invaginated endoderm and is the partial equivalent of the embolic phase of gastrulation in the frog. The blastopore is crescentic, as in

the frog, and the primitive streak is formed by closure of the blastopore. The head process forms in front of the primitive streak, which
constitutes the axis of part of the head and the trunk.

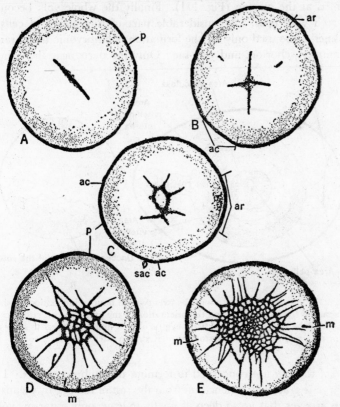

FIG. 170. Cleavage in the hen's egg. Surface views of the blastoderm and the
inner part of the marginal periblast only. The anterior margin of the blasto-
disc is toward the top of the page. A. Two cell stage about three hours after
fertilization. B. Four cells, about three and one-fourth hours after fertilization.
C. Eight cells, about four hours after fertilization. D. Thirty-four cells, about
four and three-fourths hours after fertilization. E. One hundred and fifty-four
cells upon the surface; the blastoderm averages about three cells in thickness at
this stage (about seven hours after fertilization). ac, accessory cleavage furrows.
m, radial furrows. p, inner part of marginal periblast. sac, small cell formed by
the accessory cleavage furrows. (From McEwen after Patterson.)

The medullary plate and medullary groove form much as in the
frog, beginning at the anterior end and proceeding to close gradually
from the anterior toward the posterior.

While the axial parts of the embryo are differentiating the peripheral parts of the blastoderm continue to grow around the yolk, the epibolic phase of gastrulation, new cells being continually formed at the margin (Fig. 171). Finally the whole yolk becomes covered with cells. A considerable part of this sheath of cells is destined to be used only for the formation of embryonic membranes — amnion, chorion, and yolk-sac. Only the parts near the animal

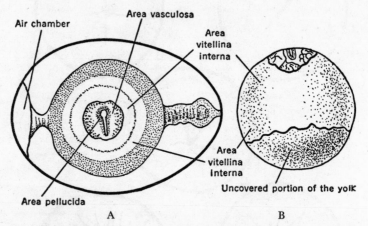

Fig. 171. A. Hen's egg at about the twenty-sixth hour of incubation, to show the zones of the blastoderm and the orientation of the embryo with reference to the axis of the shell. B. Yolk of hen's egg incubated about 50 hours to show the extent of overgrowth of the blastoderm. (Redrawn after Lillie.)

pole of the egg are concerned in forming the embryo proper. The embryo is gradually pinched off from the rest of the egg by means of deep grooves that go so deep as finally to leave only a narrow yolk-stalk between embryo and yolk. An extensive vitelline circulation covers the yolk sphere, and through this means the embryo maintains a nutritive connection with the yolk.

Like other vertebrates, the young chick (Fig. 172) develops four pharyngeal clefts (gill-slits), only one of which actually develops at all fully; this is the eustachian tube of the adult. It has been commonly stated that the bird embryo never exhibits any traces of gill filaments in these gill-slits, but Boyden has described not only in the chick but in several reptiles the transitory appearance of tissues, which he believes are undeniably rudimentary branchial filaments.

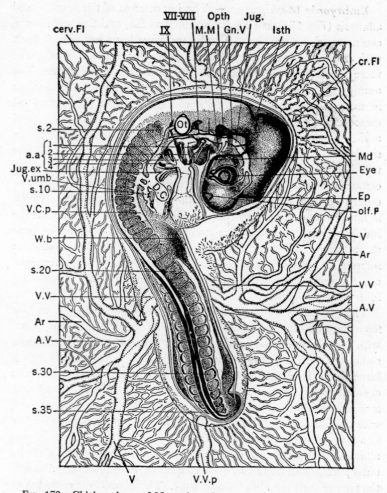

FIG. 172. Chick embryo of 35 somites, drawn as a transparent object. a.a. 1, 2, 3, 4, First, second, third, and fourth aortic arches; Ar, artery; A.V, vitelline artery; cerv.Fl, cervical flexure; cr.Fl, cranial flexure; D.C, duct of Cuvier; Ep, epiphysis; Gn.V, ganglion of trigeminus; Isth, isthmus; Jug.ex, external jugular vein; Md, mandibular arch; M.M, maxillo-mandibular branch of the trigeminus; olf.P, olfactory pit; Opth, ophthalmic branch of trigeminus; Ot, otocyst; V, vein; W.b, wing bud; V.C.p, posterior cardinal vein; V.umb, umbilical vein; V.V, vitelline vein; V.V.p, posterior vitelline vein. (From Lillie, *Development of the Chick.*)

Embryonic Membranes. — The importance of the amnion and allantois (Fig. 173) as adaptations for land life, and their role in the evolution of the terrestrial vertebrates, have been sufficiently dealt with in the chapter on reptiles. In general, the mode of origin of these membranes is the same in the bird as in the reptile. The amnion begins as a crescentic fold of the extra-embryonic blastoderm in front of the head. This fold, which consists of ectoderm and mesoderm only, grows backwards, covering the head like a hood and continues to spread over the body until it meets a smaller, but similar tail fold that has been growing forward. The two folds fuse together and completely enclose the embryo in a sac covered with ectoderm on the inside and mesoderm on the outside. Of course an outer section of the fold is also produced, called the chorion, which is lined with ectoderm on the outside and with mesoderm on the inside. Thus two complete membranes shut off the embryo from the albuminous layers and shell. The inner layer of the amnion secretes an abundant watery fluid that bathes the embryo throughout the entire embryonic period and protects it from shocks and injuries due to contacts.

The allantois begins as an outpouching of the hind-gut not far from the yolk-stalk. It pushes outward as a thin-walled sac, lined with endoderm on the inside and with mesoderm on the outside, grows out between the amnion and chorion, and expands into a large umbrella-shaped body until it fills the entire extra-embryonic coelom, or space between the chorion and amnion. Thus the amnion is covered with the distal part of the allantois and the latter is covered with chorion. In the later stages these three membranes fuse together in a number of places into a single compound structure, the chorio-allantoic membrane. The allantois becomes richly vascular on its outer surface and acts as an embryonic lung, getting oxygen through the porous shell membranes and shell. The allantois is regarded as a derivative of the ancestral allantoic urinary bladder.

The yolk-sac is at first nearly the entire egg, but as development progresses it diminishes in size as the yolk substance is assimilated by the embryo, until finally the tiny sac that remains is drawn into the body cavity of the chick through the umbilicus, and the latter closes.

Changes in Body Form during Development. — It is of interest to note that the tail of the chick of four or five days' incubation is comparatively long and slender, much like that of a lizard at an

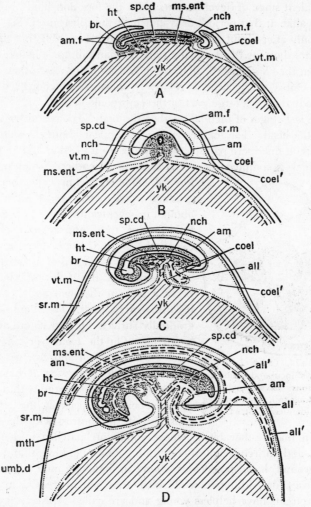

FIG. 173. Diagram illustrating the development of embryonic membranes in a bird. A. Early stage in the formation of the amnion, sagittal section. B. Slightly later stage, transverse section. C. Stage with completed amnion and commencing allantois. D. Stage in which the allantois has begun to envelop the embryo and yolk-sac. The ectoderm is represented by solid lines, the endoderm by dashed lines, and the mesoderm by dotted lines. all, allantois; all', the same growing round the embryo and yolk-sac; am, amnion; am.f, amniotic fold; an, anus; br, brain; coel, coelom; coel', extra-embryonic coelom; ht, heart; ms.ent, mesenteron; mth, mouth; nch, notochord; sp.cd, spinal chord; sr.m', serous membrane; umb.d, umbilical duct; vt.m, vitelline membrane; yk, yolk-sac. (After Parker and Haswell.)

equivalent stage of development. Also the fore and hind limbs are much alike at that period, as is shown in the illustration (Fig. 174). It is only after about ten days of incubation (Fig. 175) that the tail becomes shortened to form the typical avian tail and the fore limbs take on the characteristic features of wings. As in most other vertebrate embryos, the head is relatively enormous as compared with the body during a large part of the embryonic period, and it is only in the last stages of incubation that the body becomes much larger than the head. The feather rudiments appear about the sixth day and are at first mere papillae protruding from the skin. At hatching the chick is completely covered with down-feathers, which are the forerunners of the definitive feathers and gradually give place to the latter. On about the seventeenth day the amniotic fluid begins to disappear and on the twentieth day it is gone. On the same day the chick, by means of a sharp little "egg-tooth" on the point of the bill, pecks a hole in the shell and begins to breathe with its lungs. The allantois then gradually shrivels up and its circulation is cut off. On the twenty-first day the chick bursts the shell and emerges. It is quite a capable youngster at hatching, for it can walk, and see, and within a few minutes begins to peck at the ground. This is quite in contrast with the situation in many other birds, whose young are hatched in a naked, blind, and entirely helpless condition. As a rule, birds that nest on the ground have precocious young at hatching and are called Praecoces, or Nidifugae; while birds that nest in trees or in other safer retreats have helpless young and are called Altrices, or Nidicolae. Intermediate conditions are of course found in many species, especially in those of sea-birds, such as petrels and gulls, whose young are downy at hatching, but stay in the nest for some time.

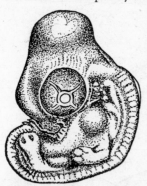

FIG. 174. Chick embryo at five days' incubation, showing precocious development of head, long tail, wing and leg nearly identical. (After Lillie.)

Nesting Habits of Birds. — Any adequate account of the nesting habits of birds would require a volume in itself, for there are countless different kinds of nests and of materials used. The more primitive nests appear to be crude affairs built on the ground, consisting of mere hollows scooped out of the sand or earth after the manner of some of the reptiles. Some birds have no nests at all but merely lay the eggs on rocks; this is probably not a primitive, but a degenerate habit. The members of the higher orders of birds, as a rule, make nests out of grasses or other materials that are suitable for weaving a fabric or basket-like container for eggs. These nests are placed in

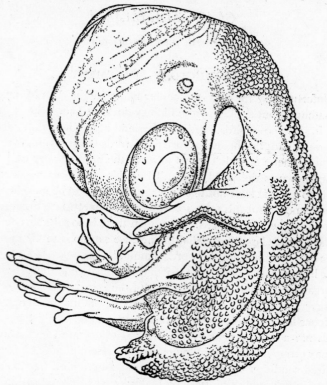

FIG. 175. Chick embryo at 10 days and 2 hours, showing differentiated wing and legs, shortened tail and feather papillae. (After Lillie.)

trees, on cliff-sides, in hollow trees, in burrows under the ground, or in caves. Clay or mud nests are common, especially among swallows. Birds that occupy territory inhabited by man are quick to adopt the various materials that man furnishes, such as string, rags, paper, and other common waste. The use made of various man-made bird houses illustrates the fact that birds are decidedly adaptable and not entirely stereotyped in their form of intelligence.

CHAPTER XXI

CLASS MAMMALIA

(General and Historical)

INTRODUCTORY STATEMENT

Unfortunately the only vernacular name for the class Mammalia is mammals, but the layman in biology does not know what a mammal is. He knows birds, reptiles, fishes and has an idea that a frog is an amphibian; but he uses a variety of words to express his idea of a mammal, none of which seems to serve the purpose very well. He sometimes uses the word "beast," but this term does not seem to apply to men, at least not to all men, nor to whales; he uses the word "quadruped," but this term seems scarcely appropriate to mammalian bipeds, whales, or bats. Since then there is no suitable common name for the class Mammalia, the best we can do is to try to introduce into common use the word, mammal.

It has generally been assumed that mammals represent the apex of organic evolution, or at least that of the chordate phylum. It is, however, not to be granted as axiomatic that the mammals represent a higher level of evolutionary attainment than do the birds; for the birds are a more recent evolutionary product, are more nearly a climax group today, and in many ways represent a more highly specialized condition than do the mammals. In only one particular do the mammals exhibit a distinctly higher order of specialization than do the birds; namely, in brain specialization, and particularly in that of the cerebral hemispheres, which have become far more complex than those of reptiles or birds through the great enlargement of the cerebral cortex, or neopallium. It has also been said that the mammals surpass the birds in specialization of the teeth and of the feet. This is true in a sense, though the toothless condition of the bird and the replacement of teeth by the bill is really a more highly specialized condition than any in which the teeth still persist; while the wing represents an extreme specialization of the fore limbs more radical than anything in the mammals except possibly the flippers of whales. It must be admitted, however, that the bird's hind limbs are rather conservative, for the acquisition of wings has limited foot specialization to some extent. The claim of the class Mammalia to supremacy in taxonomic ranking rests almost entirely upon their superiority of nervous organization and the increased intelligence that has accompanied it. Man as the exemplar of brain specialization adds immeasurably to the claim for supremacy of the class to which he belongs, for there is no dispute as to the supreme status of the human mammal. Without man the mammals would have at best a disputed claim to highest rank among the vertebrates; with man included, the mammals reign supreme.

The mammals are much more sharply differentiated from other vertebrate classes than are the birds. Modern mammals possess a large number of distinctive characteristics not shared by other vertebrates, but one group of mammals, the surviving monotremes, lacks a good many of the characters of typical mammals and at the same time possesses a considerable number of reptilian characters that higher mammals have lost. These monotremes then constitute a connecting-link group, helping to bridge the gap between reptilian ancestors and modern mammals. In this sense they play much the same role for mammals that *Archaeopteryx* and *Archaeornis* do for the birds. Another good series of connecting-link types is the large group of mammal-like reptiles to which reference has already been made and which will be discussed more fully in a later connection.

Before one can really appreciate the significance of the characters that the mammal-like reptiles contributed to mammalian evolution one must have in mind the characteristics that distinguish mammals from other vertebrates. These are listed below:

DISTINGUISHING CHARACTERS OF TYPICAL MAMMALS

Integumentary characters:

1. Hair. The skin is more or less clothed with hair, a new type of integumentary unit quite different from scales or feathers.
2. Sudoriporous (sweat) glands, whose function is that of cooling the body surface by exuding water taken from the blood stream. Evaporation of water cools the surface.
3. Sebaceous (oil) glands, whose function is that of keeping the hair and skin soft and pliable.

4. Mammary glands, whose function is that of nourishing the young.

Teeth:

5. Heterodont dentition, with differentiation into incisors, canines, and molars.
6. Thecodont teeth, each tooth embedded in an alveolar pocket of the jaw bone.
7. Diphyodont teeth, i.e., only two sets of teeth, a milk set which is later replaced by a permanent set.

Skeletal characters:

8. The skull is articulated with the atlas by two exoccipital condyles.
9. The lower jaw is composed of but one pair of bones, the dentaries.
10. The lower jaw (dentary) articulates with the squamosal bones of the skull.
11. The articulare and quadrate bones, which constituted the ancestral jaw articulation, are transformed into two bonelets of the ear apparatus, respectively the malleus and incus.
12. Turbinal bones are introduced into the nasal passages, probably serving to warm the in-breathed air and to catch bacteria and dust.
13. The long bones have diaphyses and epiphyses, that aid in bone growth.
14. The ribs articulate with vertebrae by two heads, capitulum and tuberculum.
15. The body of the vertebra is composed of three pieces, the centrum and two epiphyses.
16. Cartilaginous discs (intervertebral discs) separate the centra of adjacent vertebrae.
17. With a few exceptions, mammals possess seven cervical (neck) vertebrae.
18. The coracoid bone of the pectoral girdle is absent as a separate bone and is represented only as the coracoid process on the scapula.
19. The number of bones in the digits are two in digit I and three in the rest, a lower number than in reptiles.

Blood and circulatory system:

20. The red blood corpuscles (erythrocytes) are enucleate (without nuclei) when in the blood stream.
21. The heart is fully four-chambered.
22. There is a single left aortic arch.

Brain:

23. Great expansion of cerebral hemispheres, especially the cerebral cortex, or neopallium.
24. Corpus callosum, a massive bundle of fiber tracts connecting the two cerebral hemispheres (absent in monotremes and rudimentary in marsupials).
25. Large, complex, solid cerebellum.

Auditory mechanisms:

26. Pinna, an external ear trumpet (absent in some aquatic mammals).
27. Tympanic membrane greatly depressed at the bottom of a passage, the external auditory meatus.
28. The cochlea, auditory sense organ, is spirally coiled (not coiled in monotremes).
29. Connecting the ear drum with the inner ear (membranous labyrinth) are three sound-transmitting bonelets (ossicles): malleus (the old articulare), incus (the old quadrate), and stapes (the remains of the old hyomandibular).

Urogenital system:

30. The kidney is a metanephros.
31. There is a urinary bladder into which the ureters empty, instead of emptying into the cloaca.
32. There is usually no cloaca (present in monotremes).
33. A penis is always present.

Eggs and modes of reproduction:

34. The eggs are microscopic and with little or no yolk (except monotremes which have eggs much like those of reptiles).
35. The ovarian eggs mature in Graafian follicles.
36. Part of the oviducts are specialized to form a uterus or paired uteri.

37. Uterine gestation is the rule (monotremes lay their eggs).
38. Allantoic placenta. The ancestral allantois sometimes has the function of establishing a nutritive and excretory relation with the uterine tissues. (No placenta in monotremes and most marsupials.)
39. Viviparity. The young, except in monotremes, develop in the uterus for some time and are born alive.

Miscellaneous characters:

40. A muscular diaphragm separates the thoracic and abdominal cavities and functions chiefly in breathing.
41. Fleshy cheeks and lips cover the edges of jaws and the teeth.
42. Homoiothermous. Constant, or nearly constant, high body temperature.
43. An epiglottis guards the opening into the trachea.

Of these listed characters the following differentiate mammals from all other vertebrates: 1, 2, 3, 4, 9, 10, 11, 12, 13, 17, 18, 19, 20, 22, 23, 24, 26, 28, 29, 40, 41, 43.

The following characters are shared with mammal-like reptiles, at least to some extent: 5, 6, 7, 8, 15 (possibly 20, 21, 22, 30, 31, 33); 9, 10, 11, and 13 are in the mammal-like reptiles transitional, since they are modified in the direction of mammalian conditions.

Mammals share with birds characters 21 and 42; they share with amphibians character 8; and they share with reptiles and birds the amnion and allantois, although the latter has a changed function.

SURVEY OF MAMMALIAN ANATOMY

A detailed verbal account of mammalian anatomy would be tedious reading and rather out of place in the present connection. Instead, we shall attempt to place emphasis upon and to interpret a limited number of the more general aspects of this field.

The Mammalian Integument. — Under this head we shall discuss briefly hair; skin glands; and claws, hoofs, and nails. The possession of hair is as truly diagnostic for mammals as are feathers for birds. Even the apparently naked, glossy-skinned whales have a few bristle-like hairs on the upper lip. Sometimes hairs may be fused into scale-like or horn-like structures, as is believed to be the case in the "scales" of the scaly ant-eaters and the "horn" of the rhinoceros. Again they may be more or less covered or obscured as in the armor of the armadillos. The hair arises from a slight thickening of the

Malpighian layer of the epidermis, which subsequently invaginates so as to form a deep pocket, or follicle, of the epidermis and a dermal papilla pushes up into the bottom of the invagination after the manner of a pulp cavity in a tooth. Thus the origin and development of the hair is totally different from that of a scale or of a feather. The hair is like nothing else; it is *sui generis*. Its complex structure is shown in Figure 176.

There are many kinds of skin glands among mammals, but they may all be reduced to two fundamental types: sudoriparous, or sweat

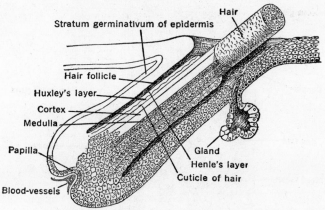

Fig. 176. Diagram, showing structural details of a hair. (From Neal and Rand.)

glands, and sebaceous glands. Generalized sweat and sebaceous glands (Fig. 177) are scattered over nearly the entire skin, while local specializations of both types occur in all mammals. The mammary glands of the monotremes are regarded by Gegenbaur as specialized sweat glands, while those of the marsupials and placentals are surely specialized sebaceous glands. A great many mammals possess scent glands located in various regions. These serve a variety of uses, principal among which are: to attract the opposite sex; to enable gregarious forms to distinguish their kind; and for defensive purposes, as in the skunk and his tribe.

Either claws, hoofs, or nails are present in all mammals except the whales; even in the latter rudiments of claws appear in the fetus and are subsequently lost. The claw seems to be the most primitive type of digital termination. The other types are doubtless specializations of the primitive claw.

Skull. — The mammalian skull is best understood if comparison be made with the reptilian skull, especially that of the higher mammal-like reptiles. The main advances over the latter are associated with four situations: great expansion of the cerebrum; changes in the nasal apparatus; introduction of a new jaw articulation; and

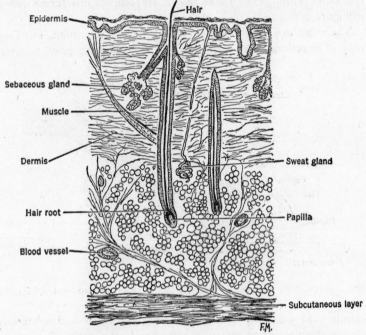

FIG. 177. Diagram of a section of mammalian skin. (From Messer.)

modification of the auditory apparatus. A certain amount of simplification also has occurred, resulting in the loss of certain bones characteristic of reptiles: prefrontals, postfrontals, preorbitals, postorbitals, basipterigoids, quadratojugals, and supratemporals. In the lower jaw simplification has gone to the extreme. Most of the bones characteristic of the reptilian jaw (angulare, surangulare, splenial, coronoid, and articulare) have either disappeared or else have been appropriated by the auditory apparatus, as will soon be explained. The only bones left in the mandible are the paired dentaries in which the teeth are embedded.

The main features of the skull may be briefly described as follows and are shown in Figure 178. There are two occipital condyles, as in therapsid reptiles but not in most other reptiles. The roof of the skull is covered by the supraoccipital, parietals, frontals, nasals. The floor is composed of basioccipital, basisphenoid, presphenoid, vomers, and mesethmoid. The side walls of the skull include petrosal, squamosals, alisphenoids, orbitosphenoids, and the small lacrimals. The lower edges of the side wall, consisting of the upper jaw, are composed of premaxillaries and maxillaries. Running as an arch from the maxilla to a process of the squamosal is the malar bone that,

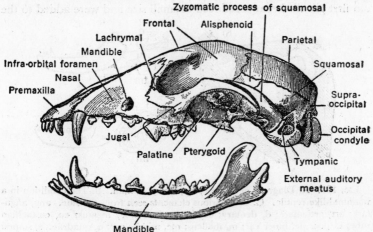

Fig. 178. Skull of a mammal (dog) with mandible detached. (From Wiedersheim.)

together with the zygomatic process, constitutes the zygomatic arch, or cheek bone. With this brief general description of the skull, let us pass to a consideration of some special features that deserve further comment.

Bones of the Nasal Apparatus. — The two nasal apertures, well separated in reptiles, are fused to form a common anterior opening. The nasal, ethmoid, and maxillary bones are extended into scroll-like structures, called turbinals, which are regarded as adaptations for warming and purifying inbreathed air. The nasal cavities, instead of opening into the front of the mouth cavity, as in most reptiles, open into a respiratory passage cut off from the mouth cavity by a false palate. This partition is formed by lateral extensions from premaxillary, maxillary, and palatine bones. This separation of respiratory and alimentary regions of the mouth cavity facilitates breathing while eating.

The Jaw and Auditory Apparatus. — It will be recalled that the reptilian lower jaw is a complex of many bones and that the end bone of the series, the articulare, articulates with the quadrate bone of the skull. The mammals underwent a shortening of the jaw, involving a loss of all bones in the jaw proper except the paired dentaries. This change involved the necessity of a new jaw articulation and the dentary acquired a more anterior articulation with the squamosal. Three of the ancestral jaw bones near the old articulation and the old first gill-slit became reduced to small size and were added to the

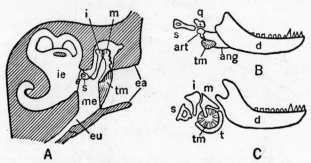

Fig. 179. A. Diagram of auditory apparatus of man. B. The condition in a mammal-like reptile. C. The various elements seen from the side. ang, angulare; art, articulare; d, dentary; ea, external auditory meatus; eu, eustachian tube; i, incus; ie, inner ear; m, malleus; me, middle ear; q, quadrate; s, stapes; t, tympanic bone; tm, tympanic membrane. (From Romer.)

ear complex. It will be recalled that in Amphibia and reptiles there was but a single bone, the stapes, connecting the ear drum with the fenestra ovalis (the opening into the membranous labyrinth where the auditory sense organs and semicircular canals lie). In the mammal this connection between drum and labyrinth consists of three bones: stapes, malleus, and incus. The stapes is the same as that of reptiles and is the inner member of the chain of three bonelets; the malleus is the bonelet attached to the ear drum and, curiously enough, is the ancestral articulare in a new guise; while the incus, ancestrally articulated with the articulare, is the old quadrate, now become the middle of the three bonelets and with a totally new function. A third old jaw bone, the angulare, without any further use as part of the jaw, has further contributed to the auditory apparatus by becoming the tympanic bone, which supports the ear drum and part of the auditory passage. These three old jaw bones, having become useless on account of the new jaw articulation, and lying conveniently close to the auditory region, "were salvaged and put to a new use" in making a more efficient organ of hearing. That this extraordinary transformation was gradual and not too much of a miracle is indicated by the fact that various stages in the change had already taken place in the mammal-like reptiles. Figure 179, A shows the auditory apparatus as it is in man; C, the various elements are seen from the side; and B, the condition in a mammal-like reptile.

To complete the account of the auditory apparatus, it should be said that a further improvement in hearing is furnished by the addi-

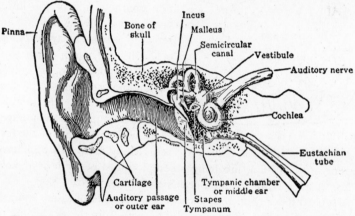

FIG. 180. Front view of human auditory apparatus. (From Woodruff.)

tion of an ear trumpet, *pinna* (Fig. 180), composed of cartilage and skin and capable of being moved about by ear muscles so as to be turned in the direction of the source of sounds. This is important in informing the mammal as to the direction of noises emanating from enemies or prey.

A still further improvement in hearing is associated with a great elongation and increased specialization of the auditory sense organ proper, the cochlea, which in higher mammals is coiled like a snail shell (Fig. 180).

Mammalian Dentition. — The teeth of mammals (Fig. 181) are attached only to the dentary, maxillary, and premaxillary bones. They are limited in number, rarely exceeding fifty-four. The incisors are generally simple in structure and with a single root; the canines, when present, are also simple and with a single root; the remaining teeth (cheek-teeth) are divided into premolars and molars, and show a wide range of complexity in structure and in number of roots. They range from simple one-cusped teeth like canines to those with a number of cusps. The primitive types of cheek-teeth are provided with conical tubercles, and are known as bunodont; a more highly specialized type of tooth has the tubercles connected by ridges, and is known as lophodont. There are usually two sets of teeth, a milk denti-tion and a permanent dentition, a condition known as diphyodont in contradistinction to the condi-tion characteristic of the lower vertebrates, in which teeth are replaced as worn away. In some of the lowest mammals there is no second dentition, or only a partial replacement of the first by the second set. The toothed whales are purely monophyo-dont, with teeth only of the first set. Many mammals also have degenerate dentition, involving a complete loss of teeth or merely a loss of incisors, or canines, or some of the molars.

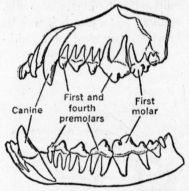

Fig. 181. Teeth of dog. (From Hegner, after Shipley and MacBride.)

A typical tooth (Fig. 182) consists of three kinds of tissue: enamel, dentine, and cement. The enamel is derived from the epithelium of the mouth cavity and is therefore ectodermal; the other constituents are dermal in origin. The teeth arise as tooth-germs quite inde-pendent of the jaws and later become embedded in sockets of the latter. The dental epithelium is at first invaginated as a continuous fold, dental lamina, covering the jaw from end to end; this fold breaks up into enamel organs. At intervals thickenings occur at the bottom of the groove, each of which becomes bell-shaped, with a dermal papilla in the hollow of the bell. The top of the bell continues to grow out as the tooth and soon ruptures the gum and protrudes as a naked cusp. Sometimes the enamel becomes folded into deep grooves and gives to the tooth a complex cross-section, as in the ungulates. The tooth remains hollow, with a pulp cavity in its center, which contains blood vessels, nerves, and connective tissue. The dentine is a bone-like material, but, unlike true bone, contains no living cells. It is, however, permeated by many fine branching and anastomosing canaliculi in which lie nerves and capillaries.

By calling the incisor teeth i; the canines, c; the premolars, p; and the molars, m; it is quite easy to give a shorthand formula for the dentition of upper and lower jaws of any mammal or group of mammals. Thus the dental formula for one side of the upper and lower jaws of a dog is:

$$i\,\frac{3}{3},\ c\,\frac{1}{1},\ p\,\frac{4}{4},\ m\,\frac{2}{3}$$

The formula for a rabbit is:

$$i\,\frac{2}{1},\ c\,\frac{0}{0},\ p\,\frac{3}{2},\ m\,\frac{3}{3}$$

The dental formulae for different groups of mammals vary considerably and these differences are usually consistent within a given group. Hence teeth are of special diagnostic importance in classification.

The Digestive System. — The mouth cavity of the mammal differs from that of the reptile or bird chiefly in that the edges of the jaws, indicated by the tooth line, are not exposed as in the lower vertebrates but are covered by flaps called lips and cheeks. These structures have much

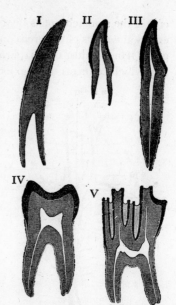

Fig. 182. Diagrammatic section of various forms of teeth. I. Incisor or tusk of elephant with pulp cavity open at base. II. Human incisor, during development, with pulp cavity open at base. III. Completely formed human incisor, opening of pulp cavity small. IV. Human molar with broad crown and two roots. V. Molar of ox, enamel deeply folded and depressions filled with cement. Enamel, black; pulp, white; dentine, horizontal lines; cement, dots. (From Hegner, after Flower and Lydekker.)

to do with the changing facial expression of mammals and are important accessories in feeding and vocalization. We have already referred to the separation of the pharynx into a nasal passage and a food passage by means of the hard palate. Entering the mouth cavity are four pairs of salivary glands. The Eustachian tubes, which are modified pharyngeal pouches, enlarge to form the middle ear cavities in which lie the auditory bonelets. The mouth opens into the oesophagus, which runs through the diaphragm to the cardiac end of the muscular stomach. The pyloric end of the stomach opens by a valve into the duodenum into which empty the ducts of pancreas and liver. The liver is a massive lobed gland lying against the diaphragm. The pancreas lies in the mesentery which connects the two loops of the U-shaped duodenum. The

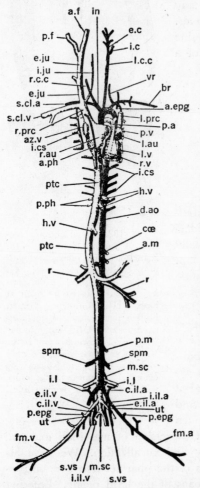

FIG. 183. Circulatory system of a mammal (*Lepus caniculus*). The heart is somewhat displaced toward the left of the subject; the arteries of the right and the veins of the left side are in great measure removed. a.epg, internal mammary artery; a.f, anterior facial vein; a.m, anterior mesenteric artery; a.ph, anterior phrenic vein; az.v, azygous vein; br, branchial artery; c.il.a, common iliac artery; c.il.v, common iliac vein; coe, coeliac artery; d.ao, dorsal aorta; e.c, external carotid artery; e.il.a, external iliac artery; e.il.v, external iliac vein; e.ju, external jugular vein; fm.a, femoral artery; fm.v, femoral vein; h.v, hepatic veins; i.c, internal carotid artery; i.cs, intercostal vessels; i.ju, internal jugular vein; i.il.a, internal iliac artery; i.il.v, internal iliac vein; i.l, iliolumbar artery and vein; in, innominate artery; l.au, left auricle; l.c.c, left common carotid artery; l.prc, left precaval vein; l.v, left ventricle; m.sc, median sacral artery; p.a, pulmonary artery; p.epg, epigastric artery and vein; p.f, posterior facial vein; p.m, posterior mesenteric artery; p.ph, posterior phrenic veins; ptc, postcaval vein; p.v, pulmonary vein; r, renal artery and vein; r.au, right auricle; r.c.c, right common carotid artery; r.prc, right precaval vein; r.v, right ventricle; s.cl.a, right subclavian artery; s.cl.v, subclavian vein; spm, spermatic artery and vein; s.vs, superior vesical artery and vein; ut, uterine artery and vein; vr, vertebral artery. (From Parker's *Zootomy*.)

small intestine varies greatly in length in different mammals, being much longer in herbivorous than in carnivorous forms. Near the junction of the large and small intestine is a caecum, which in some forms such as the rabbit is voluminous, but in carnivores and primates is reduced to the so-called vermiform appendix, a structure that sometimes is nearly solid and has no opening into the intestine. The large intestine, or colon, is relatively short and terminates at the rectum and anus. It would hardly be appropriate in the present connection to attempt a discussion of the functions of the various organs mentioned in this brief account. In general, it may be said that the digestive tract of mammals shows no spectacular advances over that in reptiles.

Circulatory System. — It would be tedious to give a description of the circulatory system in detail. In general, it differs from that of the reptile in but few important respects. The erythrocytes in their functional condition are without nuclei and can live only a short time. They are continually produced in the red bone marrow as needed. The blood is warm and is kept at a nearly constant temperature in part by an elaborate vaso-motor mechanism in the skin, involving the sweat-gland complex and the heat resulting from muscular work. The heart is fully four-chambered or double-barreled, as in the bird. The left auricle and ventricle constitute the pumping system for the systemic circulation and the right auricle and ventricle, for the pulmonary circulation. There is a single aortic arch leaving the left ventricle and arching to the left, instead of to the right as in the bird. A vestige of the right aortic arch is the innominate artery that divides to form the carotid arteries. There is nothing radically new about the venous system.

Details of the circulatory system of the rabbit are shown in Figure 183. This will serve as an interesting comparison with that of the cat, the mammal most commonly used in American laboratories.

Respiratory System. — One of the outstanding characteristics of mammals is that the perivisceral coelom is completely divided by a transverse muscular partition, the diaphragm, into an anterior pleural and a posterior peritoneal cavity. The diaphragm is convex anteriorly, but when its muscles contract it tends to flatten out and thus enlarge the thoracic cavity, causing the lungs to expand and inspire air. It is therefore plain that the diaphragm is an added adaptation for more effective breathing and hence part of the respiratory mechanism.

The essential respiratory organs are, of course, the lungs. Each lung lies in a separate pleural cavity, making it possible for one lung to be deflated without affecting the other. Each lung has a major air-tube, or bronchus, and the two bronchi unite into a median windpipe, or trachea, which is kept wide open by numerous rings of cartilage. At the top of the trachea lies the voice box, or larynx, a modified region of the windpipe composed of muscular bands, vocal cords, that are attached to cartilaginous prominences. Sound

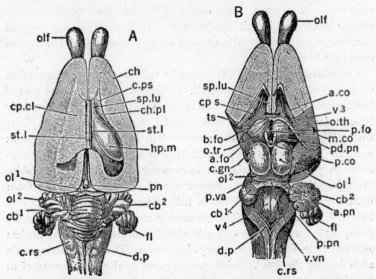

Fig. 184. Brain of rabbit, especially to show corpus callosum. (Nat. size.) In A the left parencephalon is dissected down to the level of the corpus callosum: on the right the lateral ventricle is exposed. In B the cerebral hemispheres are dissected a little below the level of the anterior genu of the corpus callosum; only the frontal lobe of the left hemisphere is retained; of the right a portion of the temporal lobe also is left; the velum interpositum and pineal body are removed, as well as a greater part of the body of the fornix, and the whole of the left posterior pillar; the cerebellum is removed with the exception of a part of the right lateral lobe. a.co, anterior commissure; a.fo, anterior pillar of fornix; a.pn, anterior peduncles of cerebellum; b.fo, body of fornix; cb¹, superior vermis of cerebellum; cb², its lateral lobe; c.gn, corpus geniculatum; c.h, cerebral hemisphere; ch.pl, choroid plexus; cp.cl, corpus callosum; cp s, corpus striatum; c.rs, corpus restiforme; d.p, dorsal pyramid; fl, flocculus; hp.m, hippocampus; m.co, middle commissure; ol¹, anterior, and ol², posterior lobes of corpus quadrigemina; olf, olfactory lobes; o.th, optic thalamus; o.tr, optic tract; p.co, posterior commissure; p.fo, posterior pillar of fornix; pn, pineal body; pd.pn, peduncle of pineal body; p.pn, posterior peduncle of cerebellum; p.va, fibers of pons Varolii forming middle peduncles of cerebellum; sp.lu, septum lucidum; st.l, stria longitudinalis; ts, taenia semicircularis; v.vn, valve of Vieussens; v³, third ventricle; v⁴, fourth ventricle. (From Parker and Haswell.)

is produced by vibrations of the edges of the stretched, flat vocal cords as expelled air passes between them. Pitch is apparently determined by the extent of pressure between the cords in closing off the air-passage. The larynx opens into the pharynx by means of a glottis covered by a flap called the epiglottis, which keeps food from entering the air-tubes.

The lungs of mammals, though not so efficient as those of birds, since they have no air-sacs nor a through draft, are much more elaborate than those of reptiles. The lung of a reptile is little more than a lobose hollow sac, while that of the mammal has the cavity so intricately subdivided into air-spaces that it appears like a sponge

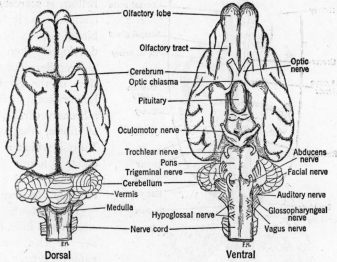

FIG. 185. Brain of a mammal, external views. (From Messer.)

in cross-section. The intervals between air-spaces are pretty well filled with capillaries and elastic connective tissue.

The Mammalian Brain. — Although the brains of certain archaic mammals were not much more highly developed than those of some of the reptiles, those of modern mammals, especially those of the more highly specialized groups, show marked advances over the brains of other vertebrates. The mammal brain (Fig. 184) is relatively large, but the cerebral hemispheres show more increase than do other parts. These hemispheres are connected by an elaborate system of commissures, which serve to correlate the two and to make them act as one organ. The corpus callosum is the most important of these commissures and it reaches a large size in placental mammals, but is rudimentary in marsupials and absent in monotremes. The cortical surface of the cerebrum in all but the most primitive mammals is much infolded into a system of convolutions, which greatly increase the surface without unduly increasing its bulk (Fig. 185). It is not strictly true that the degree of complexity of the cerebral convolutions is an index of the grade of intelligence; for the elephant has the most elaborately convoluted cerebrum, but is hardly as intelligent as many other mammals with less elaborate convolutions. The optic lobes are four in number, but in size they are small. The cerebellum is scarcely as complex as in the birds, though better developed than in any reptile. The two sides of the cerebellum are connected by a broad ventral band of fibers, the pons Varolii, which is peculiar to mammals.

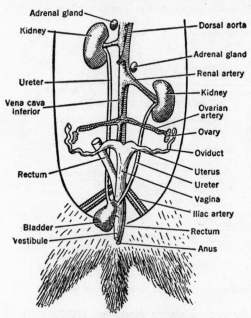

FIG. 186. Urogenital system of female rabbit, ventral view. (From De Beer.)

Urogenital Systems of Mammals. — The kidneys are compact in form and are of the metanephros type. They are usually asymmetrical in position, one lying more anteriorly than the other. The ureters lead directly to the urinary bladder, which is formed out of the remains of the allantois.

The ovaries are always paired, never single as in the bird. They are very small in size, since they typically produce minute eggs with little or no yolk. This small size of ovaries and eggs is in correlation with the habit of uterine gestation. The paired oviducts enlarge into paired uteri, which in some groups unite into a single median uterus. The urogenital system of the female rabbit is shown in Figure 186.

The testes lie at first in the body cavity, as in reptiles, and occupy positions homologous with those of the ovaries. In many mammals (monotremes, whales, elephants, armadillos, and several others excepted) the testes decend into the scrotum, an outpouching of the body cavity. The urogenital system of the male rabbit is shown in Figure 187.

ORIGIN AND EARLY EVOLUTION OF MAMMALS

There can now be but little doubt that the mammals are an off-shoot of the reptilian subclass Synapsida, and more particularly of

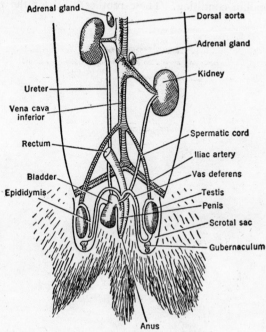

FIG. 187. Urogenital system of male rabbit, ventral view. (From De Beer.)

some type or types of Triassic Therapsida, the true mammal-like reptiles. The latter were probably derived from primitive pelyco-saurs; and these in turn from the stem reptiles, cotylosaurs.

Mammals did not gain much of a foothold in the world of life until the beginning of the Cenozoic, but they began their career long before the Mesozoic, the Age of Reptiles, and were well under way before the dinosaurs and other specialized Mesozoic reptiles had made their appearance. But the world was not ready for mam-mals until the great reptilian dynasties had passed. Nevertheless there are many evidences that the mammals were present and were living obscurely throughout nearly the whole Mesozoic Age. We may think of them as slowly improving themselves during this vast period, awaiting their chance to take over world supremacy. The Mesozoic was, so to speak, a period of training for the mammals.

THE MAMMAL-LIKE REPTILES

The therapsid reptiles approached more closely than any others the mammalian condition. These reptiles lived for the most part

FIG. 188. Mammal-like reptiles of the Lower Triassic of South Africa. Three carnivorous cynodonts are shown attacking a herbivorous contemporary reptile. (From a painting by Charles R. Knight, by permission of the Field Museum of Natural History.)

in South Africa in Triassic times. Abundant fossil remains of many types of these mammalian precursors have been unearthed from Karoo rocks of South Africa, and a few have been found in North America, which represent a parallel line of evolution. Of course nothing is known about their soft parts or of their physiological peculiarities, for only their skeletons have been preserved. It has been suggested, however, that they may have been warm-blooded

and may have given birth to living young, but this is pure speculation. All we know about them must be derived from a study of
their bones and teeth. The shape of the brain, of course, is known
from the study of the cavity of the skull. The bones and teeth, moreover, reveal the fact that these animals were taking on many mam-

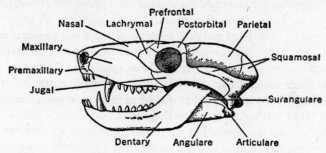

FIG. 189. Skull of a mammal-like reptile, *Nythosaurus larvatus*.
(From Lull, after Broom.)

malian characteristics. Their probable appearance in life is shown
in Figure 188.

The teeth of all were heterodont and those of some, notably the
cynodonts, were well differentiated into incisors, canines, and molars, and in general these resembled the teeth of a dog (Fig. 189).

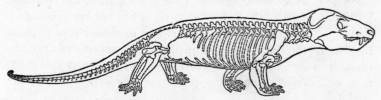

FIG. 190. Skeleton of the Lower Triassic cynodont, *Cynognathus*. About $\frac{1}{18}$ natural size. (From Gregory and Camp.)

The position and shape of the limb joints reveal that the knees and
elbows had been tucked under the body, raising the latter high off
the ground and favoring a mammalian running gait (Fig. 190).
In adjustment to this position, the femur has a knob-like head on the
side, as in mammals. In some forms the digit joints (phalanges) had
been reduced to the mammalian formula of 2–3–3–3–3, while in
others some additional joints, characteristic of reptiles in general,

appear in a much reduced state, as though about to be lost. The dentary bone of the lower jaw was greatly enlarged and the other reptilian jaw bones much reduced (Fig. 179, B). In some types the quadrate bone was very small and loosely articulated to the other jaw bones. There was a large process on the posterior end of the dentary that nearly touched the squamosal, apparently almost ready to form the new mammalian type of jaw articulation. A secondary bony palate (the hard palate), separating the nasal passages from the mouth cavity, was present almost as in mammals. The stapes is already articulated with the small, loose quadrate. There are also many other skeletal features that show mammalian trends. One might be justified in saying that if some of these therapsids continued a few steps further in the directions they had already taken they would become mammals, but we refrain from such a statement, for these particular reptiles were already rather specialized types and in some respects had gone off at a tangent from the main mammalian stock. Some of the imperfectly known later Triassic forms seem

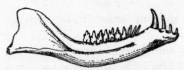

FIG. 191. Incomplete lower jaw of a North American Triassic mammal-like reptile, *Dromatherium*, formerly regarded as a primitive mammal. (From Lull, after Osborn.)

closer to the main line of mammalian descent. A North American Triassic fossil jaw (Fig. 191) was formerly regarded as that of a mammal, but now has been classed as that of a theriodont reptile close to the mammalian condition. As yet it has not been possible to find any particular type of mammal-like reptile that completely qualifies as the ancestor of the mammals. This, however, does not cast doubt on the theory that mammals were derived from some type or types of mammal-like reptiles.

PRIMITIVE MAMMALS OF THE MESOZOIC

The mammal-like reptiles which were abundant during Permian and early Triassic times gradually disappeared and were apparently gone by the end of the Triassic. True mammals doubtless arose some time during early or middle Triassic times, but we have very few fossils of them from that period. Only fragmentary remains of these early primitive mammals have been found in rocks laid down near the end of the Triassic. These have been assigned to the mammalian order Multituberculata, a group characterized by extremely large and complicated molar teeth, with many tubercles (Fig. 192).

During the succeeding period, the Jurassic, mammal fossils are more abundant and three new orders appear: Triconodonta, Symmetrodonta, and Pantotheria.

The **Triconodonta** (Fig. 193) as the name indicates, had cheek teeth with three sharp, conical cusps. They are believed to have been carnivorous, the largest of them about the size of a cat. They seem to have had a relatively short career, becoming extinct at or near the close of the Jurassic and leaving no descendants.

Fig. 192. Skull of multituberculate mammal (allothere) *Ptilodus gracilis*, Palaeocene. (Ft. Union); Wyoming. About natural size. (From Lull, after Gidley.)

The **Symmetrodonta** represent another rather unsuccessful side line of mammalian evolution. They were also carnivorous, as judged by their teeth, and were of moderate size. The teeth had three cusps arranged in a symmetrical triangle, but the cusp arrangement was entirely different from that of the Triconodonta. These forms were confined to a relatively short period near the end of the Jurassic and seem to have left no descendants.

The **Pantotheria** (sometimes called Trituberculata on account of the three tubercles on the teeth) constitute a relatively numerous series of small mammals about the size of rats or mice. They are

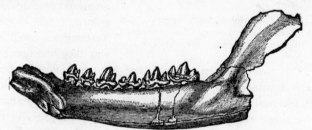

Fig. 193. Jaw of triconodont mammal, *Triconodon ferox*, Comanchian, Wyoming. Three times natural size. (From Lull, after Marsh.)

regarded as either the ancestors of later mammals or as close to the stock from which the latter were derived. The detailed structure of their teeth is such that they are believed to be the basic type from which the teeth of all higher mammals evolved. Fossil remains of pantotheres are confined to the last half of the Jurassic, but they may have survived into the Cretaceous.

Near the close of the Cretaceous the first known **Marsupials** and **Placentals** appeared. Marsupials were at first more numerous and placentals relatively rare. All these late Cretaceous forms were small insectivorous types, as judged by the teeth. Available evidences suggest that marsupials and placentals came off independently from different types of pantotheres, the marsupials probably arising somewhat earlier than the placentals. All of the Mesozoic mammals lived an obscure life during the reign of the Ruling Reptiles, but with the extinction of their reptilian rivals the situation changes.

THE CAREER OF CENOZOIC MAMMALS

At the very beginning of the Cenozoic Age (the Age of Mammals) the mammals found the land cleared of the most formidable reptiles and wide open for exploitation. The birds apparently had an equal opportunity to take over leadership, but went off upon a side line of specialization, becoming denizens of the air, leaving the land surface free for the mammals. At first the marsupials and the placentals were on a fairly equal footing. During the late Cretaceous and the early Tertiary times the marsupials had an almost world-wide dis-

Fig. 194. Cursorial archaic mammal, condylarth, *Phenacodus primaevus*. Lower Eocene, North America. (From Lull, after Osborn.)

tribution, but, before the Tertiary was well under way they had become restricted to two southern regions that became isolated from the northern continents by land subsidence. These two regions are Australasia and South America, the only regions where marsupials, with the single exception of the American opossums, survive today. These North American opossums are sometimes regarded as relatively recent migrants from South America. Apparently the marsupials in their spread over the land bodies of the world had reached Australia and South America ahead of the placentals, and these regions were then cut off before placentals had reached them. The marsupials in these places were able to survive. In all other parts of the world, however, it appears that they were unable to compete with the more efficient placentals and were exterminated in early Tertiary times.

During the Palaeocene, the first period of the Cenozoic Age, the placental mammals found the world wide open for exploitation. The earliest and most primitive placentals of this period were small forms with rather generalized food habits, but primarily insectivorous. Rather well preserved skulls of rat-sized placentals of a most primitive sort have recently been found in Cretaceous rocks of Mongolia. These are not so very different in their dentition and other features from shrews of the order Insectivora. From these stem placentals there split off a considerable number of independent evolutionary lines, most of which grew to larger size.

FIG. 195. A swamp-dwelling amblypod, *Coryphodon*, Lower Eocene, North America. (From Lull, after Osborn.)

During the Eocene, the second period of the Cenozoic, all the main orders of mammals had been established, apparently as offshoots of the ancestral insectivores. Several orders of these archaic placentals, notably Condylarthra (Fig. 194), Amblypoda, Tillodontia, and

FIG. 196. Four-horned amblypod, *Dinoceras*, the culmination of its race, Upper Eocene, Wyoming. (From Lull, after Osborn.)

Taeniodontia, became extinct before or shortly after the end of the Eocene. These mammals, especially the slow-footed amblypods (Figs. 195, 196), were small-brained and had a poorly developed neopallium. Doubtless it was this failure to keep pace with the other mammals in brain specialization and intelligence that brought about their extinction. Another order of primitive placentals, Creodonta (Fig. 197), had greater success and are regarded as ancestral to both modern Carnivora and Cetacea (whales).

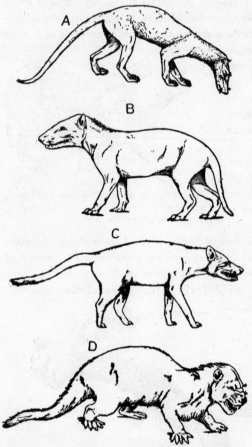

There is some evidence also that the Perissodactyla may have come off as a side line from Palaeocene condylarthran stock, but there is no evidence that any of the other orders listed above as extinct have any surviving descendants. The other orders of surviving mammals trace back to the primitive stem placentals or have branched off from each other. Placental mammals reached their height during Oligocene and Miocene times, and as a group have declined since that time. A good many orders that were well represented during these two periods are now extinct or rare. At present the Rodentia, Artiodactyla, Carnivora, Chiroptera, and Primates are holding their own. All the other orders are on the wane and some are even bordering on extinction. Most of the orders

FIG. 197. Creodonts. A. *Tritemnodon*, a primitive hyaenodont, Middle Eocene, North America. (After Scott.) B. *Hyaenodon*, the last survivor of the archaic carnivores, Lower Oligocene, North America and Old World. (After Osborn.) C. The dog-like *Dromocyon*, Middle Eocene, North America. (After Osborn.) D. *Patriofelis*, Middle Eocene, North America. (All from Lull, after Osborn.)

of placental mammals are doomed except as man sees fit to preserve them.

The evolutionary history of placental mammals may be conveniently visualized by reference to Figure 198, where one may get an idea of the time of origin, time of extinction (if extinct) and period

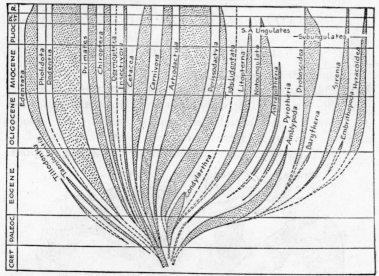

Fig. 198. Diagram indicating the relationships, time of origin, and periods of greatest success of the orders of placental mammals. (From Romer.)

of greatest abundance of each of the many orders. This diagram also shows the interrelations of the orders in so far as they have been determined.

The classification of mammals adopted in this book is found at the end of Chapter I, and need not be repeated here. The assemblages of placental mammal orders are those suggested by W. K. Gregory in his scholarly volume *The Orders of Mammals*.

CHAPTER XXII

MONOTREMES AND MARSUPIALS

I. MONOTREMATA (PROTOTHERIA)

The monotremes are sometimes referred to as "living fossils," implying that the surviving types represent a very primitive level of mammalian evolution. Actually they constitute a sort of connecting-link between mammals and their reptilian ancestors and serve to bridge the gap between these two classes in somewhat the same fashion that *Archaeopteryx* connects birds with the Ruling Reptiles.

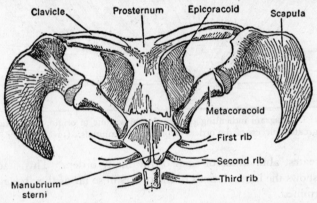

Fig. 199. Pectoral arch and sternum of *Ornithorhynchus*. (From Wiedersheim.)

Monotremes are fully mammalian in some respects, but in other respects almost as fully reptilian. One might designate them as unfinished mammals. Like typical mammals they have hair, sweat and oil glands, and mammary glands of a sort, though these are regarded by Gegenbaur as derivatives of sweat glands, while those of all other mammals are modified sebaceous glands. The cerebral cortex is only moderately developed; the jaw is composed of dentaries only; the three ear bonelets are proportionately larger than in higher mammals; an external ear pinna is present in one genus; the ear drum is depressed; the cochlea is only slightly coiled; the circulatory system is almost fully mammalian; a diaphragm is present; and in several other ways they are typically mammalian.

They are reptilian, or at least transitional between mammals and reptiles, in a great many respects:

1. The pectoral girdle is distinctly reptilian in that it possesses separate large coracoid bones, an interclavicle, and lacks the spine or supraspinous area (Fig. 199).

2. The pelvic girdle possesses epipubic, or marsupial bones, extending from the front of the pelvis.

3. The ribs, except the cervicals, are one-headed, the tuberculum being absent.

4. Cervical ribs, absent in higher mammals but present in all reptiles, are well represented.

5. The vertebrae are for the most part without epiphyses.

6. In many ways the bones of the skull are reptilian or else transitional. The lacrimal is absent, the jugal reduced or absent, traces of a reptilian prevomer are present, there is no auditory bulla, and several other skull characters suggest the reptilian condition.

7. They are not fully homoiothermous in that there is a fluctuation of body temperature in health of as much as 15° Centigrade.

8. The paired oviducts are separate throughout and open by two separate genital pores into the cloaca.

9. There is a rather shallow cloaca. (The term Monotremata refers to the fact that there is but one opening externally, that of the cloaca.)

10. They lay eggs that are in most respects like those of reptiles.

11. The embryonic development, including yolk-sac circulation, amnion, and allantois, is strikingly reptilian.

12. There is no corpus callosum connecting the cerebral hemispheres.

13. The cochlea is a simple process of the sacculus as in reptiles and is not coiled as in higher mammals.

It appears then that the monotremes are roughly about half-and-half in their mammalian and reptilian characters. They are, however, without doubt mammals, but mammals that have failed to complete many of the evolutionary transformations characteristic of higher mammals.

Were teeth at all well developed in the monotremes it would be possible perhaps to determine from them the affinities of this isolated group with some early fossil types, but only a few embryonic teeth

are developed and these disappear in the adult. Thus the monotremes lack all of the characteristic tooth features that are diagnostic
of mammalian orders.

The prevailing view as to the taxonomic status of the monotremes
is that they represent the end product of a slender evolutionary line
of mammal-like forms that probably arose from some different
mammal-like reptile stock than that which gave rise to any other
mammalian groups. It is believed that they originated during the
Triassic along with the Multituberculata, but were not derived from
the latter. There is almost no fossil record of monotremes, only one
extinct Echidna-like fossil from the Pleistocene of Australia having
been found.

In view of these considerations we shall regard the monotremes
as in no sense ancestral to higher mammals, but as a side line of
mammalian evolution. They probably represent conditions parallel
to those passed through by the mammal-like reptiles that were ancestral to higher mammals. The present status of the surviving
monotremes is that they are extremely primitive in many important
respects, degenerate in others, and highly specialized in still others.
These two groups, ant-eaters and platypus, are specialized along
totally different lines for two utterly different modes of life. We shall
devote some pages to an account of their natural history.

NATURAL HISTORY OF MONOTREMES

Family 1. Echidnidae. — This family contains two genera,
Echidna and *Proechidna*. *Echidna aculeata* (Fig. 200, D), the Australian spiny ant-eater, is the best known species. It is found in New
Guinea, Tasmania, and Australia, and several local subspecies are
distinguished. Its characters may be dealt with under two categories: those that are cenogenetic, adaptations for the ant-eating
habit; and those that are palingenetic or primitive.

Echidna is a typical ant-eater in all of its adaptations. It has a
heavy protective covering of quill-like spines, with an underlying
layer of coarse hair. The snout is long and tapering, reminding one
rather strongly of a bird's bill. The tongue is extremely long and
extensible and is covered with a sticky salivary secretion, which
holds the ants when the tongue is thrust into ant-holes. The claws
are very long and powerful and are used for tearing down ant-
hills or termite nests and for making burrows. As in ant-eaters of

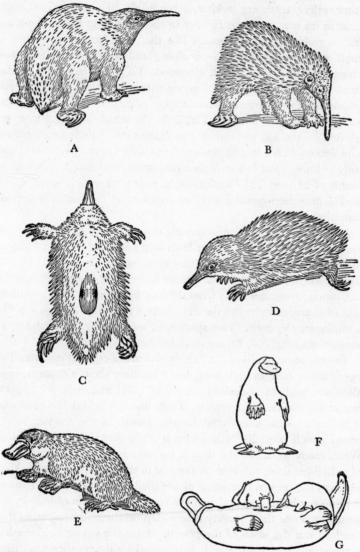

FIG. 200. Group of Monotremata. A. *Proechidna bruijnii.* B. *Proechidna nigro-aculeata.* C. *Echidna aculeata;* ventral aspect to show brood pouch. D. *Echidna aculeata.* E. *Ornithorhynchus anatinus.* F. *Ornithorhynchus* standing up like a penguin. G. *Ornithorhynchus* female allowing young to obtain milky secretion from the diffuse abdominal mammary glands. (All redrawn, A, B, F, G, after Brehm; C, after Haacke; D and E, after Vogt and Specht.)

other orders, teeth are lacking in the adult. Two other characters seem in no way to relate *Echidna* to the ant-eating habit; these are first, a rudimentary tail, much like that of a bird, and second, a small spur connected with a peculiar gland on the heel, a structure whose function is not well understood. Of somewhat more fundamental importance are the following characters: the cerebral hemispheres are fairly large and moderately convoluted; there is a temporary "marsupial pouch" (Fig. 200, C), which seems to have no relation to the marsupium of the marsupials, but is more nearly homologous with a broad, hollowed-out teat; the temperature of the body is lower than in the higher mammals, and has a variation in health of at least 15° Centigrade, a character which seems to be intermediate between the poikilothermous and the homoiothermous conditions.

Proechidna, a New Guinea species, differs from *Echidna* in the following particulars: the toes on both fore and hind feet are reduced to three large and two rudimentary elements; the beak is longer and is curved downward; the back is more arched; the external lobe of the ear, pinna, protrudes freely from the hair of the head. The combination of characters gives to the *Proechidna* a ridiculous resemblance to a miniature elephant. Two species, *P. bruijnii* (Fig. 200, A) and *P. nigroaculeata* (Fig. 200, B), are distinguished.

The breeding habits of the Echidnidae are of especial interest. The egg is about half an inch long, has a leathery shell, a thick layer of albumen, and an abundant supply of yolk, and is in all respects essentially like that of a reptile. Only one egg is laid at a time and it is immediately transferred by the mouth of the mother to the brood pouch (Fig. 200, C), where it undergoes a short incubation. When ready to hatch, the shell is broken, as in the bird, by means of a shell-breaking tubercle on the end of the snout; the mother then removes the broken fragments of the shell. The just-hatched young is in a very immature and helpless condition and lies quietly in the pouch for some time, merely able to lap up the milky secretion that exudes from the walls of the pouch. After the young Echidna has reached a considerable size it is removed by the mother from time to time in order to give it exercise, but it is put back into the pouch to be suckled. There is among Echidnidae really no need of a nest, for the egg is kept safely in a pouch. After a time, however, the mother leaves the young in the burrow while she pursues her nocturnal occupation of ant-hunting. This burrow with its enlarged terminal chamber is a safe retreat for the youngster when later he ventures forth to learn the ant-eating game for himself.

Family 2.   Ornithorhynchidae. — This family consists of but the single species *Ornithorhynchus anatinus* (Fig. 200, E), the duck-bill platypus, a native of southern Australia and Tasmania. When the first specimen of this strange beast was exhibited in England it was believed to be a fake, on a par with the composite mermaids then in vogue. It was described as a furry quadruped with the bill and feet of a duck; a very apt characterization. The animal is about eighteen inches long, with a heavy coat of soft brown fur. The feet are five-toed and webbed, the webbing on the fore feet extending well beyond the tips of the toes, but that of the hind feet being about as it is in a water bird. Both feet are armed with sharp claws. The bird-like "bill" is very wide and flat and is covered with soft, naked skin that flares out at the base into sensitive flaps; this "bill" covering is highly sensitive owing to the abundance of sense organs that are scattered over its surface. There are no teeth in the adult, but instead, broad, horny plates line the inside of the "bill"; these are used for crushing the shells of bivalves and water snails, which constitute its chief food. The young platypus has a set of milk teeth, all molars and eight or ten in number; these are gradually worn off and then replaced by plates. No permanent teeth are present. The eyes are small and beady; there

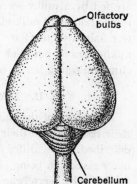

FIG. 201. Brain of *Ornithorhynchus*, dorsal view, natural size. Note lack of cerebral convolutions. (From Parker and Haswell.)

is no external ear lobe; the male has a spur on the heel like that of the Echidnidae, but larger in size. The tail is large and dorsoventrally flattened; it is used as a rudder in swimming and diving much as in the beaver.

The brain of *Ornithorhynchus* (Fig. 201) is the most primitive brain known for a living mammal. It is comparatively quite small, and the cerebral hemispheres are smooth and, like those of a reptile, entirely lacking in convolutions. The habits of this creature are purely aquatic, not unlike those of a muskrat. It lives in stagnant, weedy ponds or streams, feeding chiefly on mollusks, crustaceans, and worms that are secured by scooping up the muddy bottom with the paddle-shaped "bill."   Provender is stored in capacious cheek pockets and carried to the burrow, where it is eaten at leisure. The burrow is dug deep into the bank of the stream, beginning below the water line and sloping upward until at a distance of twenty-five to fifty feet it terminates in a large, dry chamber with top ventilation. This chamber is comfortably lined with reeds and rushes.

Breeding Habits of Ornithorhynchus. — The eggs to the number of two or three are laid in a nest of grasses, quite like a simple bird's nest. They are somewhat smaller than those of *Echidna* and have a rather tough, flexible shell, yellowish-white in color. They are incubated while still in the nest by means of the body heat of the mother; hence there is no brood pouch. When the young hatch they are fed by a milky secretion which exudes from the diffusely scattered abdominal milk-glands. The young squeezes the milk from the wet hair with the flat "bill." When the youngsters are older the mother lies on her back (Fig. 200, G) and the ludicrous little fellows climb on top of her in order to feed to better advantage.

II. MARSUPIALIA (DIDELPHIA)

The origin of the marsupials, their early wide distribution, and their restriction to their present narrow confines have already been described. They differ from monotremes in having sebaceous mammary glands, in being viviparous; in having teats; in possessing two-headed ribs; vertebrae with epiphyses; no separate coracoid; no interclavicle, cervical ribs absent, etc. In these respects they are also like placental mammals. The marsupials differ from placentals in having a feebly developed or no corpus callosum; epipubic (marsupial) bones attached to the pubis; a marsupial pouch of some sort in nearly all forms; double vagina (a character referred to in the term Didelphia); eggs, though minute, somewhat larger than in placentals, with a thin albumen layer and sometimes a vestigial shell; in giving birth to extremely immature young which must complete their development in the pouch; and in having a cloaca, but this is usually incompletely developed.

EGG, DEVELOPMENT, BIRTH, AND SUCKLING OF THE OPOSSUM

Hartmann has recently made an extensive study of the embryology and birth of the Virginia opossum, which may serve to illustrate the situation in marsupials in general.

The eggs are very much smaller than those of monotremes, but somewhat larger than those of placentals. There is a thin layer of albumen and a definite amount of yolk. The eggs and young embryos lie free in the uterus and absorb some nutriment from fluids that fill the uterus. The young are born seven days after the eggs are fertilized in an extremely immature condition. They are said to have the appearance of tiny pink grubs about half an inch long. Though so embryonic in most respects, the fore legs are precociously large and strong and look like flippers. Contrary to earlier accounts which state that the mother places the young in the pouch, these tiny larvae, for such they seem to be, make the journey up to the pouch under their own power, pushing aside the hair of the mother's abdomen with their strong "flippers." When they reach the pouch they crawl into it and search for the teats. Each swallows a teat all the way down to the stomach and clamps on to it with a precociously developed larval mouth. So strongly do they hold the teats that, after they have once fastened firmly to them, they can not be pulled off. The teat will pull off before they will let go of it.

The pouch young feed upon milk and grow rapidly. After they have grown large and active they loosen their semipermanent hold on the teats and come out of the pouch, hanging on to the mother's tail with their own prehensile tails.

It is obvious that the eggs and developmental conditions of the marsupials are somewhat intermediate between those of monotremes and those of placentals, but it is not believed that the three stages constitute a phylogenetic series. As has been said, the placentals have not descended from marsupials, but both marsupials and placentals were probably derived independently from different types of the extinct Pantotheria. The fact that one type of marsupial, *Perameles* (Fig. 235), has a poorly developed allantoic placenta suggests that the ancestors of modern marsupials may have had a placental mode of gestation, and that the present non-placental condition characteristic of most marsupials is a secondary, degenerate character.

THE SUBORDERS OF MARSUPIALS

The present classification of marsupials is in a state of flux and may be soon changed, but for the present we may distinguish three

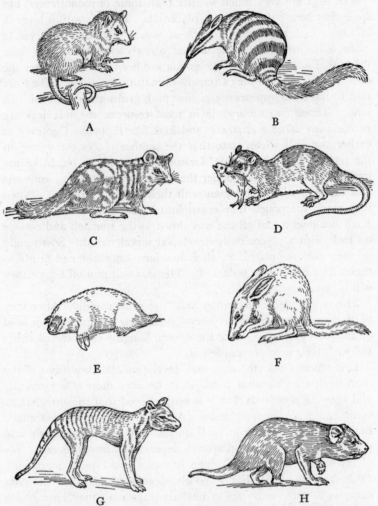

Fig. 202. Group of Marsupials (Polyprotodonts). A. Virginia opossum, *Didelphys virginiana*. B. Banded ant-eater, *Myrmecobius fasciatus*. C. Native cat, *Dasyurus viverrinus*. D. Water opossum, *Chironectes minima*. E. Marsupial mole, *Notoryctes typhlops*. F. Rabbit bandicoot, *Peragole lagotis*. G. Thylacine or Tasmanian wolf, *Thylacinus cynocephalus*. H. Tasmanian devil, *Sarcophilus ursinus*. (All redrawn, A after Vogt and Specht; D, after Lydekker; B, after Flower and Lydekker; E, after Beddard; others, after Brehm.)

suborders: Polyprotodontia, Diprotodontia, and Caenolestoidea. We shall give a brief taxonomic description of these three subdivisions after a general statement about their adaptive radiation. It is of great interest to note a striking parallelism between the marsupials and the placentals in the general adaptive types developed in the two groups. This situation affords a good illustration of convergent evolution, which may be defined as the development of unrelated groups along parallel lines in adaptation to similar environmental conditions. Thus we find among the Australian marsupials a marsupial mole (Fig. 202, E), *Notoryctes*, with most of its adaptive features similar to those of placental moles. *Dasyurus* (Fig. 202, C) is regarded as a fair replica of a cat; *Thylacinus* (Fig. 202, G) is a moderately good imitation of a dog; the rabbit bandicoot (Fig. 202, F) resembles a rabbit; some of the phalangers (Fig. 203, F) suggest squirrels; *Phascolomys* (Fig. 203, G) looks a good deal like a small bear; *Myrmecobius* (Fig. 202, B) is a counterpart of the ant-eaters; and *Chironectes* (Fig. 202, D) is the best the marsupials can do for an otter. There are no real ungulates among the marsupials, but the large kangaroo, *Macropus* (Fig. 203, A), occupies an ecological niche very similar to that of the antelopes and behaves much like an antelope.

Suborder I. Polyprotodontia

This group, which consists mainly of insectivorous and carnivorous types, is more primitive than are the herbivorous diprotodonts. The polyprotodonts are characterized by the possession of four or five incisors on each side of the upper jaw and one or two fewer in the lower jaw; both canines and molars have the typical carnivorous shape. They are confined to Australasia, with the exception of the American opossums.

Family 1. Didelphidae (the Opossums). — Of all living marsupials the opossums appear to be the most generalized in both structure and habits. The family is exclusively American, especially South American, but they seem to be distantly related to the Australian Dasyuridae. The Virginia opossum (Fig. 202, A), *Didelphys virginiana*, is the best known North American member of the family and deserves special mention. It is distinctly arboreal, with a prehensile tail adapted for clinging to branches and for use as a hold-fast by the young, who wind their tails about the arched tail of the mother. The opossum is omnivorous, eating fruit, insects, birds, reptiles, and their eggs. There is a distinct pouch in which the young are suckled and carried. The animal is nocturnal in habit, sleeping in hollow trees during the day. The death-feigning instinct has received the proverbial description "playing 'possum." Important genera of the family are: *Didelphys, Marmosa, Chironectes,* and *Metachirus;* there are about twenty-five species. *Marmosa murina* is a tiny opossum about the size of a small rat; *Chironectes* is an aquatic type with webbed feet and about the size of a muskrat. It is the only aquatic marsupial (Fig. 202, D).

Family 2. Myrmecobiidae (Banded Ant-eaters). — This small family is represented by a single species, *Myrmecobius fasciatus* (Fig. 202, B), an animal about the size of a cat, with only slight specializations for the ant-eating habit. Its snout is moderately prolonged; its tongue is very long and extensible and is covered with the customary sticky secretion; the tail is covered with long, coarse hair; the claws are only moderately heavy. Instead of being toothless like ant-eaters of other subclasses they have an unusually large number of small teeth, ranging from 50 to 54. In this respect and in several others they resemble the Mesozoic marsupials. *Myrmecobius* has no pouch.

Family 3. Dasyuridae (Carnivorous Marsupials). — This is a somewhat heterogeneous family of marsupials, ranging from mouse-like to badger-like types. They may or may not have a pouch. *Dasyurus viverrinus,* the "native cat" (Fig. 202, C), is less cat-like in appearance than marten-like. It feeds largely on birds and their eggs. *Sarcophilus ursinus,* the "Tasmanian devil" (Fig. 202, H), is an animal about the size and shape of a badger. It has the reputation of being one of the most ferocious of animals, with a devilish "yelling growl." Native Australians say, however, that it is rather a slinking than an openly pugnacious creature. *Phascologale* is a genus of small animals not unlike some of the smaller American opossums in appearance and habits. *Sminthopsis* is a genus of pouched "mice." *Antechinomys* is a genus of pouched jumping "mice," with long ears and legs.

Family 4. Thylacynidae (Thylacynes). — This family is represented by the single species *Thylacinus cynocephalus* (Fig. 202, G), which receives the name of the "Tasmanian wolf." The creature is less like a wolf than like some of the smaller members of the cat family, but the Australians had to have some sort of "wolf," and this is the nearest approach that the marsupials can afford. It is a predaceous animal, almost as large as a small wolf, with a dog-like head and a series of tiger-like bands across the back and tail.

Family 5. Peramelidae (Bandicoots). — There are three genera in this family. *Perameles* is a genus of twelve species of medium-sized forms, with the pouch opening backwards. *Peragole* (Fig. 202, F) is a genus of two species of "rabbit bandicoots," which have the habit of burrowing in the soil for grubs and other soil insects. *Chaeropus castanotis* is the "pig-footed bandicoot," also a burrowing form, with only two toes on the fore feet.

Family 6. Notoryctidae (Marsupial, or Pouched Moles). — This family is represented by a single species, *Notoryctes typhlops* (Fig. 202, E), a south Australian mole-like animal, with silky reddish-gold fur, which harmonizes with the color of the arid soil in which it burrows. It has a complete set of mole-like adaptations and leads a thoroughly mole-like life. The eyes are rudimentary; there are no external ear lobes; the fore feet are armed with extremely heavy burrowing claws, the third and fourth being much more conspicuous than the rest; the tail is very short and stumpy.

Suborder 2. Diprotodontia

The members of this division are mainly herbivorous. Their dentition is not unlike that of the rodents, the incisors being of the gnawing type, usually two pairs above and one pair below. The canines are either small or absent; the molars have either tubercles or transverse ridges. This group contains the largest and most highly specialized of the marsupials.

Family 7. Phalangeridae (Phalangers). — This is one of the largest marsupial families and consists mostly of arboreal forms. They are characterized by having five fingers and toes, with the second and third phalanges bound together by an integumentary bond; the hallux is usually opposable. The pouch is well developed; the tail is usually long. The following are some of the more important genera: *Tarsipes*, the long-snouted phalanger; *Acrobates*, the pigmy flying phalanger; *Distaechurus*, the pentailed phalanger; *Dromicia*, the dormouse phalanger; *Petaurus*, the true flying phalangers; *Tricosurus*, the true phalangers; *Phascolarctus*, the koala.

The true phalangers (Fig. 203, F) are fairly large forms, more or less fox-like in form and sometimes known as "brush-tailed opossums." The flying phalangers are much like our flying squirrels in structure and habits; they are not genuine flyers but merely soarers

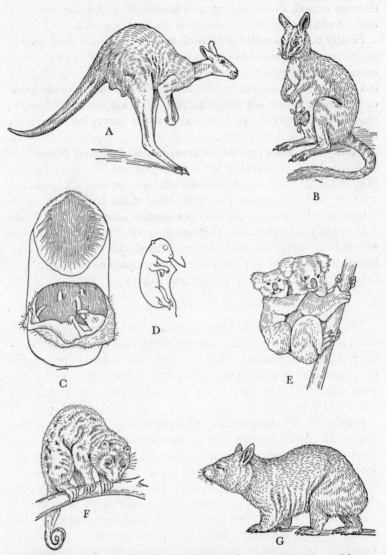

FIG. 203. Group of Marsupials (Diprotodonts). A. Red kangaroo, *Macropus rufus* (after Lydekker). B. Rock wallaby, *Petrogale xanthopus* (after Vogt and Specht). C. Young kangaroo attached to nipple in pouch of mother; pouch laid back to show interior (after Brehm). D. Lateral view of same removed from pouch (after Parker and Haswell). E. Koala, *Phascolarctus cinereus*, carrying young on back (after Brehm). F. *Phalanger maculatus*. G. Wombat, *Phascolomys ursinus* (after Lydekker).

that parachute from tree to tree by means of folds of skin stretched between the fore and hind limbs. The koala is a curious slow-moving, nocturnal animal that feeds almost exclusively on the leaves of the gum tree. It has been called "marsupial bear," but is really more like a large "Teddy bear" than anything else, as the illustration (Fig. 203, E) plainly attests.

Family 8. Macropodidae (Kangaroos, Wallabies, etc.). — The kangaroos are mostly terrestrial forms, but some of them appear to be secondarily arboreal. The hind legs are very large and powerful and usually the fourth and fifth toes are much enlarged into a sort of hoof. The tail is always long and heavy at the base. *Macropus rufus* (Fig. 203, A) is the largest of the marsupials, attaining a length of five and a half feet, exclusive of the tail. They are very fleet of foot, progressing by great leaps of the long hind legs covering twenty feet at a jump. The fore legs are of no use in running and appear to be merely for grasping food and for handling the young. The genus *Petrogale* (Fig. 203, B) includes kangaroos that live among the rocks, using the long tail as a balancing pole as they leap from rock to rock. *Dendrolagus* (the tree kangaroo) is very different in its habits from any of the other members of the family. The foot structure indicates that the arboreal habit has been superimposed upon an ancestral cursorial habit, for there is the same great enlargement of the fourth and fifth toes as in the other kangaroos.

Family 9. Phascolomyidae (Wombats). — This family consists of but one genus, *Phascolomys*. It is in general appearance something like a small bear (Fig. 203, G) or a heavily built marmot. It lives entirely on the ground and moves about with a sort of shuffling plantigrade gait much after the manner of a bear. It is shy and gentle, though it can put up a vigorous defense with teeth and claws if forced to do so. In habits it is nocturnal, spending the daytime in burrows or holes among the rocks.

Suborder 3. Caenolestoidea

This suborder consists of a number of extinct forms and three living genera of so-called marsupial shrews, found in small numbers in the Andean foothills of South America. These genera, *Caenolestes*, *Orolestes*, and *Rhyncholestes*, are definitely isolated from one another today, but are doubtless derived from a very ancient common stock. Until rather recently these animals were classed as primitive diprotodonts, but an extensive anatomical study of them by W. H. Osgood has thrown great doubt on this classification. In a sense the caenolestids seem to be somewhat intermediate between the poly-protodonts and the diprotodonts. They have a primitive diprotodont dentition, but a foot structure more like that of the polyprotodonts. Osgood believes that the ancestral caenolestids were probably North American forms that may have also given rise to an early diproto-dont stock that migrated across the Alaska-Kamchatka land bridge and down to Australian territory before the latter was cut off from southern Asia.

In general appearance, *Caenolestes* is one of the most generalized of mammals reminding one more of shrews than anything else. Most of its anatomical characters are primitive and generalized, a fact in harmony with its very close resemblance to the extinct members of its group that lived in Miocene times. The name Caenolestes means "a modern representative of an ancient group."

CHAPTER XXIII

ORDERS OF PLACENTAL MAMMALS

INTRODUCTORY STATEMENT

Definition. — This is a great group of present-day mammals, including about 95 per cent of all living mammalian species. They are characterized by the following features: no marsupium; no epipubic bones; the young always nourished for a considerable time in the uterus by means of a placenta; young born in a relatively advanced state and not attached to teats in semipermanent fashion; no cloaca; always a good-sized corpus callosum.

The most primitive placental mammals are now believed to be more nearly representative of the ancestral mammalian prototype than are the monotremes or marsupials. Certain members of the order Insectivora have been selected as the most generalized of living mammals. Osborn selected as his mammalian prototype the tree shrew *Tupaia* (Fig. 204, B), while Lull selected as his, *Gymnura* (Fig. 204, A), a large rat-like animal related to the hedgehogs. The most specialized mammals are undoubtedly the whales, if structural modification be taken as the criterion; but man outranks all other mammals in brain and nervous specialization, and therefore in intelligence.

The fifteen orders of placental mammals as listed in the general classification at the end of Chapter I, are grouped into several assemblages, or infraclasses, on the basis of anatomical and embryological criteria too technical for discussion in a volume of this sort. Suffice it to say that, according to W. K. Gregory and other leading mammalogists, there are grounds for the belief that four main assemblages of orders exist that might be called: (1) the *insectivore assemblage* (including Insectivora, Dermoptera, Chiroptera, and Primates); (2) the *edentate assemblage* (including Edentata, Pholidota, and Tubulidentata); (3) the *carnivore assemblage* (including Carnivora and Cetacea); and (4) the *ungulate assemblage* (including Perissodactyla, Artiodactyla, Hyracoidea, Proboscidea, and Sirenia). This leaves the order Rodentia standing alone, though it is closer to the insectivore assemblage than to any other. Some of the smaller, more obscure orders of placental mammals will receive but little attention, while some of the large, highly successful orders will be dealt with rather fully.

ORDER INSECTIVORA (HEDGEHOGS, MOLES, AND SHREWS)

These are primitive, rather small, furry animals, that feed largely on insects. They are for the most part nocturnal and terrestrial in habit, as the first mammals are believed to have been. Some of them have been specialized slightly for an arboreal habit; others have been rather profoundly modified for a fossorial life. In bodily proportions they are as a rule quite generalized, fitting well the role assigned to them of persistently primitive mammals.

The members of the shrew family (Fig. 204, B) are rather rat-like in form and more or less plantigrade in attitude. There is nothing especially striking or noteworthy about these animals except their lack of specialized characters. It has already been pointed out that various authorities on mammalian morphology have selected the shrews as the most generalized of living placental mammals.

The hedgehog family, including the genera *Erinaceus*, *Hylomys*, and *Gymnura*, are in general a little more specialized than are the shrews, though Lull considers *Gymnura* (Fig. 204, A) the most primitive living placental mammal. The true hedgehog is characterized by its armor of quills, which are much like those of the porcupine in structure.

The true moles (Fig. 204, C) are profoundly specialized for a subterranian burrowing habit and resemble in their adaptations the marsupial mole. They have rudimentary eyes, no ear lobes, short tail, and heavy digging claws. The golden mole (*Chrysochloris*) of South Africa is a beautiful creature with iridescent golden fur. Moles feed chiefly on earthworms and dig long tunnels just beneath the turf, and on this account are the bane of lawn-keepers and gardeners. No less than nine families of Insectivora have been distinguished, but lack of space forbids a detailed description of them.

ORDER DERMOPTERA

This is an order containing but a single species, *Galeopithecus volans* (Fig. 205), the so-called "flying lemur." It is a bat-like creature, nearly as large as a cat, with membranes stretched between the

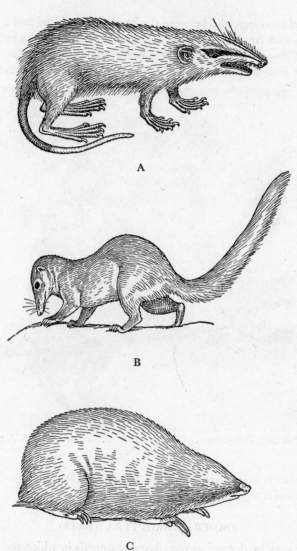

A

B

C

FIG. 204. Group of Insectivora. A. *Gymnura rafflesii*, believed by Lull to be the most primitive insectivore (after Horsfield and Vigors). B. *Tupaia*, the tree shrew, considered by Osborn as near the prototype form of all higher placental mammals (after Osborn). C. Golden mole, *Chrysochloris trevelyani* (after Günther). (All redrawn.)

fore and hind legs, also between the head and the hand and between the tail and the hind feet. In anatomical and embryological characters *Galeopithecus* resembles not only shrews of the order Insectivora, but the fruit-bats of the order Chiroptera and lemurs of the order

Fig. 205. *Galeopithecus.* (From Parker and Haswell, after Vogt and Specht.)

Primates. It helps to integrate the Insectivora-Dermoptera-Chiroptera-Primate assemblage of placental orders.

ORDER CHIROPTERA (BATS)

Bats may be defined as true flying mammals in which the fingers of the fore limb are greatly elongated to support, like the ribs of a fan, a membranous wing-plane. They do not merely soar or glide like the "flying lemur" or the flying squirrels, but actually propel themselves with rapid wing-strokes as effectively as do many of the birds. Extra planing surface is acquired by a stretch of membrane running from the hind limbs to the tail. The knees of bats are turned backwards, a position that would require dislocation of the hip in any other mammal. Many of the bats have large delicate ears and extremely complicated folds of sensitive membrane surrounding the nostrils (Fig. 206, B, C, D). These are believed to be organs of a sixth sense (kinaesthetic sense) that gives warning of the nearness of solid objects in the dark. It is said that bats living in caves that have absolutely no light fly about in swarms at a high speed and never collide with one another nor with the walls or roof of the cave. "There can be little doubt," says W. K. Gregory, "that the Chiroptera are an offshoot of late Mesozoic or early Tertiary arboreal insectivores, which must have resembled *Galeopithecus* in many characters." Bats are divided into two suborders: Microchiroptera and Megachiroptera, of which the latter are the more primitive.

Suborder 1. Megachiroptera (Fruit-eating Bats). — These are rather large animals and are sometimes called "flying foxes." They occur in India, Australasia, Ceylon, Africa, and Madagascar. The best known is *Pteropus*, a large bat with a wing-spread of over five feet, though the body is only about a foot in length. Their main food consists of figs and guava. They are distinctly social in habit and move about in droves of considerable size. Another well-known species is the collared fox-bat (*Xantharpyia collaris*) which is shown in its customary resting position with its young clinging to the abdomen of the mother (Fig. 206, A).

Suborder 2. Microchiroptera (Insectivorous Bats). — These are small bats (Fig. 206, B) with practically cosmopolitan range on account of their great powers of flight. At least five hundred species are known. They are decidedly nocturnal in habit, taking up the role of birds while the latter are asleep. "Blind as a bat" is a familiar aphorism that has its basis in the fact that the bat's eyes are so sensitive to lights of high intensity that they are blinded by the broad daylight. At night bats skim rapidly and dexterously through the air catching insects on the wing with remarkable expertness. In the daytime they spend their time sleeping in caves or other dark sheltered places, hanging up-side-down by means of the claws of their hind feet. They are decidedly gregarious, living in colonies of thousands within the narrow confines of certain small caves. A common American species is the "brown bat" (*Eptesicus fuscus*); another common species of the eastern parts of North America is the "little brown bat" (*Myotis lucifugus*), which is less than three and a half inches in length. The vampire (*Desmodus rotundus*) is a bat of rather large size,

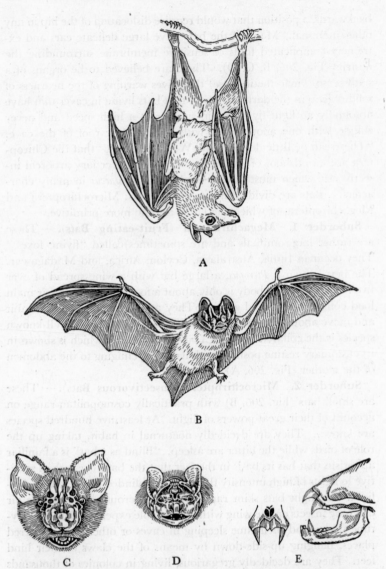

FIG. 206. Chiroptera (bats). A. Collared fox-bat, *Xantharpyia collaris*, and young. (After Sclater.) B. *Synotus barbastellus*. (After Vogt and Specht.) C. Face of *Triaenops persicus*, showing nasal folds. (After Dobson.) D. Face of *Centurio senex*. (After Dobson.) E. Dentition of vampire, *Desmondus rufus*, to show sharpness of teeth. (After Flower and Lydekker.)

native to South America. True to its reputation it lives the life of a blood-sucker, attacking horses and cattle and occasionally men. Its mode of attack is to fasten its razor-edged front teeth (Fig. 206, E) in the throat and to sever a vein or an artery, after which it proceeds to gorge itself with blood. Bats of one curious family, the Molossidae, are of interest because they have become secondarily terrestrial, appearing to be more at home on their feet than one would expect of a bat; for they run about almost like mice. This is quite in contrast to the usual situation among bats, which move about on the land with extreme awkwardness. When the typical bat crawls it hooks the thumb-nail in front and pushes with its feet behind, a pitiably helpless mode of locomotion.

ORDER PRIMATES (LEMURS, MONKEYS, APES, AND MAN)

The traditional position allotted to the primates is the last and highest order of mammals, but it has come to be realized that the group is on the whole more generalized than several other orders, and is undoubtedly more closely related to Insectivora, Dermoptera, and Chiroptera than to any other orders. The derivation of the earliest lemurs from large-brained arboreal insectivores (somewhat like *Tupaia*) is strongly indicated by a score of anatomical and embryological characters. The primates may be defined as primarily arboreal animals with prehensile digits; with thumb and great toe shorter than the other digits and more or less opposable to the latter; with plantigrade walking position of the feet; with terminal, flattened "nails" instead of claws; with hair covering the entire body except the palms and soles and parts of the face; with a single pair of usually pectoral mammae; with the eyes directed anteriorly instead of laterally; the orbit completely surrounded with bone; a clavicle always present; the stomach simple; and the cerebrum unusually large and well convoluted.

Probably the best among many classifications of the primates is the following:

Suborder 1.   Lemuroidea (lemurs or "half-apes")
Suborder 2.   Tarsioidea
Suborder 3.   Anthropoidea
  Series 1.   Platyrrhini (New World monkeys)
    Family 1.   Hapalidae (marmosets)

Family 2. Cebidae (capuchins, howler monkeys, spider monkeys, etc.)
Series 2. Catarrhini (Old World monkeys, apes, and man)
    Family 1. Cercopithecidae (monkeys, baboons, macaques, etc.)
    Family 2. Simiidae (man-like, or anthropoid apes)
    Family 3. Hominidae (men)

Suborder 1. Lemuroidea (Lemurs). — The lemurs (Fig. 207, A) are much the most ancient and the most generalized of the primates, and therefore show less wide departures from the insectivore condition than do the anthropoids. They are exclusively arboreal, mostly nocturnal, and extremely timid and retiring. In appearance they strike one as intermediate between a squirrel and a monkey. The brain is comparatively unspecialized, the cerebral hemispheres being so small as not even to cover the hind-brain. The second finger retains the ancestral claw, but the rest of the fingers have flat nails. The lemurs have their headquarters in Madagascar, but are also found in the tropical forests of Africa and Malaysia. During the Eocene Period they lived both in North America and in Europe, a fact indicative of the antiquity of the group.

Chiromys madagascariensis, the "aye-aye," is a rather primitive squirrel-like lemur with long incisor teeth; a bushy tail; only the thumb has a "nail," the other digits being provided with claws; the mammae are abdominal, a primitive position; it has but one young at a birth. The "aye-aye" has a plaintive voice resembling the native name; it leads a prowling, furtive life, always in pairs. A nest of twigs is made in the tops of trees.

The more modernized lemurs may be exemplified by the ruffed lemur, the mouse lemur, and the slow loris. Of all the lemurs the ruffed lemur (*Lemur varius*) is probably the most monkey-like. It has a rather long, bushy tail, a fox-like face and the full primate dentition. The voice is loud; they are diurnal as well as nocturnal in habit. The mouse lemur (*Chirogale coquereli*) is a native of Madagascar; it is very small in size, with soft, fluffy fur and of generalized proportions. The slow loris (*Nycticebus tardigradus*) is an aberrant lemur, native of East Indian and Malayan territories. It is extremely deliberate in its movements, moving about among the trees chattering and whistling as though without a care in the world. Like other lemurs, it is looked upon with superstitious dread by the natives, who regard it as a beast of ill omen.

Suborder 2. Tarsioidea. — *Tarsius spectrum* (Fig. 208), a native of the Malay Islands, is a strange little creature, with enormous

FIG. 207. Group of Primates. A. Smith's dwarf lemur, *Microcebus smithii.* B. Spider monkey, *Ateles ater.* C. Drill or mandrill, *Papio leucophaeus.* D. Gibbon, *Hylobates lar.* E and F. Chimpanzee, *Pan pygmaeus.* (Redrawn, A and B, after Beddard; rest after Lydekker.)

eyes that give it the appearance of wearing spectacles, a character from which it derives it specific name. The digits are armed with adhesive pads and have small flat nails. The tail is long and tufted at the end. They live in pairs in holes in hollow trees, and are mainly insectivorous and decidedly nocturnal. The mother carries the young about by taking hold of the neck skin with the teeth, after the manner of a mother cat. *Tarsius* has an almost smooth cerebrum and a low order of intelligence. Some writers regard *Tarsius* as a lemur, classing it as one family of Lemuroidea, but it differs from the latter

Fig. 208. *Tarsius spectrum.* (From Lull.)

in so many ways that recent authorities have assigned it to a separate suborder. One of the most peculiar features of *Tarsius*, responsible for its generic name, is the great elongation of some of the tarsal bones of the foot.

Suborder 3. Anthropoidea (Monkeys, Apes, Man). — The anthropoids are decidedly more highly organized than are the lemurs. They are characterized by the possession of: 32 to 36 teeth; completely closed orbit; pectoral mammae; prehensile hands and feet (except in man); cerebral hemispheres richly convoluted and covering the cerebellum.

Series 1. Platyrrhini (New World Monkeys). These primates are distinguished by the broad nasal septum; the thumb is not opposable, but usually reduced to a small vestige; the tail is long and prehensile; there are no cheek pockets or pouches; there are no callosities on the ischium.

Family 1. Hapalidae. These are the marmosets, animals about the size of large squirrels, quite extensively used as pets. They have a very generalized diet, eating fruit, eggs, and insects, and have claws instead of nails on the digits.

Family 2. Cebidae. Most of the common South American monkeys (Fig. 207, B) belong to this family. Several species of them are familiar to everyone as companions of the Italian organ-grinder. They are all rather slender and have exceptionally long, more or less prehensile tails. The howler monkeys are noted for their prodigious voice, which is produced by means of a specially modified sounding apparatus. The commonest of the Cebidae are the capuchins, companions of the hand-organ.

Series 2. Catarrhini (Old World Monkeys, Apes, and Man). This series of primates is characterized by: narrow nasal septum, with nostrils directed downward; all have 32 teeth, as in man; non-prehensile or rudimentary tail; the great toe fully opposable, except in man; the thumb always opposable.

Family 1. Cercopithecidae (Baboons, Mandrills, and Macaques). The baboons and macaques (Fig. 207, C) are characterized by: quadrupedal habit of locomotion; more or less dog-like heads; ischial or rump callosities; no vermiform appendix; narrow chests, a character associated with the quadrupedal habit; very large canine teeth; cheek pockets. They are omnivorous in diet, as are the other Catarrhini. One of the most striking characters of members of this family is the brightness of their coloring, especially that of nose, cheeks, and rump. Bright blue, scarlet, and lilac colors are the commonest tints. In habits they combine those of the arboreal with those of the terrestrial types. They are good fighters and are able to cope with many of the predaceous terrestrial animals that inhabit Asiatic and African forests.

Family 2. Simiidae (Anthropoid Apes). The members of this family have long been objects of especial interest on account of their close relationship to man. In no sense are they to be thought of as ancestral to man; rather it would appear that they are distant "cousins," derived from a common ancestral stock. Doubtless, were we to discover this common ancestor, we should be inclined to call it an ape, but it certainly was not very much like any of the present-day apes.

The family may be defined as follows: tail rudimentary as in man; no cheek pouches; no ischial callosities except in the gibbon; arms longer than legs; the great toe fully opposable; the shoulders broad; somewhat bipedal habits; always a vermiform appendix; hair mainly on the ventral side of the body and on the limbs. The number of species is not great and there is so general an interest in them that we may spare the space to give a brief description of the principal ones.

FIG. 209. The orang-utang, *Simia satyrus*, sitting in its nest. (From Weysse, after Shipley and McBride.)

The gibbons (Fig. 207, D), of which there are several species, are all assigned to the genus *Hylobates*. One species, *H. syndactylus*, is called the siamang. These rather small apes are all inhabitants of southeastern Asia. They are remarkable for their exceedingly long arms that touch the ground when they stand erect. They have a small rump callosity similar to that of the baboons. Their dentition is adapted for a fruit-eating habit, though the canines are large and saber-like for self-defense. The skull is rounded and without the sagittal crest characteristic of the gorilla. They have a very erect posture both in walking and in sitting, the head being set upon the neck much as in man. The gibbon has a tremendous voice, much more voluminous than that of a Caruso, though it weighs not more than about sixty pounds. They live in heavily wooded mountain slopes, remaining largely in the trees, through which they are capable of making amazing speed. With its long arms the gibbon swings along with a hand-stride of twenty to forty feet, and never misses a hold, though it must calculate the distances with great nicety or fall from great heights to the ground. Any animal that can use its arms and hands in this way must have a finely developed brain back of it; indeed the gibbon's brain development is exceptional, especially in the visual and co-ordination centers. When on the ground the gibbon walks erectly but very awkwardly, balancing itself by touching the knuckles of the hands to the ground. It is evidently about nine-tenths an arboreal creature, using the ground only when trees are not available.

The orang, represented by but one species, *Simia satyrus* (Fig. 209), is a large ape native to Sumatra and Borneo. It is relatively short and stocky, and has reddish hair. Though it is only about four feet in height it has an arm-spread of over seven feet. The head is short and broad and the eyes very close together. The skull has a sagittal crest for the attachment of the powerful neck muscles; the jaw is deep and massive and is used both for tearing open fruits and in fighting. The hands are the chief weapons, and are relied upon rather than the teeth. The heavy weight of the orang makes it a less efficient climber than is the gibbon and its mode of climbing is much more deliberate and man-like. It builds its nest in trees by breaking off branches and arranging them platform-fashion in the crotch where two large limbs meet. The orang appears to be the only purely herbivorous member of the apes; its diet is said to consist exclusively of fruits. On the ground it runs on all fours in an awkward and ineffective way.

The chimpanzee (Fig. 207, E and F), *Pan* (*Anthropopithecus*) *pygmaeus*, is an African ape with black hair and a height of about five feet; it is less bulky than the orang. These characters make the chimpanzee a better climber than the orang, though not so expert as the gibbon. The head is larger than that of the orang, and the brow ridges are very prominent. There is a pronounced sagittal crest on the skull for the attachment of the neck musculature. The jaws are prognathous and resemble those of prehistoric man. It builds nests much like those of the orang. Some authorities distinguish

FIG. 210. Order PRIMATES. *Gorilla gorilla*, a gorilla. Note large head, small ears, short lips, large canine teeth, ridges above eyes, and absence of a chin. The gorilla walks on the backs of its fingers. Height about 5½ feet, weight 500 pounds. (Drawn by R. Bruce Horsfall. From Hegner.)

several species of chimpanzees. They are largely but not exclusively fruit-eaters. Their range is rather limited, being confined to central equatorial Africa. There is no doubt of the close affinities of chimpanzees and gorillas and some authorities would place them in the same genus.

The gorilla, represented by but one species, *Gorilla gorilla* (Fig. 210), is much the largest and fiercest of the anthropoid apes. It is native to the tropical African forests and is confined to a very restricted territory. It stands about five feet in height, but is so massive in build that it frequently reaches a weight of between four and five hundred pounds. If it had legs in proportion to its arms and trunk it would be a giant of at least seven feet in height. The gorilla has become highly specialized as a muscular brute, man as a creature of intelligence and finesse. The skull has a much heavier sagittal ridge than that of any of the other apes, and this is accompanied by a neck musculature of tremendous strength. The jaws are prognathous and very powerful, with large canine teeth, and the brow ridges are very prominent. All of these characters are much more pronounced in the old males than in the young males or in the females, a condition that suggests strongly their highly specialized character. The gorilla has an almost black skin and the hair is black and coarse. In habits the gorilla appears to be transitional between the arboreal and the terrestrial types. Both hands and feet approach the human type, especially in young individuals, though the great toe remains completely opposable. Gorillas are gregarious, living in bands of considerable size, with an old male at the head of each band. They will not run from man or from any other creature, but stand their ground and put up a ferocious fight with both hands and teeth. The statement has often been made that the gorilla uses sticks or clubs in fighting, but this has never been confirmed by a reliable authority. From the purely brutish physical standpoint the anthropoid apes have attained a higher degree of specialization than any other primate, but they fall far short of man in nervous specialization.

Family 3. Hominidae (Man). The human family is, structurally speaking, closely related to the Simiidae; in fact, the Simiidae and the Hominidae are more closely related than are the Simiidae and the Cercopithecidae. The chief differences between man and the anthropoid apes are viewed as the direct result of the acquisition by man of terrestrial habits, erect posture, and larger brain, all of which acquisitions are undoubtedly closely correlated. These primary human adaptations are accompanied by secondary changes. Erect posture, for example, involves a series of adjustments, such as alterations in the curvatures of the spine, changes in the structure of the legs, loss of grasping power of the great toe, and increased length of legs. The following comparison between man and the anthropoid apes is made by Gregory:

"The anthropoids are chiefly frugivorous and typically arboreal; when upon the ground they run poorly and (except in the case of the gibbons) use the fore limbs in progressing. Thus they are confined to forested regions. Man, on the other hand, is omnivorous, entirely terrestrial, erect, bipedal and cursorial, an inhabitant primarily of open country. The anthropoids use their powerful canine tusks and more or less procumbent incisors for tearing open the rough rinds of large fruits and for fighting. Primitive man, on the contrary, uses his small canines and more erect incisors partly for tearing off the flesh of animals, which he has killed in the chase with weapons made and thrown or wielded by human hands. The implements and weapons also usually make it unnecessary for man to use his teeth in fighting and functionally they compensate for the reduced and more or less defective development of his dentition."

Although some authors recognize four living species of man, the best authorities now admit of but a single species, *Homo sapiens*. Possibly the minor divisions are the equivalent of subspecies, races, or varieties. Four races are distinguished by Lull:

Australoid race: skull long; eyebrows very prominent; teeth large, especially the canines; tall and long-limbed; skin brown; hair black, long and wooly. Habitat: Australia, Dekkan, Hindustan.

Negroid race: skull long; forehead round; nasal bones flattened; teeth sloping; skin, eyes, and hair black; hair short and wooly. Habitat: Madagascar and Africa from the Sahara desert to Cape of Good Hope.

Mongoloid race: skull broad and short; nose flat; eyes small and oblique; stature short and thick-set; skin golden brown; hair coarse, straight and black; beard scanty. Habitat: east of a line drawn from Lapland to Siam; Chinese, Tartars, Japanese, Malays, Eskimos, North and South American Indians.

Caucasoid race is usually subdivided into three varieties:

A. Mediterranean: short; slender; long-headed; with hair and eyes dark brown to black.

B. Alpine: medium height; stocky build; round-headed; hair and eyes dark brown or black, but in the north often hazel or gray, probably due to admixture with the northern varieties.

C. Nordic: tall; long-headed; hair flaxen, red, or light brown; eyes blue, gray, or green.

Habitat of Caucasoid race: mainly Europe and North America: includes also Moors, Berbers, Egyptians, Kurds, Persians, Afghans, Hindus, Turks, Jews, and Armenians.

THE IMMEDIATE ANCESTORS OF MAN

According to Gregory, man arose from an early, large-brained anthropoid stock, not far from the chimpanzee-gorilla group. Evidences point toward central Asia as the place of origin and early development of the prehuman Hominidae. The time of origin is believed to have been not later than early Pliocene and not earlier than Miocene times; thus dating back some hundreds of thousands of years. The earliest fossil remains of the Hominidae consist of the relics of the Java "ape-man," *Pithecanthropus erectus* (Fig. 211). Fragmentary remains of this creature, consisting of a skull-cap, a thigh bone, and two upper molar teeth, indicate that it was intermediate between the most primitive type of present-day man and the highest of the living apes. *Sinanthropus pekinensis* (the Pekin man) is now known from a number of skulls and teeth and constitutes an extinct genus of the man family a step more advanced than *Pithecanthropus*, connecting the latter with the genus *Homo*. McGregor has reconstructed

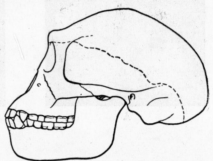

FIG. 211. Skull of the Java ape-man, *Pithecanthropus erectus*. (From Lull, after Dubois.)

busts of *Pithecanthropus*, of the most primitive of extinct human species (*Homo neanderthalensis*), and of *Homo sapiens*, a series which strikingly shows the gradual evolution away from apish and toward human features (Fig. 212).

The science of anthropology concerns itself, among other things, with the study of races of man, past and present, a field that can not be more than touched upon in a volume dealing with vertebrate zoology. Our main purpose has been to place man in his biological setting among his fellow mammals.

ORDER RODENTIA (GNAWING MAMMALS)

This order is the largest order of mammals and contains more genera and species than any other. It is a natural order, clearly defined. Rodents resemble the insectivores more closely anatomically and embryologically than any other mammals. In some respects they are even more primitive than surviving insectivores, a fact that has led Gregory to the view that they may have split off from the primitive placental stem even earlier than the insectivores.

The rodents are for the most part rather small mammals, though

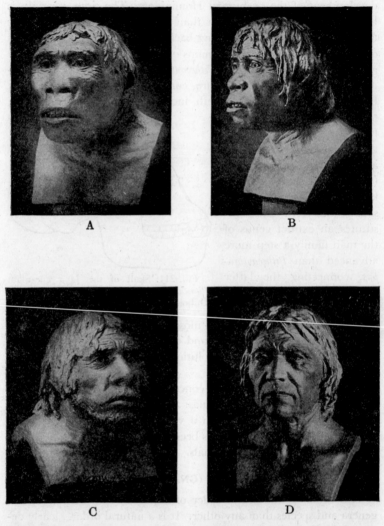

FIG. 212. Restoration of prehistoric men, after models by J. H. McGregor.
A. *Pithecanthropus erectus*, the Ape-man of Java. B. *Eoanthropus dawsoni*, the Piltdown
man. C. *Homo neanderthalensis*, the Neanderthal man. D. *Homo sapiens*, the Crô-
Magnon man. (Courtesy of Professor McGregor.)

a few of them have reached a considerable size. It has been claimed by some authorities that there are more species of rodents living to-day than of all other mammals combined. Unquestionably they are the most typical mammalian group today, as well as the most success-ful. Because they are so extremely prolific, because they are omnivo-rous, and because many of them lead a nocturnal burrowing life, they seem likely to be the main mammalian rivals of man in the next geological period. The rodents are characterized by absence of canine teeth; and the incisors are long and strong, and persistently growing, with enamel confined chiefly to the anterior edge. This arrangement of the enamel makes the teeth wear down to a chisel edge, which is self-sharpening with use. The brain is smooth, with few furrows, and the intelligence is usually rather low. The testes are usually abdominal in position; the placenta is discoidal and deciduate. Two suborders are distinguished: Duplicidentata (hares and pikas) and Simplicidentata (rodents proper).

Suborder 1. Duplicidentata (Hares and Pikas). — These animals are characterized by two pairs of incisor teeth in the upper jaw, the inner being small and lying behind the outer. The tail is short. The group is regarded by some biologists as a distinct order.

Family 1. Leporidae (the hares) are distinguished by long ears, long hind legs, and short though obvious tail.

Family 2. Lagomyidae (Pikas) are distinguished by short ears, short hind legs, and no external evidences of a tail.

Suborder 2. Simplicidentata (True Rodents). — The mem-bers of this suborder are divided into three sections: represented by squirrel-like, rat-like, and porcupine-like rodents.

Section 1. Sciuromorpha (Squirrel-like Rodents). This large section includes the squirrels proper, the flying squirrels, the ground squir-rels and chipmunks, the gophers, the prairie dogs, the marmots, the beavers, and others. The flying squirrels (Fig. 213, A) are really gliding animals, with a membrane stretched between the fore and hind limbs. The prairie dogs are burrowing rodents of the western plains, that live in large colonies. The habits of the beaver (Fig. 213, D) are too well known to require description here. They are threatened with extinction on account of their highly desirable fur. No other rodent is so highly modified for aquatic life as is the beaver.

Section 2. Myomorpha (Rat-like Rodents). This is the largest mod-ern group of mammals in point of numbers of species and of individ-uals. At least a hundred genera and nearly five hundred species

FIG. 213. Group of Rodentia. A. Flying squirrel, *Sciuropterus volucella* (after Lydekker). B. Long-tailed marmot, *Arctomys caudatus* (after Beddard). C. Egyptian jerboa, *Dipus jaculus* (after Lydekker). D. Beaver, *Castor fiber* (after Lydekker). E. Agouti, *Dasyprocta aguti* (after Beddard). F. European porcupine, *Hystrix cristata* (after Beddard).

have been distinguished. The group includes: dormice, field-mice, rats and mice proper, mole rats, jumping mice (Fig. 213, C), and the so-called African flying squirrels. They exhibit a very wide range of adaptive specializations, being terrestrial, subterrestrial, arboreal, cursorial, jumping, aquatic, and volant. They do serious damage to the world's food supply and are responsible for the spread of some of the worst plagues that man has to contend with.

Section 3. Hystricomorpha (Porcupine-like Rodents). This is a somewhat heterogeneous group and is not very accurately described as "porcupine-like," since many types appear quite unlike porcupines. There are eight families, including: "water-rats," cavies, guinea-pigs, agoutis (Fig. 213, E), chinchillas, ground porcupines, and tree porcupines. The cavies are South American and West Indian forms that reach a length of four or five feet. They are terrestrial in habit, with small ears and short tail. The chinchilla is a small squirrel-like animal native to the Andes; the fur is soft and gray and is highly prized. The Canada porcupine is a heavy-bodied terrestrial and arboreal form that gnaws off the bark of trees, eats water-lily leaves and roots. It is armed with short quills that are nearly hidden in the long fur. Its equipment is purely for passive defense, except that, when attacked, it lashes the tail and thus drives in its largest quills. Dogs are often injured when they are unwise enough to attack the porcupine, for they get their mouths full of barbed quills that are extremely difficult to remove. The European porcupine (Fig. 213, F) is considerably larger than its American relative, having a body length of about three feet. It has quills nearly a foot in length, those on the tail being hollow so as to produce a rattling sound when the animal is disturbed. A great crest of coarse hair surmounts the head and hangs down like a mane. In spite of the prevalent reports to that effect, the porcupine never shoots its quills.

ORDER EDENTATA (XENARTHRA)

This group is believed to be a surviving remnant of an archaic group. They have become highly specialized in several ways and exhibit many evidences of racial senescence. The name of the order implies a total lack of teeth and is therefore not appropriate for either the armadillos or the sloths; the ant-bears alone are quite toothless. The dentition of the toothed edentates is peculiar in that there are no incisors or canines and the teeth in the definitive condition are without enamel. The testes are abdominal; the clavicle is always present;

Fig. 214. Edentata, Pholidota, and Tubulidentata.   A. Great ant-eater, *Myrmecophaga jubata*.   B. Two-toed sloth, *Chaelopus didactylus*.   C. Texas nine-banded armadillo, *Dasypus novemcinctus texanus*.   D. The aard-vark, *Orycteropus capensis*.   E. Short-tailed pangolin, *Manis temminckii*.   (All redrawn, A, D, E, after Lydekker; B, after Beddard; C, after Newman.)

there is an additional pair of zygapophyses on the posterior dorsal and lumbar vertebrae. The Edentata are strictly American in distribution and have been limited to this territory from the first. In adaptive characters the three main types differ widely from one another.

Suborder 1. Pilosa (Hairy Edentates). — The hairy edentates belong to two quite distinct families: The Myrmecophagidae (ant-bears), and Bradipodidae (sloths).

Family 1. Myrmecophagidae (Ant-bears). These are among the strangest animals now living. They are truly edentate, have a long slender snout, long sticky tongue, heavy front claws, and long, coarse hair, characters that we have already found to be adaptive features of the ant-eating type of mammal, no matter to what group it belongs. *Myrmecophaga tridactyla*, the great ant-bear, is a large animal with a total length from end of snout to tip of tail of at least seven feet. It is very powerful and quite formidable when attacked. One swipe of the great hooked claws has been known completely to eviscerate a large dog. *M. jubata* (Fig. 214, A) is somewhat smaller but quite similar. The *Tamandua* is a still smaller ant-bear with arboreal habits and a long prehensile tail. *Cyclopes* is the smallest of the ant-bears. Although called ant-eaters, they subsist chiefly on termites, sometimes incorrectly called "white ants."

Family 2. Bradipodidae (Sloths). The sloths (Fig. 214, B), in spite of their marked external differences, exhibit many fundamental resemblances to the ant-bears. They are highly specialized for arboreal life. Their strong hooked claws which are much like those of the ant-bears are used as hooks for suspending them from branches. They always progress up-side-down, hanging from the under side of a branch. In accord with this habitually inverted position the heavy hair slopes from the belly toward the back; similarly the hair on the limbs slopes from the feet towards the body. It seems likely that this peculiar position of the hair serves the purpose of effectually shedding the rain. An interesting fact has been discovered about the hair: it is sometimes green in color, due to the presence in the hollows of the individual hairs of numerous cells of a green alga. This greenish coloring doubtless serves as a protective adaptation. The face of the sloth is extremely flat, in very marked contrast with the elongated face of the ant-bears. There are only four or five teeth in each half of each jaw. The sloths are very peculiar in that they have an excessive number of trunk vertebrae, as many as 23 being present in some species. The neck vertebrae are also exceptional for mammals, in that they depart consistently from the number seven, which is so characteristic for mammals, in having six, eight, or nine. They are largely insectivorous in diet. *Bradypus*, the three-toed sloth, and *Chaelopus*, the two-toed sloth, are the best known members of the family.

Suborder 2. Loricata (Armored Edentates; Armadillos). — The living armadillos belong to the family Dasypodidae and are much more numerous in species than are the Pilosa. At least seven genera and over twenty species have been distinguished. They are characterized by having a well-developed dermal skeleton, composed of numerous bony plates, in which hairs are embedded, and which are covered with horny scales. They have numerous teeth, which in the adult are without enamel; but in the embryonic stages a well-defined enamel layer has been discovered, which subsequently wears off. Incisors and canines are not found in the adult upper jaw, but embryonic rudiments of these teeth have been described. Although lacking some kinds of teeth, the number of cheek teeth may be as high as forty in each jaw. The armadillos range from moderately large animals of three feet or more in length to small forms about the size of a rat. Only a few of the species can receive mention here. The little *Chlamydophorus* has a solid unjointed armature and is considered primitive in this respect. *Euphractus sexcinctus* (the peludo) is a decidedly hairy type. *Tolypeutes* has three movable bands and rolls up into a ball. *Priodontes* is the giant among armadillos, being three feet long to the base of the tail and having thirteen movable bands in the armor.

Dasypus novemcinctus (the nine-banded armadillo) is the only North American armadillo and therefore deserves especial attention. It is really a South American species that has migrated northward through Central America and now inhabits Mexico and southern Texas. It is a medium-sized animal that lives in burrows in the daytime and forages for insects at night. Its ears are long and close together and remind one of a donkey's ears. It is a source of satisfaction to be able to contribute an adequate illustration (Fig. 214, C) of this interesting species to take the place of the atrocious figure of Flower and Lydekker, which was evidently drawn from a badly stuffed specimen. Perhaps this armadillo deserves especial mention on account of its unique embryological features. It produces regularly, with rare exceptions, four young at a birth, that are always all four of the same sex. A study of the early developmental history has revealed the fact that this is a case of specific polyembryony, in which the four individuals are produced from a single fertilized egg, that divides at a very early period into four embryos. Thus each set of young consists of identical quadruplets. There is a single chorion, but four separate amnia. This case is taken as evidence that in mammals sex is determined at the time of fertilization, since the four division products of a single egg are invariably of the same sex.

Extinct Edentata. — The best known extinct edentates are the giant ground sloths, of which *Mylodon* is a type, and the giant armadillos, of which *Glyptodon* is the classic example. *Mylodon* was as large and as heavy as a rhinoceros, and *Glyptodon* was sixteen feet long.

ORDER PHOLIDOTA (SCALY ANT-EATERS)

This is a small order formerly included within the order Edentata, but now given separate ordinal status on account of the discovery of morphological differences more fundamental than the resemblances that formerly led to their classification as edentates. The order consists of the pangolins, or scaly ant-eaters, which are placed in the family *Manidae* and the genus *Manis*. *Manis gigantea* is a fairly large and massive animal, about six feet in length, tail included. They are African and oriental in distribution. The most striking feature of these animals is the scaly covering, or what appears to be an armor composed of large pointed overlapping scales, which are sometimes regarded as reptilian scales, sometimes as fused hairs, but are probably new specialized structures. Scattered true hairs occur between these "scales." The species shown in the illustration is *Manis temminckii* (Fig. 214, E).

The pangolins are ant-eaters, doubtless also termite eaters, and possess all of the characteristic adaptations already mentioned for several other ant-eaters: the long snout, sticky tongue, integumentary protection from ants, and heavy claws for digging into ant and termite galleries. The Japanese have a legend concerning their feeding habits which is interesting, if true. After stirring up a colony of ants they are said to erect the scales so as to allow ants to crawl under them. The scales are then clamped down so as to hold the ants, and then the animal goes in for a swim. When submerged in the water the scales are lifted and the ants washed out so that they float about on the surface, where they are easily picked up by means of the long tongue. The Malays have a similar legend. It seems unlikely that this story is a pure fabrication.

ORDER TUBULIDENTATA

This order contains only the curious aard-vark, *Orycteropus* (Fig. 214, D) of South Africa. These curious animals were formerly classed as edentates, but are now known to be unique in a number of characters and have therefore been accorded separate ordinal value. They too are ant-eaters and have the slender snout, long tongue, and strong claws characteristic of this habitus. The skin is very thick and covered with sparse hair.

ORDER CARNIVORA (FLESH EATERS)

This order comprises an immense group that dates back to early Tertiary times and may have arisen independently, along with insectivores, rodents, edentates, and ungulates from the main stem of ancestral Mesozoic placental mammals. The order is subdivided into three suborders: Creodontia, Fissipedia, and Pinnipedia.

Suborder 1.   Creodontia. — This is an extinct group of some importance for our purposes inasmuch as it is regarded not only as ancestral to modern carnivores, but there are also evidences that the whales were derived from early carnivores related to the creodonts.

The Eocene creodonts were numerous and varied in type and most of them seem to have become extinct, without leaving descendants. One group of them, however, evolved into the surviving fissipede carnivores. Figure 197 shows the probable external appearance of several of the best-known genera and these roughly resemble modern carnivores. The most striking difference between creodonts and modern carnivores is that of brain size and specialization, their brains being small and poorly developed.

Suborder 2.   Fissipedia (Terrestrial Carnivores). — The dentition (Fig. 181) is probably the best diagnostic feature of this group; they have six incisors of small size in each jaw, canines are large and strong, the last premolar and the first molar are "carnassial" or cutting teeth, and the last two molars are crushing teeth. The fissiped carnivores have a world-wide distribution, being native to all of the large continental bodies except Australia. The principal family groups are: the cats, the civets, the hyaenas, the dogs, the raccoons, the weasels, and the bears.

Fig. 215. Group of fissiped Carnivora. A. Canada lynx, *Felis canadensis* (after Fuertes). B. Civet cat, *Viverra civetta* (after Beddard). C. Spotted hyaena, *Crocuta maculata* (after Beddard). D. Gray or timber wolf, *Canis nubilus* (after Fuertes). E. Raccoon, *Procyon lotor* (after Feurtes). F. Badger, *Taxidea taxus* (after Fuertes). G. Otter, *Lutra canadensis* (after Fuertes). H. Largest of the bears, Alaska brown bear, *Ursus gyas* (after Fuertes). (All figures redrawn, those after Fuertes in National Geographic Magazine, simplified and more or less modified.)

Family 1. Felidae (Cats). This is much the largest and most dominant of the carnivore families. The carnassial teeth are highly perfected shearing organs, canines especially long and curved, and molars are somewhat reduced. The claws are retractile, an arrangement that gives the cats a quiet tread when stalking their prey. The typical genus, *Felis*, includes such cats as the lions, tigers, leopards, lynxes, jaguars, ocelots, pumas, and many smaller types. The domestic cat is believed to be a descendant of the eastern wild species, *Felis caffra*, first domesticated by the Egyptians and considered by them a sacred animal. The Canada lynx (Fig. 215, A) is a short-tailed, somewhat aberrant type of cat.

Family 2. Viverridae (Civets). The civets (Fig. 215, B) and their kin, which comprise this family are rather small, more or less cat-like carnivores that are native to Ethiopian and oriental regions. The claws are incompletely retractile and they have more teeth than the true cats. The civets proper are decidedly feline in appearance and are usually marked with black and white spots or stripes. The fossa is a very cat-like carnivore; it is the largest carnivore native to Madagascar. The mongoose is a small, extremely active animal of oriental countries. It is noted for its ability to kill snakes, especially the deadly cobra.

Family 3. Hyaenidae (Hyaenas). These animals (Fig. 215, C) are in appearance and habits intermediate between the cats and the dogs. They are either spotted or striped. The voice is said to be almost human in sound and stories are told of human beings lured to their death by following their cries.

Family 4. Canidae (Dogs). The dog family includes the wolves (Fig. 215, D), foxes, coyotes, and the dingo of Australia, which is believed to be an imported species. The domestic dogs are believed to have been derived from several wild stocks, some of which may have become extinct. In many ways the dogs are the most primitive of the carnivores: the dentition is quite generalized, the claws are less specialized than in other groups and in several other ways they appear to resemble the ancestral carnivores. They have been associated with man for a very long period, and are as cosmopolitan in their distribution as man is, because wherever man goes he takes his dogs, even to the North Pole.

Family 5. Procyonidae (Raccoons). This is an American family of carnivores that in some ways is intermediate between the dogs and the bears. They have plantigrade feet and grinding teeth like the bears, but in other respects are more like the dogs. The common raccoon (*Procyon*) is a familiar type (Fig. 215, E) around streams and lakes, where it catches crayfish, clams, and sometimes fish, without, however, going very far into the water. The clown-like pandas are regarded as aberrant raccoons.

Family 6. Mustelidae. This is a large family of bloodthirsty, predaceous creatures, including: weasels, polecats, badgers (Fig. 215, F),

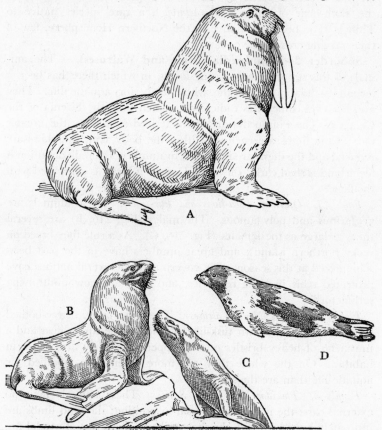

Fig. 216. Pinniped Carnivora. A. Pacific walrus, *Odobenus obesus*. B. Male, and C, female, of Steller sea-lion, *Eumetopias jubata*. D. Greenland seal, *Phoca groenlandica*. (All redrawn after Fuertes.)

martens, wolverines, sables, minks, ermines, ferrets, stoats, skunks, otters (Fig. 215, G), and other less known types. For the most part they give off a nauseous musky odor, which is most marked in the skunks. They are among the most important of our fur-bearing animals. Representatives of the family are native to all the continental bodies except Australia and Madagascar.

Family 7. Ursidae (*Bears*). The bears (Fig. 215, H) are the largest of modern carnivores and are characterized most sharply by their plantigrade walk and the short tail. Most bears belong to the genus *Ursus*, but several other genera are distinguished, such as *Melurus*, the sloth-bear of India, and *Aeluropus*, a rare species native to Thibet. The bears are native to the Northern Hemisphere, few of them having crossed the equator.

Suborder 3. Pinnipedia (Seals and Walruses). — The animals of this suborder are marine forms, in which there has been a secondary adaptation of the whole body for aquatic life. They are, however, much less radically modified than the Sirenia or the Cetacea. The Pinnipedia are characterized as follows: the greater part of the limbs are enclosed within the body skin; the claws are reduced and the digits are increased in number; the milk dentition is feeble and is shed early; the cranial cavity is large as compared with the face.

Family 1. Otariidae (*Sea-lions and Fur-seals*). These animals are gregarious and polygamous. The males (Fig. 216, B) are several times as large as the females (Fig. 216, C). As a rule they breed on rocky northern islands; and great numbers have in the past been slaughtered at this season. The governments of several nations have protected seals in their rookeries, and they are now multiplying satisfactorily.

Family 2. Trichechidae (*Walruses*). These are large, heavy-bodied forms (Fig. 216, A) with tusk-like canines in the upper jaws and a mustache of heavy bristles on the upper lip. They are Arctic in habitat. On the whole they are more extensively modified for aquatic life than are the sea-lions.

Family 3. Phocidae (*The True Seals*). These animals have no external ears; the nostrils are dorsal in position; the hind limbs are intimately bound up with the short tail to make a sort of caudal fin, which is used as a very effective swimming organ. The fore limbs are rather small and fin-like, and the whole body is decidedly spindle-shaped. The seals are much more highly specialized for marine life than are either the sea-lions or the walruses. One of the commonest of the seals is *Phoca groenlandica* (Fig. 216, D), a small spotted animal about four or five feet long.

ORDER CETACEA (WHALES AND DOLPHINS)

This assemblage of large aquatic mammals is profoundly modified for marine life. They are unquestionably the most highly specialized structurally of all mammals, although certain of their characters are persistently primitive. In older classifications they have usually been placed among the earlier orders, because they are least like man, who was looked upon as the ultimate goal of organic evolution. The statement that the whales are the most highly specialized mammals is backed up by the following criteria of specialization: 1, the whales are farthest removed from the generalized types of mammals in all of their adaptive characters; 2, they have undergone losses or extreme reduction of such typical mammalian structures as hair, teeth (in some groups), claws, and hind limbs; 3, the skeleton of the fore limbs is secondarily specialized by the addition of several extra joints in the digits; 4, they have reached a size unrivaled in the world's history, far surpassing that of the giant reptiles of Mesozoic times; 5, the stomach is one of the most complex among mammals; 6, the skull of some of the whales is the most asymmetrical and otherwise specialized among mammals.

There are many evidences that the whales were derived from early Eocene creodonts, the first carnivores. The earliest of the whales were elongated, aquatic carnivores with head and teeth much like those of other carnivores. The extinct *Zeuglodon* certainly was much more like a carnivore than anything else. These primitive whales are assigned to the suborder Zeuglodontia and modern whales to two suborders, Odontoceti and Mystacoceti.

Suborder 1. Odontoceti (Toothed Whales). — This suborder includes the sperm whales, narwhals, beaked whales, porpoises, and dolphins. They are characterized by the presence of teeth and absence of whalebone; by the possession of a single nostril or blow hole; by marked asymmetry of the skull; and by having at least some of the ribs two-headed.

The sperm whale or cachalot (Fig. 217, C), *Physeter*, is probably the largest animal that ever lived, and the writer was fortunate enough to have been able to examine and to record the measurements of what is now believed to have been the largest specimen ever authentically described. This was the well-known Port Arthur whale, that came ashore on the north coast of the Gulf of Mexico in March, 1910. This animal measured on a straight line from snout

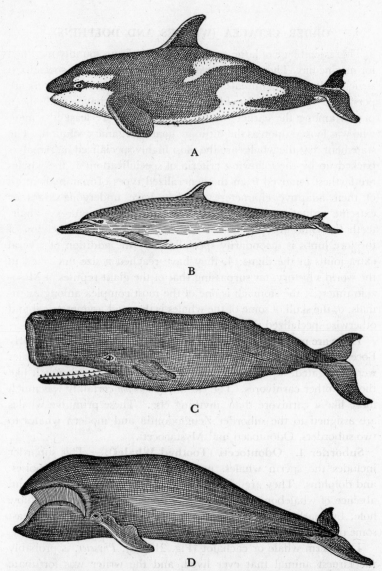

FIG. 217. Group of Cetacea. A. Killer whale, *Orca gladiator* (after True). B. Common dolphin, *Delphinus delphis* (after Reinhardt). C. Sperm whale, *Physeter macrocephalus*. D. Southern right whale, *Baloena australis*. (C and D, after Beddard.)

to end of flukes (not following curvatures as is usually done) sixty-three and a half feet. Its circumference in front of the flippers was thirty-seven feet; it was twelve feet in height at the shoulders. This enormous animal did not impress one as a long, slender type, but as distinctly stocky, retaining its great diameter from the end of the snout to within about fifteen feet from the tail. The lower jaw of the sperm whale is long and narrow and is armed with from forty to forty-eight conical teeth that fit into the toothless groove of the upper jaw. These whales are monophyodont, having only one set of teeth. A large cavity in the skull is filled with a liquid oil, spermaceti, which is a valuable product. This reservoir of light oil is believed to be largely of hydrostatic value, in that it must be quite buoyant. The huge skull is the most highly modified skull known for a mammal. The right maxillary and left nasal bones are much larger than their fellows, the right nasal being vestigial. The top of the skull has a great bony crest running diagonally instead of mesially as in other skulls. The seven cervical vertebrae are largely fused into a short immovable neck. The sperm whale is valuable for spermaceti, for oil made from blubber, and for ambergris. The latter is a very valuable product said to be worth its weight in gold, and is a cumulative by-product of intestinal digestion, having a composition somewhat like cholesterin. Ambergris is used in imparting long-lasting quality to fine perfumes and even minute quantities add value to considerable volumes of perfume. The food of the sperm whale consists largely of giant squids, as may be judged by the remains of the latter found in the whale's stomach.

One of the most fish-like of the toothed whales is the killer whale (Fig. 217, A), *Orca*, a small species that has the reputation of killing larger whales.

Beaked whales are animals of moderate size, seldom more than thirty feet in length; they have a prolonged muzzle armed with numerous teeth. They are quite slender and doubtless have done duty as "sea serpents." Dolphins and porpoises (Fig. 223, B) are small toothed whales of rather generalized structure. They have teeth in both jaws, and the head is more mammal-like than that of other whales. According to Flower, there are nineteen genera of these small whales, and they comprise a considerable majority of all existing cetaceans. They are distinctly gregarious, running in schools of considerable size. Their habit of leaping out of the water at intervals makes them an interesting sight for ocean travelers. Closely allied to the porpoises is the narwhal, a form in which the teeth are reduced to a single tusk in the upper jaw, which protrudes out in front like a spear. This tusk is twisted in structure like a rawhide ox-whip and is limited to the males, who use it in fencing contests among themselves.

Suborder 2. Mystacoceti (Whalebone Whales). — The whale-bone, or baleen whales (Fig. 217, D) are the last word in adaptive

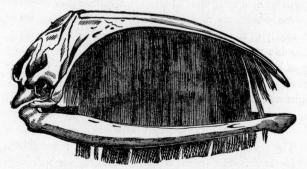

Fig. 218. Skull of baleen whale, *Baloena mysticetus*. (From Weysse, after Claus and Sedgwick.)

specialization among mammals. The teeth are rudimentary and functionless, present in the young but replaced in the adult by baleen. The nostrils are paired; the skull is symmetrical; the sternum is single; the ribs are one-headed, articulating only with the trans-verse processes of the vertebrae. The group is composed exclusively of large forms, the only one that is less than a giant being the pygmy right whale, which is only about fifteen feet in length. Baleen, or whalebone, is a horny material developed from the epithelial lining of the upper jaws. It is disposed in curtain-like plates (Fig. 218), frayed out into fringes at the bottom. The plates reach a length of twelve or more feet and are triangular, with the greatest width at the top. As many as three hundred and seventy blades or curtains, placed with their edges an inch or so apart, have been counted in a single mouth. The function of the baleen is that of a strainer. The great beast rushes through the water with the mouth wide open, gathering in fishes or whatever else happens to be in the way. Then the mouth closes and the water is forced out between the sheets of baleen, while fishes, etc., are retained and swallowed. Such huge creatures require vast quantities of food and can not become very numerous. Formerly whalebone was a commercial product of some importance, used chiefly as stays in women's garments. Many substitutes, however, have been discovered and, moreover, stays have gone out of fashion; so that the market value of the commodity has been greatly depressed. A single large whale produces several tons of whalebone, and, since a ton used to be worth about ten thousand dollars, the capture of a single baleen whale meant a small fortune to the whaler.

Rorquals are a type of whalebone whale with comparatively small heads, a distinct dorsal fin, and with a throat deeply corrugated into longitudinal furrows. The flipper has only four fingers, but each finger is very long, having many extra joints. They range in length from forty to nearly seventy feet; one species has a record of eighty-five feet in length. Though longer, they are less bulky than sperm whales, probably equaling the latter in weight. The cervical vertebrae are all separate.

Right whales are the more typical baleen whales. They have no dorsal fin; the head is very large, being about one-fourth of the entire length; the baleen is very long; the throat is not corrugated; the cervical vertebrae are fused into a solid mass. The Greenland right whale is, perhaps, the best known of all whales. It has a very limited distribution, being confined to the Arctic Ocean. It grows to be about seventy feet in length. The pursuit of whaling used to be one of the most romantic and dangerous of human occupations; but with the advent of whaling guns, with which the great creatures may be harpooned at a safe distance, the danger is largely eliminated, though much of the romance remains. The southern right whale, a close relative of the Greenland species, has a wide range, avoiding only the Arctic regions. The two species never occur in the same territory. It was less prized by the whaler on account of the relatively short and coarse whalebone.

Whales as a whole are much less numerous than they were a century ago and it seems probable that, unless some protection is given them, they are likely to become extinct before another century rolls by. Man seems to have no compunctions in his lust for commercial profit, and even these noble creatures of the deep may soon go the ways of the giants of ages past.

THE UNGULATE ORDERS

The last great group of placental mammal orders are often called ungulates, or hoofed mammals. They were probably all derived from a very generalized early Eocene stock that split off from the main stem along with the insectivore assemblage, the rodents, and the carnivore assemblage. Many orders have now become extinct, but the surviving orders are so numerous that we shall entirely omit the extinct ones from this account.

ORDER PERISSODACTYLA (ODD-TOED UNGULATES)

In this group the middle digit of both fore and hind feet is pre-eminent and carries most of the weight. The axis of the limb

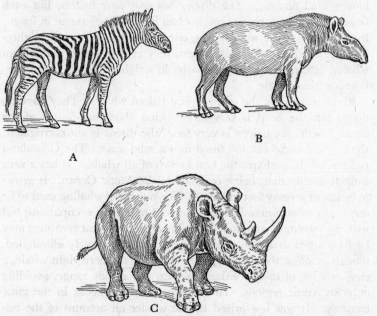

FIG. 219. Group of Perissodactyla (odd-toed ungulates). A. Burchell's zebra, *Equus burchelli*. B. American tapir, *Tapirus terrestris*. C. African rhinoceros, *Rhinoceros bicornis*. (Redrawn and modified: A, B, after Beddard; C, after Lydekker.)

passes through the third digit. The teeth of the odd-toed ungulates are usually lophodont, a type characterized by the presence of enamel ridges running back and forth across the grinding surface. The present-day perissodactyls are grouped into three families: Equidae, Tapiridae, and Rhinocerotidae.

Family 1. Equidae (Horses, Asses, and Zebras). The members of the horse family (Fig. 219, A) are characterized by the possession of but a single functional toe, the third toe, on each foot. The second and fourth toes are represented by vestigial remnants, called "splint bones." The molar teeth are highly complex in structure and wear down through most of the life of the individual, so that the age of any specimen may be arrived at by the amount of wear upon the teeth. All of the modern Equidae are placed in the single genus *Equus*. Perhaps the most convincing record of the ancestry of any vertebrate group is that of the horse (Fig. 4). With respect to toes, teeth, and general form, the gradual perfection of the present highly specialized cursorial grazing type may be traced back through an unbroken line of ancestors to a very generalized ungulate type with four functional toes, generalized teeth, and comparatively small size. The horse has played and is still playing an extremely important role in the progress of human civilization.

Family 2. Tapiridae (Tapirs). The tapirs (Fig. 219, B) are the most generalized of modern odd-toed ungulates. They are characterized by moderate size and by a short, highly flexible proboscis produced by elongation of nose and upper lip. The dentition is more generalized than that of the horses, there being forty-two teeth, a number very close to that of the most primitive placental mammals. There are four toes on the fore feet and three on the hind feet. The tapirs are confined to South and Central America and to the Malay Peninsula.

Family 3. Rhinocerotidae (Rhinoceroses). This family consists of a few species of large, massive animals, whose general appearance is familiar to all (Fig. 219, C). They are distinguished by the presence of one or two median "horns" on the nose, but these structures are not true horns, being composed of an agglomeration of hair-like structures fastened to a prominence of the nasal bones. There are usually three, sometimes four, toes on the fore feet, but in either case the third toe is the most important; the hind feet always have three toes. The upper lip is long and more or less prehensile, but not elongated into a proboscis as in the tapirs. The skin is extremely thick and the hair very sparse. They are fierce and intractable, charging at an enemy with great fury and stopping at nothing. Only guns of large caliber and hard-hitting qualities will stop their mad rush. They have a fairly wide distribution, being native to both India and Africa. The fossil record of the ancestry of the rhinoceros is almost as complete as that of the horse, and the two groups appear to converge upon a common ancestral group. The early rhinoceroses must have looked more like horses than do the present forms, which have grown heavy of limb and body and are no longer typically cursorial.

ORDER ARTIODACTYLA (EVEN-TOED UNGULATES)

The mammals of this group are: swine, hippopotami, peccaries, camels, deer, moose, elk, giraffes, pronghorns, cattle, buffaloes, gnus, antelopes, gazelles, yaks, sheep, ibex, goats, and many other less well-known types. They are, in general, purely terrestrial, though some of them are semiaquatic. For the most part they are cursorial, though some are heavy-bodied and not very fleet of foot. They have hoofs on two or four toes. The stomach usually has several chambers in adaption to a purely herbivorous diet.

Group 1. Suina (*Swine-like Ungulates*). This group consists of three families, represented respectively by the hippopotami, swine proper, and peccaries. The *Hippopotamus* (Fig. 220, A) is a large heavy-bodied aquatic "hog," with four hoofs on each foot. It is native of Africa, as is also the pygmy hippopotamus, a dwarf species found in Liberia. The swine proper include the European wild-hog, the wart hog (Fig. 220, B), and several other types. The peccaries are swift, cursorial, hog-like creatures, that run in large packs, and on account of their sheer numbers, are said to be very dangerous to meet.

Group 2. Ruminantia (*Ruminants*). These ungulates "chew their cud," by which is meant that they swallow their food rapidly and afterwards regurgitate it into the mouth for further mastication. Three assemblages of these forms are distinguished: A, *Tragulina* (mouse deer); B, *Tylopoda* (camels, llamas); C, *Pecora* (deer, antelopes, oxen, giraffes, goats, and sheep).

The chevrotains, or mouse deer, are intermediate between the swine and the ruminants, and are the most primitive of the ruminants. The camels (Fig. 220, C) are a small group of well-known types, confined to arid regions of the Old World. Camels are not known in the wild state; all are domestic or feral. The ancestral history of the camel family is now almost as well worked out as that of the horse. Proverbial for the camels are two characters: that of living for long periods without water, and the use of the fatty humps for food when compelled to fast. Both of these characters may be considered as adaptations for desert life and have made it a highly

FIG. 220. Group of Artiodactyla (even-toed ungulates). A. Hippopotamus, *Hippopotamus amphibia*. B. Wart hog, *Phacochoerus aethiopicus*. C. The Bactrian camel, *Camelus bactrianus*. D. Wapiti, or American elk, *Cervus canadensis*. E. Giraffe, *Giraffa camelopardalis*. F. Ibex, *Capra sinaitica*. (Redrawn and somewhat modified; A, C, after Lydekker, B, E, F, after Beddard, D, after Fuertes.)

valuable beast of burden and transport across the arid trails of the Asiatic and African deserts. On this account they have earned the cognomen "ships of the desert." The camel is very valuable for its hair, which is used in making fabrics highly prized for their richness, softness, and wool-like characteristics. The llamas, sometimes called alpacas and vicunas, are creatures with camel-like characters, but more generalized in several respects; in fact they are sometimes regarded as primitive camels of the New World, for they are native to South America. They are of value chiefly for their rather thin hair, which is coarser than that of the camel and is the material out of which are made vicuna or alpaca fabrics. The llamas have the disgusting habit when irritated of forcibly spitting the contents of the stomach at the object of their annoyance.

The deer family is a very large one and includes such well-known types as elk, moose, reindeer, etc. They are characterized by the possession of antlers in the male sex, and in the reindeer in both sexes. The antlers vary in degree of elaborateness in the different genera, ranging from the small, unbranched horns, as in *Cervulus*, to the complex branching antlers of the elk (Fig. 220, D). In all cases they are solid bony structures, as opposed to the hollow horns of the Bovidae. About sixty species of deer are known, the majority of which are Old World forms. The moose is the king of the deer family on account of its great size and its fighting qualities. The reindeer is the most northerly of the deer, occupying circumpolar territory. The musk-deer is an exceptional type in that it has no horns, but instead is possessed of long, sharp tusks, probably used in digging roots for food.

The giraffe family (Fig. 220, E) comprises a small group of highly specialized ruminants distinguished by their great height, long neck, and slender legs. The horns differ from all others in that they are merely prominences of the frontal bones of the skull covered with skin and hair. Africa is the home of the giraffe, as well as that of the okapi, a small, less specialized member of the giraffe family, somewhat like an antelope in general appearance.

The cattle family (Bovidae) is much the largest family of ruminants. It includes oxen, bison, yak, sheep, goats, ibexes (Fig. 220, F), gnus, antelopes, and several other less familiar types. The most prominent distinguishing character of the group is the horns, which are hollow, composed of keratin, and usually present in both sexes. A large number of the Bovidae have been domesticated, and most of them are so familiar that no description of the different species is necessary.

ORDER HYRACOIDEA (CONEYS)

This small order consists of but one living genus of primitive ungulates. The coney (Fig. 221), *Hyrax* or *Procavia*, bears a strong

FIG. 221. Coneys or hyraces, *Hyrax abyssinicus*. (From Lull, after Brehm.)

resemblance to certain rodents, the short ears and reduced tail being especially like those of the cavies. They are unlike the ungulates and like the rodents in that the incisor teeth grow from persistent pulps. In certain other respects they resemble primitive ungulates.

Some of the coneys live among rocks, while others are partly arboreal. The Scriptures describe them as "exceeding wise" and as "feeble folk," but the observation that he "cheweth the cud but divideth not the hoof" is without foundation on either count; for they are not ruminants, and there are four hoofs in front and three behind.

ORDER PROBOSCIDEA (ELEPHANTS)

This group comprises the largest and in many respects the most highly specialized of terrestrial mammals. They are characterized

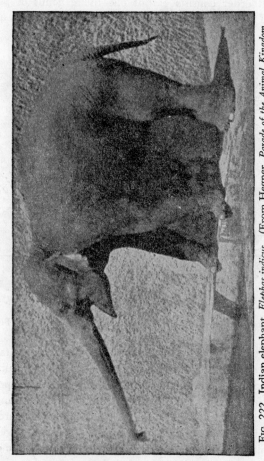

Fig. 222. Indian elephant, *Elephas indicus*. (From Hegner, *Parade of the Animal Kingdom.* Photo by Hegner.)

by the elongation of the nose and upper lip into a very long trunk; by the possession of five functional digits on both fore and hind feet; by the specialization of the incisor teeth of the upper jaw into great tusks; and by the extreme type of lophodont molar teeth. The skull is immensely thick and its bones contain large air cavities;

Fig. 223. African elephant, *Elephas africanus*. (Redrawn after Beddard.)

there is no clavicle; the cerebral hemispheres are much convoluted, but they do not cover the cerebellum; the testes are abdominal in position.

Elephants walk with the legs stiff, almost as if they were jointless, an adaptation for bearing the great weight; for it would require great muscular effort to support the huge bulk of these animals upon a bent type of limb. Two families of Proboscidia are distinguished: Elephantidae and Dinotheridae. The latter were Miocene forms characterized by great downwardly directed tusks of the lower jaw.

There are but two living species of elephant, the Indian elephant (Fig. 222), *Elephas indicus*, and the African elephant (Fig. 223), *E. africanus*. The African species is the larger, and has much larger ears. The largest specimen on record is probably the notorious "Jumbo," which was about eleven feet high at the shoulder. African elephants are wild and intractable as compared with their Indian cousins; and therefore are seldom seen in circus parades. The Indian elephant is the common circus elephant, a smaller and more manageable type. In its native country it is used extensively as an equipage, as a beast of burden and for handling heavy timber. As a species, however, they are not dependable, some being vicious and others perfectly docile in disposition. In nature they are creatures of the jungle and are purely herbivorous. They are capable of defending themselves against all enemies except man.

Elephants have been credited with extraordinary memory, but in all probability an exceptionally keen sense of smell plays a prominent part in their memory, an enemy being associated with a special odor. Even in human beings, whose sense of smell is at best rudimentary, memories of all sorts are inextricably bound up with odors.

Elephants live to a great age, probably in the neighborhood of two hundred years. In this connection the peculiar arrangement of the molar teeth is of interest; for as the molar teeth that first emerge are worn off by long years of use other molars gradually replace them. The grinding teeth are arranged as though in the arc of a circle, so that only two or at most three on each jaw are in contact at one time. When the front ones wear out the rest move up and take their places, until in very old animals only the last teeth are present. This dentition is, in some respects, the most specialized found among vertebrates.

Among the best known recently extinct types of elephants are the mammoth and the mastodon. The mammoth was more nearly like the Indian elephant than any other species, but was much larger. Its tusks were enormous, one being known to weigh two hundred and fifty pounds. These tusks are extremely durable as is demonstrated by the fact that much of the ivory now in use in the form of billiard balls, etc., has been made from them, though their original owners have been dead for thousands of years. The mastodon was about as high as the Indian elephant, seven to nine feet, but was much more stockily built and longer bodied. The tusks were sometimes as much as nine feet or more in length.

The evolution of the peculiar characters of modern elephants is well shown in a series of extinct forms. The earliest proboscidian appears to have been a form like *Maeritherium* (Fig. 224, F'), which, though rather generalized in most respects, shows the beginnings of elephantine characters in the air cells in the back of the skull, in the enlarged second incisors, or incipient tusks, and the primitive lophodont molars. It was, however, only about three and a half feet high. Transitional stages are shown in *Palaeomastodon* (Fig. 224, E'), in *Trilophodon* (Fig. 224, D'), and in *Stegodon* (Fig. 224, C'),

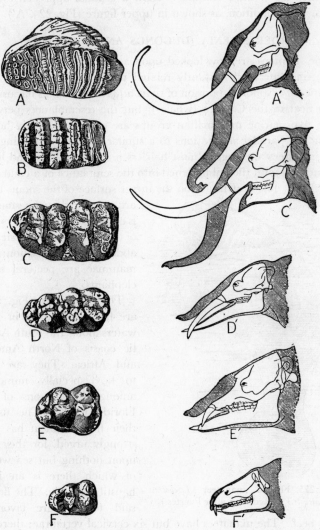

Fig. 224. Evolution of head and molar teeth of mastodons and elephants. A, A'. *Elephas*, Pleistocene. B. *Stegodon*, Pliocene. C, C'. *Mastodon*, Pleistocene. D, D'. *Trilophodon*, Miocene. E, E'. *Palaeomastodon*, Oligocene. F, F'. *Maeritherium*, Eocene. (From Lull.)

in which all of these characters show a gradual approach toward the present condition, as shown in upper figure (Fig. 224, A').

ORDER SIRENIA (DUGONGS AND MANATEES)

The sirenians are now looked upon as an aquatic offshoot of an early ungulate stock distantly related to the proboscidians. The traditional taxonomic position of these aquatic mammals has usually been next to the Cetacea (whales), but the resemblances between these two marine mammalian groups are evidently largely homoplastic, or parallel adaptations to a similar habitat. Both dugongs and manatees are large, almost hairless mammals, with hind limbs absent, and with the tail flattened into the semblance of a caudal fin or a fluke. The nostrils are on the upper surface of the snout; there are no clavicles; the stomach is complex and resembles that of the ungulates; the testes are abdominal in position; the mammae are pectoral as in elephants.

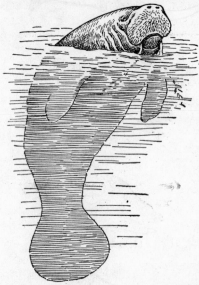

FIG. 225. Florida manatee, *Trichechus latirostris*. (Redrawn after Fuertes.)

The manatees (Fig. 225) are fairly abundant in fresh waters along the south Atlantic coasts of North America and Africa. They are said to be especially numerous among the lagoons of the Florida Coast. The use of their flesh as meat has been strongly urged, for they feed upon nothing but sea weeds, of which there is an inexhaustible supply. The flesh is said to compare favorably with beef. The manatees have but six cervical vertebrae; there are as many as twenty molar teeth, which seem to continue to increase during life. In these two respects they are almost unique among mammals.

The dugong (Fig. 226), *Halicore*, is an oriental and Australian species, with whale-like tail-flukes instead of the rhomboidal type of tail paddle seen in the manatee. It is more extensively specialized for aquatic life than the manatee, for the nostrils are more dorsal, the tail is more fish-like, and the digits have no claws. It is said that the dugong is responsible for most of the mermaid legends, for when

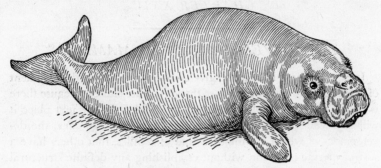

FIG. 226. Dugong, *Halicore dugong*. (Redrawn after Lydekker.)

the female holds her young to her pectoral breast by means of one flipper while swimming with the other, she presents a slightly human aspect.

CHAPTER XXIV

THE DEVELOPMENT OF MAMMALS

It is much more difficult to give a concise account of development of mammals than of any other of the vertebrate classes, because there is such a wide range of diversity of conditions. In the first place it will be recalled that some of the mammals lay large eggs, the development of which is similar to that of reptiles, that others have a sort of uterine gestation without establishing any definite structural

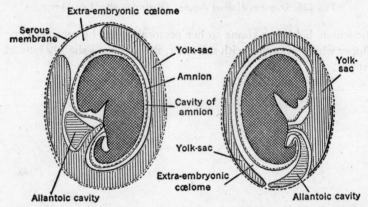

FIG. 227. Fetal membranes of *Hypsiprymnus*. (From Parker and Haswell.)

FIG. 228. Fetal membranes of *Phascolarctus*. (From Parker and Haswell.)

connection between the fetal and the uterine membranes, and that still others have various types of placental gestation. We may quickly dispose of the situation involved in the egg-laying mammals by saying that their mode of development is essentially reptilian, similar to that of the bird already described, and need not be discussed here.

The marsupials present a wide variety of conditions. Their eggs though minute are somewhat larger than those of the placental mammals. The embryo has a brief period of uterine gestation, though no fixed nor definite uterine attachment is, as a rule, established.

In most marsupials a large part of the surface of the egg is covered over by the compressed and expanded yolk-sac, which aids in the absorption of nutriment derived from uterine fluids. This condition is illustrated in *Hypsiprymnus* (Fig. 227). In *Phascolarctus* (Fig. 228), in addition to the extensive yolk-sac, a primitive type of allantoic placenta comes to the surface to aid in food absorption, but no vascular villi invade the uterine mucosa. Only in *Perameles* (the bandicoot) does the allantois attain anything like an intimate nutritive relation with maternal tissues. This consists of simple allantoic placenta (Fig. 229) in which folds and ridges of the fetal allantois interlock with those of the uterine wall, lacking only villi

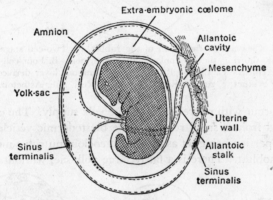

FIG. 229. Fetal membranes of *Perameles*. (From Parker and Haswell.)

to make this placenta fully equivalent to those of some placental mammals. In this connection we might revert to the view held by several leading authorities that the conditions found in the marsupials of today are not primitive but largely degenerate, and that *Perameles* with its primitive placenta (Fig. 229) represents a more nearly primitive condition than any other living marsupial so far studied. Such a view would involve the corollary that both modern marsupials and modern placental mammals have been derived from a primitive placental ancestry. It may well be that some of the Pantotheria, now regarded as common ancestors of both marsupials and placentals, had a primitive placental mode of gestation.

Conditions in Placental Mammals. — Some of the simpler types of placenta, such as that of the pig and the horse, are not unlike those seen in the marsupial, *Perameles*, but in others, as for example the primates, the armadillos, etc., the conditions are very much modified. A volume could be written about the great variety of placental conditions among mammals.

The **egg** of the placental mammal is extremely small and essentially yolkless, yet many developmental changes take place that

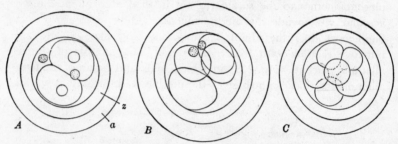

FIG. 230. Cleavage of the ovum of the rabbit. A. Two-cell stage, 24 hours after coitus, showing the two polar bodies separated. B. Four-cell stage, $25\frac{1}{2}$ hours after coitus. C. Eight-cell stage. a, albuminous layer derived from the wall of the oviduct; z, zona radiata. (From Kellicott, after Assheton.)

seem to occur with reference to a large yolk supply. The embryo is developed from a small region of the blastodermic vesicle, the remaining portion being set aside as a precocious nutritive membrane, the trophoblast. There is a fairly large yolk-sac, without any yolk

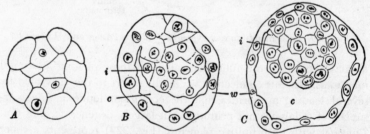

FIG. 231. Morula and early blastodermic vesicles of the rabbit. The zona radiata and albuminous layer are not shown. A. Section through a morula stage, 47 hours after coitus. B. Section through very young vesicle, 80 hours after coitus. C. Section through more advanced vesicle, 83 hours after coitus; taken from uterus. c, cavity of blastodermic vesicle; i, inner cell mass; w, wall of the blastodermic vesicle (trophoblast). (From Kellicott, after Assheton.)

content, upon which a vitelline circulation develops which serves no function associated with yolk absorption. Amnion, chorion, and allantois form much as in birds, though secondary modifications of all of these membranes are found in various groups. All of these conditions seem to admit of but one interpretation: that the small, yolkless mammalian ovum is the lineal descendant of a large-yolked egg similar to that of the monotremes or the reptiles, and that the yolk has been lost in connection with the habit of uterine gestation. With all the conservativeness of the typical germ-cell, however, the mammal egg persists in behaving much as though it had a large supply of yolk upon which it had to depend for nourishing the embryo.

Cleavage and Early De-velopment in a Placental Mammal.—It is not easy to compare the cleavage (Fig. 230) of the mammalian ovum with that of any other form. It appears deceptively simple, but we know that this apparent simplicity is a camouflage, for subsequent events reveal that the apparent holoblastic cleav-age gives results that are similar to those resulting from a rep-tilian type of meroblastic cleav-

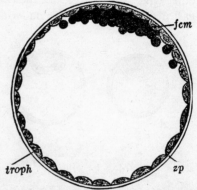

Fig. 232. Section through the fully formed blastodermic vesicle of the rab-bit. *fcm*, granular cells of inner cell mass; *troph*, trophoblast; *zp*, zona pellucida. (From Kellicott, after Quain.)

age. It appears that the first two cleavages are total and equal, just as in amphioxus. After that the cleavages are not easy to follow, since the cells seem to shift about and not to retain their original positions.

The blastula stage takes the form of a solid mass of cells, the morula (Fig. 231, A), in which a peripheral layer of cells, the tro-phoblast, is distinguished from the inner-cell-mass. Subsequently (Fig. 231, B and C) the trophoblast separates from the inner-cell-mass except at the animal pole and a large cavity filled with fluid appears between the two layers. The trophoblast layer is a temporary structure serving as a sort of primitive placenta for the young embryo and helping the latter to gain its first connection with the uterine membrane. A specialized region of the trophoblast, called the "Träger," sends short papillae into the uterine mucosa, opening the way for the true placental villi that come later. The inner-cell-mass forms the entire embryo, together with the embryonic membranes, amnion, chorion, allantois, and yolk-sac. At first a round ball of cells, the inner-cell-mass (Fig. 232) flattens out to form a thin lens-shaped body in contact with the attached part of the trophoblast. Later two layers form, ectoderm and endoderm, by a sorting out of two types of cells, or a migration inwards of the endoderm cells. This process is the equivalent of the first step in gastrulation, but can not readily be compared with the equivalent process in any other type of embryo. Once the two-layered germinal disc, or early gastrula, is formed, the remainder of the process of embryogenesis is

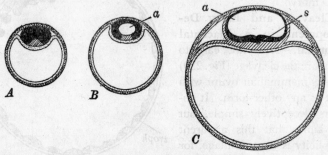

Fig. 233. Diagram of the formation of the amnion in the Insectivora. Black, embryonic ectoderm; heavy stipples, trophoblast; light stipples, endoderm, oblique ruling, mesoderm. A, before the appearance of the amniotic cavity; inner cell mass differentiated into ectoderm and mesoderm; endoderm extending completely around the wall of the vesicle. B, the amniotic cavity (*a*) appearing in the ectoderm. C, enlargement of the amniotic cavity. Mesoderm expanded and split into somatic and splanchnic layers, separated by the coelom. *s*, primitive streak. (From Kellicott, after Keibel.)

much like that of the reptiles or birds and need not be further described.

The development of the embryonic membranes, however, differs in many ways from that seen in the bird. The layer of endoderm, at first confined to the upper part of the vesicle, spreads until it forms a complete inner lining for the trophoblast. The gut of the embryo is pinched off from the upper part, leaving an empty yolk-sac below, connected with the gut-endoderm by a slender yolk-stalk. The amnion sometimes forms as in the chick (Fig. 173), by folds of the somatopleure, which also produces the outer layer, or chorion; but sometimes the amnion forms precociously by means of a cavity opening up in the midst of the ectodermic mass, a short-cut method used by the insectivores (Fig. 233), bats, rodents, armadillos, and man. The allantois forms as in birds, but frequently remains rudimentary, as in man (Fig. 235). In some cases, as in the pig, horse,

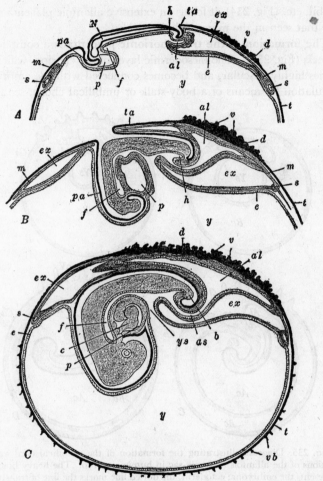

Fig. 234. Diagram of the formation of the embryonic membranes and append-ages of the rabbit. A, at the end of the ninth day; B, early the tenth day; C, at end of tenth day. Ectoderm, black; endoderm, dotted; mesoderm, gray. *al*, al-lantois; *as*, allantoic stalk; *b*, tail bud; *c*, heart; *d*, trophoderm; *e*, endoderm; *ex*, exocoelom; *f*, foregut; *h*, hind-gut; *m*, mesoderm; *N*, central nervous system; *p*, pericardial cavity; *pa*, proamnion; *s*, marginal sinus (sinus terminalis); *t*, tro-phoblast; *ta*, tail-fold of amnion; *v*, trophodermal villi; *vb*, trophoblastic villi; *y*, cavity of yolk-sac; *ys*, yolk-stalk. (From Kellicott, after Van Beneden and Julin.)

rabbit, etc. (Fig. 234), it forms an extensive allantoic placenta much like that seen in the marsupial, *Perameles*.

The formation of the true chorionic placenta is a complicated process (Fig. 235). The mesodermic layer of the chorion, which becomes highly vascular, and becomes connected with the embryonic circulation by means of a body-stalk or umbilical chord, sends out

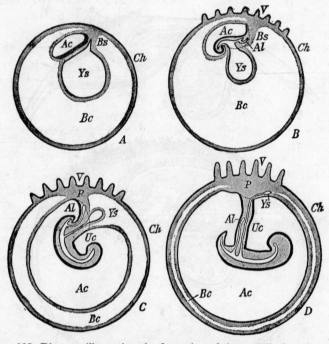

FIG. 235. Diagram illustrating the formation of the umbilical cord and the relations of the allantois and yolk-sac in human embryo. The heavy black line represents the embryonic ectoderm; the dotted line marks the line of transition of the body (embryonic) ectoderm and that of the amnion. Stippled areas, mesoderm. *Ac*, amniotic cavity; *Al*, allantoic cavity; *Al*, allantois; *Bc*, exocoelom; *Bs*, body stalk; *Ch*, chorion; *P*, placenta; *Uc*, umbilical cord; *V*, chorionic (trophodermic) villi; *Ys*, yolk-sac. (From Kellicott, after McMurrich.)

branching processes, chorionic villi, into the uterine tissues, which penetrate the uterine lymph cavities and absorb liquid nutriment by osmosis directly from the maternal supply. The maternal tissues become thick and congested in these regions, and the fetal and maternal tissues together constitute the definitive placenta. The entire chorion is at first provided with simple villi, but later only certain regions retain the villi and act as placental areas. Frequently the placental area is discoidal in shape, as in the primates, in some of the edentates, and in many of the rodents; sometimes the placental area is band-like or zonary, as in the carnivores; and in the case of some of the ungulates it is cotyledonous, in which case thick knots of villi are scattered over almost the entire chorion, separated by extensive non-villous areas.

Parturition, or birth, takes place at widely different stages of maturity in the different mammalian groups. In some species, as in cattle and horses, the young at birth are well advanced and, within a few hours after birth, are able to walk or even to run, and require little parental care except in connection with mammary feeding. In other species, as in the carnivores and rodents, the young are born naked, blind, and helpless and need much care for a considerable period. The human infant, while not as immature as some of those just mentioned, is decidedly helpless and needs care longer than any other creature.

Mammalian embryology is so highly diverse in its range from lowest to highest groups that one is overcome with a sense of futility when attempting to give a brief summary of a few of its outstanding features. If the present account does nothing more than excite an interest in this fascinating field it will have accomplished its purpose.

INDEX